C000228572

18 TINY DEATHS

18 TINY DEATHS

THE UNTOLD STORY OF **FRANCES GLESSNER LEE**
& THE INVENTION OF MODERN FORENSICS

BRUCE GOLDFARB

ENDEAVOUR

An Hachette UK Company
www.hachette.co.uk

First published in Great Britain in 2020 by Endeavour,
an imprint of Octopus Publishing Group Ltd
Carmelite House
50 Victoria Embankment
London EC4Y 0DZ
www.octopusbooks.co.uk

ISBN (Hardback): 978-1-91306-803-5
ISBN (Paperback): 978-1-91306-804-2

A CIP catalogue record for this book is available from the British Library.

Printed and bound in the UK

10 9 8 7 6 5 4 3 2 1

Publishing Director: Claudia Connal
Senior Editor: Pollyanna Poulter
Art Director: Juliette Norsworthy
Picture Research Manager: Giulia Hetherington
Senior Production Manager: Peter Hunt

For Bridgett, Kaya and Quinn

'The investigator [...] has a twofold responsibility: to clear the innocent as well as to expose the guilty [...] – the Truth in a Nutshell.'

Frances Glessner Lee

Contents

List of Key Characters

The Glessner Family

John Jacob Glessner
Sarah Frances Macbeth Glessner – wife of John Jacob Glessner, known as Frances Macbeth
John George Macbeth Glessner – son of John Jacob and Frances Macbeth Glessner, known as George
Frances Glessner Lee – daughter of John Jacob and Frances Macbeth Glessner, known in childhood as Fanny and referred to later in this book as Lee or Captain Lee

Glessner Family Friends

George Burgess Magrath, MD – Harvard classmate of George Glessner, medical examiner for the Northern District of Suffolk County
Isaac Scott – designer, craftsman and artist who made furniture and decorative objects for the Glessners

Harvard Medical School

James Bryant Conant – President of Harvard University, 1933–53

C Sidney Burwell, MD – Dean of Harvard Medical School, 1935–49

Alan R Moritz, MD – Chairman of the Department of Legal Medicine, 1937–49

Richard Ford, MD – Chairman of the Department of Legal Medicine, 1949–65

Others

Roger Lee, MD – prominent Boston internist and personal physician of George Burgess Magrath and Frances Glessner Lee, to whom he was not related

Alan Gregg, MD – director of the Medical Sciences Division of the Rockefeller Foundation, in charge of funding projects to improve medicine

Erle Stanley Gardner – bestselling author of the Perry Mason novels

Foreword

Foreword

I first encountered Frances Glessner Lee's dioramas as a young doctor in 2003, when I travelled to Baltimore to interview for a position at the Maryland Office of the Chief Medical Examiner. The chief, Dr David Fowler, asked if I had seen the Nutshell Studies. I told him, honestly, that I had no idea what he was talking about. Fowler then escorted me into a dark room and switched on the lights. Pushed into a corner, some hidden under sheets to keep the dust off, were a bunch of little boxes, and inside those, enclosed in plexiglass, I discovered a precious and intricate world of violence and death.

The Nutshell Studies of Unexplained Death are miniature death scenes. I scrutinized them. In one of the tiny rooms, I noticed the dotted pattern on the tiled floor and the incredibly precise floral wallpaper. Another showed a wooden cabin with a kitchen and bunk beds. There were snowshoes in the attic, a pot on the counter. I played with dolls' houses as a girl and would regularly beg my father to drive us to the miniatures store hours away from our home in order to purchase supplies for my own tiny world, but I had never seen dolls' houses this sophisticated before. To make plates for my dolls, I would pop out the plastic liner inside bottle caps. The plates in the Nutshell Studies were made of porcelain. *Porcelain!* The labels on the cans stacked on the kitchen shelves and the headlines on the newspapers were legible. I couldn't stop peering at the details.

Among those details, of course, were the blood spatters on the wallpaper, the grotesquely charred remains of a body on a burned bed, a man with a purple head hanging from a noose. These were no ordinary dolls' houses. This was not child's play. What was I looking at? Who made these? And the most compelling question: what had happened here, in each of these stories frozen in miniature?

I had come to the interview in Baltimore after two years of training as a forensic pathologist at the New York City Office of the Chief Medical Examiner (OCME). Part of my education there included going to death scenes with the medico-legal investigators from the office, learning what to look for at a scene and what I might find there that would help inform my final determination of cause and manner of death in the sudden, unexpected and violent stories we were tasked by law with investigating. This is how you learn death investigation anywhere – through on-the-job training.

Still, there was always something uncomfortably voyeuristic about entering someone's home unannounced and going through their medicine cabinet, rubbish bins and refrigerator as part of the process of trying to find out why they were lying dead on the floor. The investigators at the New York City OCME were certified professionals, and they told me where to focus my attention and what to look – and smell and listen and feel – for. The medicine cabinet would hold evidence of the deceased's ailments. A big bottle of antacids could mean they suffered from gastrointestinal problems, but it could also be a clue pointing to undiagnosed heart disease. Prescription drug bottles might indicate whether those medicines were being used as directed, underutilized or abused. The wastebasket might hold unpaid bills, eviction notices or an abandoned draft of a suicide note. The refrigerator could be full of food or empty except for a single vodka bottle. If the food was fresh, so was the body, most likely. If it was rotting... then it could help us confirm the degree of decomposition we were observing in the deceased, in an effort to hammer down the time of death.

Everything at a death scene is part of the story, and it was the details I would find there that mattered most. I couldn't interview the patient. The surrounding environment was the medical history I would rely upon the next day, in the morgue, when I would perform the forensic autopsy and add those findings to the findings from the scene. As my mentor, the late Dr Charles Hirsch, long-serving chief medical examiner for the city of New York, taught all of us who were fortunate enough to work for him, the autopsy is only *part* of the death investigation.

It was during my autopsy training in New York that I also learned the scene findings weren't necessarily revealing. They could be irrelevant. They could be misleading. At the scene, the gun in the dead man's hand and the witness who said that he was depressed suggested a suicide; but in the morgue, the absence of powder burns or stippling on his bare skin told me the gun had to have been fired from at least 75cm (30in) away. He had been murdered, and the scene staged to look like a suicide. The dead woman in her apartment appeared to have died peacefully in her sleep. The next day, in the morgue, her naked dissected body showed the deep bruises under the unblemished skin of her neck, and the petechial haemorrhages in the whites of her eyes were witness to homicidal strangulation. I learned that what you see at the scene can inform what you see in the morgue, but it cannot replace it.

Peering into the unique and incomparable scenes encased in the Nutshell Studies, I was taken back in time to a period in history when death investigation was beginning to emerge as a scientific discipline, and doctors were just starting to challenge the primacy of coroners and police detectives in distinguishing criminal acts from other types of death. Here was the work of both a gifted artisan and a medical expert, joining her skills to create something more than science and deeper than art. The exhibits were designed to be functional, educational and fully decipherable – but the interpretation of each scene could change based on the medical information provided by autopsy findings. There is something about peering into a room from above, at dolls rather than at moving, living people (or their no-longer-moving, no-longer-living bodies), that allows you the time and space to train your eye, that makes you notice the details. I realized the Nutshell Studies were my on-the-job training with the New York OCME death investigators, but in miniature. The skills I had learned from those investigators in life-size apartments and homes, businesses and construction sites could be honed here, too, from many types of scene at once, and in minute detail. I was awed by the time and effort it must have taken to create such elaborate, complex and perplexing scenarios, and by how much could be gleaned from close observation of them.

When I first viewed those dioramas, stashed away in the back room of the Baltimore OCME's office, they had been in storage for years, and they were not in the best shape. Their only pupils seemed to be the staff of the medical examiner's office, who occasionally brought in visitors to look at them as historical curiosities. There was no way for the public to see them. As far as I knew, despite their age and condition, they were still being used for training death investigators. Still, it seemed to me a sad fate for such a remarkable body of work.

In subsequent years, and with the dedicated attention of Bruce Goldfarb, an administrator at the Baltimore OCME and the author of this book, Frances Lee's Nutshell Studies of Unexplained Death have been repaired, renovated and preserved. They were displayed at the Smithsonian Institution in 2017 and 2018, and they have been publicized in books and magazines and on the internet. This book is a culmination of years of historical research using primary sources, including the papers of Frances Glessner Lee herself. It is the story of how one stubborn, intelligent and creative self-taught woman immersed herself in a passion that had immense repercussions in the fields of both medicine and the law. Goldfarb places Frances Glessner Lee and her intelligence, influence, wealth and forceful personality in context within the world of medico-legal death investigation. As this absorbing and evocative book will show you, Frances Glessner Lee should be recognized as the matriarch of the modern practice of forensic pathology.

Her 18 Tiny Deaths have made a whole world of difference.

Dr Judy Melinek, forensic pathologist and co-author (with T J Mitchell) of the memoir *Working Stiff: Two Years, 262 Bodies, and the Making of a Medical Examiner* and *First Cut*, the debut in a series of forensic noir detective novels

CHAPTER 1

Legal Medicine

1944

Seventeen pathologists and medical examiners, all dressed in dark suits and ties, sat around a long table in a wood-panelled conference room on the third floor of Building E-1 of Harvard Medical School. It was the autumn of 1944. Thousands of miles away, war ravaged Europe and the Pacific islands. The men had gathered to attend a seminar on legal medicine, a field that would later be known as forensic science: the application of medicine to matters of law and justice.

Dr Alan R Moritz broke the grim news to the group. Unfortunately, Captain Frances Glessner Lee, her preferred title since being made an officer in the New Hampshire State Police the previous year, was unable to attend the seminar as planned. She had fractured her right tibia in a fall and subsequently suffered two heart attacks.[1]

As trained professionals affiliated with one of America's most prestigious medical institutions, the men well understood the grave prognostic implications for a woman almost sixty-seven years of age with a constellation of health problems. The heart attacks were the latest setback of encroaching infirmity that increasingly limited Lee's ability to function day to day. Now she faced a long period of strict bed rest under the watchful care of a physician.

For Moritz, one of the nation's leading pathologists, Lee's absence was a personal and professional loss. The seminar participants, for their part, would miss the benefit of her encyclopaedic knowledge of legal medicine as well as the civilizing effect of her presence.

Lee's seminar curriculum was intended to provide the men with specialized knowledge to probe unexpected and unexplained deaths, including how to estimate the time of death, assess decomposition and other postmortem changes, differentiate blunt- and sharp-force injuries and explore related areas of death investigation. No other medical school in America offered anything like it.

Lee was an improbable figure to assume the mantle of authority in the emerging field of legal medicine. A decorous grandmother with a preference for brimless Queen Mary hats and black dresses she sewed herself, she was an independently wealthy scion of Chicago society in the Gilded Age – a term coined by author Mark Twain for the last few decades of the nineteenth century, which he considered glittering on the surface but corrupt underneath. Often a difficult woman with impossibly exacting standards and an almost fanatical sense of purpose, Lee was more than just a guiding presence for Harvard's legal medicine programme. By the force of her personality and the spending of a substantial portion of her personal wealth, she was nearly single-handedly responsible for the establishment of legal medicine in the United States and her influence was recognized at Scotland Yard and around the world.

As a reformer, educator and advocate, her influence on the field was immeasurable. This genteel matron was respected as one of legal medicine's leading authorities. But getting to that point had not been easy. 'Men are dubious of an elderly woman with a cause,' Lee once said. 'My problem is to convince them that I am not trying to butt in or run anything. Also, I have to sell them on the fact that I know what I am talking about.'[2]

In the seven years since Lee had approved hiring Moritz to chair the country's first academic programme in legal medicine, the two had been working on an innovative project that could potentially revolutionize the investigation of unexpected and suspicious deaths: an intensive week-long seminar on legal medicine for police officers. The ambitious curriculum they had mapped out was groundbreaking, intended to train police in modern scientific forensic methods.

For the better part of two years, Lee had also been working obsessively on a series of intricately detailed scale-model dioramas designed to teach crime-scene observation: the identification of clues that might be important in determining the cause and manner of deaths that were unexpected, sudden or the result of injury. She called the models the 'Nutshell Studies of Unexplained Death'. Now, because of her illness, Lee's and Moritz's plans seemed doomed.

'The models are none of them finished and none of them can be finished,' Lee wrote to Moritz while recuperating at The Rocks, her 1,500-acre estate near Littleton, New Hampshire. 'I hope you will agree with me that under these circumstances the Police Seminar should not be held.'[3]

In the Building E-1 conference room, the men paused in their sombre studies to draft a resolution for Moritz to deliver to Lee:

Resolved, that Mrs Frances G Lee shall have the everlasting gratitude of all those attending the Seminar in Legal Medicine at Harvard Medical School in 1944, and that all those present extend their profound thanks and appreciation for her philanthropy, which has made possible the holding of these seminars, which, in turn, have done so much to advance the cause of legal medicine; and that it is the sincere hope of all of those present that Mrs Lee will soon be fully restored to her normal health and activities.[4]

* * *

To appreciate Captain Lee's pioneering work in legal medicine, it is necessary to travel back in time and understand how societies have dealt with death, especially unexpected or unexplained death, over the centuries.

A little more than 1.4 million Americans died during the year of 1944, according to the Vital Statistics of the United States. Most of them were at home or in hospitals. Their deaths were attended by a doctor, nurse or family member. They were known to have an illness or disease, became progressively worse and then died.

Historically, however, about one in five deaths are sudden and unexpected.[5] These involve people not known to be ill, who die by violence or injury or under unexplained circumstances. Of these 283,000 or so questionable deaths in the US in 1944, no more than one or two per cent – a few thousand at most – were investigated by qualified medical examiners: doctors with specialized training to diagnose the cause and manner of death. At that time, only a handful of East Coast cities – Boston, New York, Baltimore and Newark – had competent medical examiners who were trained in legal medicine and had properly equipped offices. The vast majority of the United States still used the coroner system, an archaic throwback to medieval England.

Despite its universality as an inevitable fact, the occasion of death has always held a special place in human experience. Intellectually, we know it happens to all of us and everyone we know, but when somebody dies it's still shocking and upsetting. The need for answers is deeply rooted. What happened? Why did this person die?

The earliest methodical inquiries into the nature of a death were mostly concerned with suicide. Through human history, suicide has been viewed as an act of defiance against God or authority or a crime against oneself known as *felo de se*. Soldiers of the Roman Empire who took their own lives were considered deserters. Some cemeteries prohibited the burial of a person who had died by their own hand.[6]

In medieval England, the 'keeper of the pleas of the Crown', an official known as the 'crowner' (later corrupted into coroner), served as the royal judicial representative and had a variety of responsibilities. One of his primary duties was collecting money owed to the monarchy: mainly taxes and fines. He was tasked with serving writs from the court – orders and summonses; he was also authorized to seize royal fishes: sturgeon, porpoise and other sea creatures fit only for the palate of a king – and to investigate shipwrecks and treasure troves. It was his job to make sure the Crown received its share.

Coroners also investigated deaths that were sudden or apparently unnatural, mainly to determine whether the deceased was murdered or a suicide. They were responsible for answering two questions: what caused this death and who was responsible for it? One is a medical question, while the other is a matter of criminal justice.[7] Early coroners didn't need any knowledge of medicine or the law. They held an inquest, a process that was part investigation and part adjudication. To do this, they called together an inquest jury of ten or twelve men (only adult males were allowed to participate), most of whom were illiterate farmers and many of whom had probably known the deceased or been witnesses to the death.

The coroner and the inquest jury were required to observe the dead body, often at the place where the death had occurred or the body was found. The inquest had to be held *super visum corporis* ('upon viewing of the body').

Failure to view the body invalidated the proceedings. If there was no body to view, an inquest could not be held at all. The jury had to get a good look at it, not just a quick peek. They were required to examine it for signs of violence and note the presence of wounds.

Of course, without a foundation of basic medical knowledge, there is little to learn from looking at a dead body. Nonetheless, after viewing the body and hearing from witnesses, the jury rendered a verdict by holding a vote. It wasn't very scientific.

If it was decided that the deceased had been murdered, the inquest was then required to name the killer. The coroner was authorized to charge the accused and arrest him, and it was the duty of the local sheriff to hold the accused in jail until trial. The coroner heard confessions, when they were offered, and confiscated all the property – home, land, possessions – of those who were convicted and executed. Since killing yourself was a crime against the Crown, the coroner took a deceased's property too.

When the English colonized parts of America, they brought their common law with them. In the USA, today's sheriff, justice of the peace and coroner are lingering vestiges of the Middle Ages.

Maryland acquired its first coroner in 1637, three years after the colony was founded, when Thomas Baldridge, a tobacco farmer, was appointed sheriff and coroner of St Mary's County. He was given the rather vague instruction to 'Doe all and everything…the office of sheriff or coroner of any county in England doe.'[8] A more detailed description of his duties was issued in 1640:

> Upon notice or suspicion of any person that hath or shall come to his or her death entirely within the limits of that hundred [an administrative division] as you conveniently may to view the dead body and to charge

the said persons with an oath truly to inquire and true verdict to grant how the person viewed came upon his or her death according to the evidence.[9]

Two days after being appointed coroner, on 31 January 1637, Baldridge held his first inquest. A jury of twelve freemen, all tobacco farmers, was summoned to view the body of John Bryant, who had been killed while chopping down a tree. Joseph Edlow, also a tobacco farmer, had been with Bryant when it happened.[10]

Testifying under oath, Edlow told the inquest jury that he had warned Bryant to get out of the way. 'John, have a care of your selfe, for the tree is falling,' he recalled telling his friend. Edlow said that Bryant stepped back five or six paces. As the tree toppled, it glanced off another tree and rebounded onto Bryant, crushing him beneath its weight. 'The said John Bryant spake not one word after,' the inquest record noted.

Baldridge and the jury examined Bryant's body and noted 'two scratches under his chinne on the left side'. They did about as well as could be expected of a group of untrained tobacco farmers, reaching the conclusion that Bryant died because 'his bloud bulke broke'.

As coroner, it was Baldridge's duty to bury the body as well as to sell off Bryant's property to settle his debts. The record of Bryant's inquest includes a dreary inventory of his earthly possessions: 'two suits & an old doublett', stockings and drawers, bowls and spoons, a few scraps of furniture, a canoe, a cock and hen, and his servant, Elias Beach.

* * *

The course of human history is overall one of continual progress and advancement. Our lives were improved immeasurably by breathtaking developments in agriculture, sanitation, transportation and medicine. We tamed electricity, built railroads and invented telephones. But for the better part of three centuries, little changed in how unnatural deaths were investigated in America. For most of the country, the process remained a peculiar anachronism, a holdover from the thirteenth century bearing little relation to modern science-based medicine.

The coroner was a local official with a jurisdiction within a county or city. He might have been a sheriff, magistrate or justice of the peace; he could also have been a woodworker, baker or butcher; in many places, he was the local undertaker. The coroner got the job by being elected to office, or by being appointed to office by elected officials. As such, the position was inherently political. He didn't get the job on the basis of his diligence and expertise but for his political affiliations and loyalties. Keeping the job depended on remaining in the good graces of voters or political leaders. Since the coroner didn't necessarily know anything about medicine, he had help in determining the cause of each death from a doctor, known variously as the coroner's physician, medical referee or medical examiner.

Some might argue that a coroner's inquest may have been good enough back in the day when America was mostly rural and agrarian. Most sudden deaths were likely to be from accidents or natural causes like heart attack or stroke. On the rare occasions of a suspicious death, the culprit usually didn't have the opportunity to travel far from the scene. There were often witnesses. Identifying a body wasn't an issue because there were generally family or neighbours nearby. Most people didn't travel far from where they were born, so everybody knew everybody and their business. Perhaps twelve uninformed minds using common sense were better than nothing at all.

The deficiencies of the system, however, grew more apparent as the population of urban areas swelled and the

opportunities for crime increased. Within a few blocks in a
big city, tens of thousands lived in ramshackle tenements.
Cities teemed with vulnerable populations: transients,
immigrants, people who had left the farm to seek work. A
perpetrator could quickly distance himself from his deeds
by streetcar or train. It was easy to vanish in a place like
New York, Philadelphia, Chicago or Boston, and that made
investigating suspicious deaths more difficult.[11]

Additionally, throughout most of the country, the
coroner system was notoriously corrupt and incompetent.
The coroner was in a position ripe for bribery, kickbacks
and extortion. He could send bodies to undertakers willing
to line his pockets. In some jurisdictions, the coroner was
authorized to file charges and set bail in cases of homicide or
criminal negligence, such as a workplace death – problems
that could be resolved with money and influence.

Authorizing coroners to call inquests at their own
discretion, for which the coroner and the inquest jurors were
paid by the case, essentially gave coroners a free hand in the
public treasury. Inquest juries were packed with cronies and
associates who could be trusted to rubber-stamp whatever
conclusion was preferred by police or prosecutors. Rather
than being an asset to criminal justice, coroners often became
a detriment. They unnecessarily delayed charges in cases of
homicide and, due to their ineptitude, made basic errors in
the performance of their duties. Coroners were often terrible
witnesses in court, giving testimony that was unreliable and
useless to prosecutors.

The men who served as coroners' physicians were often
no better, largely incompetent and indifferent. In the 1920s,
Columbia University criminal-justice professor Raymond
Moley conducted a study of coroner cases in Cuyahoga
County, Ohio, which includes the city of Cleveland. He
found a plethora of nonsensical causes of death, such as
'could be suicide or murder'; 'aunt said she complained of

pneumonia, looked like narcotism'; 'looks suspicious of strychnine poisoning'; 'found dead'; 'head severed from body'; 'could be assault or diabetes'; 'diabetes, tuberculosis, or nervous indigestion'; and 'found crushed'.[12]

In 1914, a man by the name of Leonard Wallstein, New York City's commissioner of accounts, conducted an investigation of the city's coroner system. The commissioner of accounts is similar to an inspector general, with the authority to issue subpoenas for documents and to compel testimony.[13] Word of the investigation lit a fire under coroners who had been sitting on long-overdue reports. Within a month of Wallstein's investigation being announced, coroners filed reports on 431 potentially criminal deaths, nearly 200 of which were more than a year old and sixty-three of which were more than three years old.

After hearings with scores of witnesses, including all the city's coroners and coroners' physicians, Wallstein issued a scathing report in January 1915. Of all the men holding office as coroner, 'not one was thoroughly qualified by training or experience for the adequate performance of his duties', he wrote.

Of the sixty-five men who had served as coroner since New York City was consolidated in 1898, only nineteen were doctors. The report noted that eight were undertakers, seven were 'politicians and chronic office-holders', six were real-estate dealers, two were saloon keepers, two were plumbers and the remainder had previously worked in a variety of occupations that included printer, auctioneer, butcher, musician, milkman and woodcarver.

George LeBrun, who served as a coroner's secretary for four decades, said in his testimony that New York City's coroners were 'outrageous crooks who dispensed "justice" for cash. Their only interest in each new case was to discover how they could extort money, and they used their office for blackmail purposes.'[14]

According to Wallstein's report, coroners' physicians were 'drawn from the ranks of mediocrity'. Good doctors with thriving practices didn't want to be bothered with examining dead bodies in the middle of the night or to be inconvenienced by entanglement in a legal proceeding. Doctors willing to serve as coroners' physicians were motivated by a steady source of easy money. They often did a cursory, superficial examination of a body or none at all. The report documented instances of doctors signing stacks of death certificates at the morgue with barely a glance at the bodies.

The cause of death certified by coroners was often questionable to the point of absurdity. In one example, a man had his cause of death listed as rupture of a thoracic aneurysm, a diagnosis that had somehow been made without the benefit of an autopsy. The coroner's report failed to mention that the man was found holding in his right hand a .38-calibre revolver with one spent round and a lethal bullet wound in his mouth.

Wallstein's investigators reviewed 800 death certificates and found a 'complete lack of evidence to justify the certified cause of death' in forty per cent of the documents. When coroners' physicians were asked why they chose one diagnosis over another with similar signs and symptoms, they often admitted an inability to explain their conclusions. They seemed to pluck diagnoses out of thin air.

The cause of death certified by coroners was so untrustworthy that health department officials testified that the city's vital statistics would be more accurate if death certificates signed by coroners were excluded altogether.

This is not to say that all coroners were corrupt or incompetent. Certainly, there were decent men with integrity who conducted their duty in good faith. By the same token, some medical examiners were doctors unfit for the task. In their defence, doctors weren't taught much about death in medical school, since the patients they were expected to treat were living. Diagnosing cause and manner of death was not part of the curriculum at that time.

Until midway through the twentieth century, police were also utterly unequipped for scientific homicide investigations. Few police departments required a college degree for employment, and many police officers didn't even graduate from secondary school. As with coroners, many were unable to read and write, particularly in smaller towns and rural areas. Training for the job was minimal.

At the scene of a death, the police were often a hindrance, likely to destroy evidence by walking through blood, moving the body, handling a weapon or putting their fingers through bullet holes in clothing. What happened during those first moments influenced everything that subsequently happened in the investigation. If the police didn't handle the scene properly – if they overlooked signs of foul play or failed to preserve evidence that was critical for determining the cause and manner of death – the case was bungled from the beginning.

In the mid- to late 1800s, the reputation of coroners in Boston, Massachusetts, was as bad as anywhere. There was no limit to the number of coroners the governor could appoint. The designation of coroner was a valuable plum to hand out as a political favour, practically a licence to steal. Before the office of medical examiner was established in 1877, Boston had forty-three coroners. The city of New York, with three times the population of Boston, had four for the entire jurisdiction. Suffolk County, Massachusetts – which includes the city of Boston – had more coroners than New York City, Philadelphia, New Orleans, Chicago, San Francisco, Baltimore and Washington, DC, combined.[15]

'You have in the coroner an officer armed practically with the utmost power of the law,' said prominent Boston attorney Theodore Tyndale:

He decides in the first place, upon his discretion, whether an inquest be necessary or not; it is obvious how large are the opportunities for corruption in this direction: that for a man whose cupidity or possibly culpability and fear are stronger than his honor and integrity, it would not be difficult to thwart justice and close the door to all judicial investigation of a crime by corruptly declaring an inquest unnecessary, and even aiding in the removal of suspicion and the concealment of the evidence and traces by authorizing a speedy burial. But if he may thus on the one hand shield the guilty and endanger the public safety, on the other the opportunities for a man prompted by malice or vindictiveness or the desire of cheap notoriety are enough, truly, to make us tremble.[16]

The scandal that brought matters to a head in Boston began when the body of a newborn baby was found in a rubbish bin. One of the city's district coroners convened an inquest, which returned a verdict of 'death at the hands of a person unknown'. Each member of the inquest jury earned two dollars and the coroner ten. But rather than show some decency, coroners saw an opportunity. The body of the baby was dumped in another district for another coroner to hold another inquest and dump the body again. Four times this decomposing baby was exploited until word of the appalling practice got out.[17]

That was the end of the coroner system in Boston. In 1877, lawmakers abolished coroners and inquests and placed a competent doctor in charge of death investigations.

This, then, was the world Frances Glessner Lee made it her mission to change. Before her time, progress in the field of death investigation had been slow, lurching forward only when scandals shocked the public's sensibilities. It was her goal to modernize the investigation of sudden and unexplained deaths.

* * *

The police department of Chicago, Illinois, is older than the city itself. On 31 January 1835, two years before the city was incorporated, the Illinois General Assembly authorized Chicago to establish its own police force. Seven months later, Orsemus Morrison was elected the town's first constable.[18]

As constable, Morrison carried the 'staff of office', a whitewashed wood baton that was more ornament than weapon, to indicate the authority of his elected position. His duties included collecting fines and taxes and serving as coroner of Cook County – in which Chicago sits – by leading inquest juries in cases of questionable deaths.

The first death that Morrison investigated was that of a visiting Frenchman found dead in the autumn of 1835. He was discovered in the early morning, half-buried in a muddy pit in 'the woods': an area densely overgrown with foliage bounded by LaSalle, Washington and Randolph streets – the location of the present-day City Hall. Morrison called an inquest jury. The deceased, they were told, had been staying at a hotel and had gone out for an evening walk. He had been drinking and apparently got lost and became mired in the mud pit, where he fell victim to the elements. The jury concluded that the man had frozen to death by misadventure. No evidence suggested otherwise.[19]

At the time of Morrison's tenure as constable, Chicago had fewer than 4,500 inhabitants. Favourably located in proximity to the Great Lakes, railroads and the Mississippi River, it rapidly grew into a major centre of manufacturing and distribution. Agricultural equipment sold through Chicago transformed the country's vast prairies into productive farmland. Cattle and hogs raised on farms throughout the Midwest were sent to Chicago for slaughter and from there, along with corn and grain, were shipped throughout the United States. The city became home to some of the country's largest manufacturers and some of its wealthiest families.

During the 1800s, the population of Chicago rose at a breathtaking rate. By 1860, it was more than 100,000; in the next decade, it nearly tripled, approaching 300,000. Among the legion of young people migrating there during this period of growth were John Jacob Glessner and his wife, Frances Macbeth.

The son of a newspaper publisher, Glessner was born in 1842 and spent his formative years in Zanesville, Ohio. At the age of twenty, he struck out on his own and took a position as bookkeeper at Warder, Child & Co. in Springfield, an industrial town in the southwest part of the state. Warder, Child & Co., a maker of reapers, mowers and planters, was one of the largest farm-equipment companies in the country. In Springfield, Glessner rented a room with the Macbeth family, where he met and fell in love with Frances, a young schoolteacher. He rapidly advanced his station in Warder, Child & Co. Adept in the world of business, he seemed destined for success.[20]

In 1869, the firm's principals decided to open an office in Chicago to increase their share of agricultural markets in the Midwest. Glessner asked to head the new operation, so long as he was given authority to run the business as he saw fit, and he was appointed as a vice president of the company. He and Frances were married at her parents' home in Springfield, then, after a visit to his parents in Zanesville, they took the train to begin their new lives in Chicago.

On 2 October 1871, one week before the Great Chicago Fire that destroyed almost a third of the city, the Glessners celebrated the birth of their first child, George Macbeth. A daughter, Frances, arrived on 25 March 1878. A plump and healthy baby, she was known as Fanny.

As Glessner's career advanced, his personal wealth grew accordingly. As a junior partner, his share of the company's profits in 1877 was $39,600 – close to £700,000 in present-day value. By the time he was forty years old, Glessner was a dollar millionaire, with a net worth of about £21 million in today's currency. He was among the wealthiest men in Chicago.

Eventually, five major agricultural machinery companies – including Warder, Bushnell & Glessner (the successor of Warder, Child & Co.) – merged to form the International Harvester Company. At its inception, the company was valued at $150 million – over two and a half billion pounds in modern terms. By then the last active principal of Warder, Bushnell & Glessner, John Jacob Glessner was elected chairman of International Harvester's executive committee. He suddenly owned a piece of the largest manufacturing company in the world, and his family's security was set for generations.

This wealth allowed Frances Macbeth and John Jacob to indulge their shared passions for music and the arts. They enjoyed live performances, attending the opera and musical events at venues throughout Chicago, and raised George and Fanny to appreciate the same fine arts. Most of all, the Glessners enjoyed classical symphonic music. John Jacob was one of a group of prominent Chicagoans who provided the funding to establish the Chicago Symphony Orchestra in 1891. He was a staunch supporter and benefactor of the orchestra for the rest of his life.

The Glessners were also enthusiasts of cultural and intellectual self-improvement. John Jacob was active in the Literary Club, while Frances Macbeth took lessons in literature, French, Italian and German. They enjoyed acquiring fine furniture, art and decorative objects for their home.

During a visit to the Interstate Industrial Exposition in 1875, the Glessners admired black walnut furniture carved by Isaac Scott.[21] Scott was an artist, woodworker and designer particularly known for art furniture. The Glessners commissioned him to build a bookcase for their home. It was the beginning of a close personal friendship that lasted the remainder of Scott's life. Over a period of years, he designed furniture, pottery, picture frames, embroidered works, pewter and other decorative items for the family.

Such wealth seemed to assure a life of comfort and security for the Glessner children.

CHAPTER 2

The Sunny Street of the Sifted Few

1878–1898

Privilege is no immunity to misfortune. George Glessner developed severe hay fever at around the age of four. By the time Fanny was born, his doctor advised the family to spend summers away from the filthy, pollen-filled air of Chicago and take George to the country for respite from his symptoms.

The Glessners heard about an area in the White Mountains of New Hampshire with a reputation for being practically pollen-free. Frances Macbeth had taken ill since Fanny's birth, so in the summer of 1878 she remained in Chicago with the baby while George was sent to New Hampshire with Frances's sisters, Helen and Lizzie.

After a two-day train ride, the group arrived in Littleton, New Hampshire, about 40km (25 miles) west of Mount Washington. George experienced little relief from his symptoms, until Helen Macbeth consulted a local homeopath who concluded that George wasn't 'far enough into the mountains'. He recommended a hotel about 22km (14 miles) away, the Twin Mountain House. 'Aunt Helen made the move and George was very much better almost overnight,' Fanny recalled in her journal many years later.[1] She described the Twin Mountain House as a 'great barn of a place'. It was an impressively grand three-storey wood-frame structure, with the upper floor boasting a steeply sloping mansard roof. 'Of course there was no plumbing.'[2]

Many guests, including the Glessner family, returned to the Twin Mountain House summer after summer. John Jacob remained in Chicago for much of the time, but made frequent visits. Another regular was Henry Ward Beecher, a celebrated clergyman who was also an outspoken abolitionist and suffragist (and brother of Harriet Beecher Stowe, author of the hugely successful anti-slavery novel *Uncle Tom's Cabin*). Beecher had recently been embroiled in scandal, his reputation soiled by an adulterous relationship with his assistant's wife and the subsequent high-profile lawsuit brought by the wronged husband.[3]

At Twin Mountain House, five-year-old Fanny befriended Beecher. 'He took a fancy to me as I did to him,' she recalled. 'In the middle of the morning he would go into the bar for a lemonade and often took me with him. I would sit on his knee with a little glass of ice-cold lemonade.'[4]

One morning, during a visit with his family, John Jacob walked down the stairs and saw Fanny and Beecher sitting together, having their lemonades. He stopped in his tracks, disapproving of his young daughter being in the company of unsavoury characters. He spoke with his wife. 'My dear, a summer hotel is not a good place to bring up children,' he told her. 'I think if we're going to have to come up here year after year for George's hay fever, that we will have to have a home of our own.'[5]

Touring the area in a horse-drawn buggy, the Glessners found a prominent hill that had been cleared of timber, leaving a rough, rocky pasture strewn with boulders. The view was spectacular, with Mount Washington to the east and the towns of Bethlehem, Littleton and

Scythefactoryville spread out below. For $23,000 – about £430,000 in today's terms – they purchased a hundred acres of farmland, which included a farmhouse and a few assorted ramshackle buildings. On this property, Isaac Scott designed a nineteen-room mansion built on a high prominence overlooking the White Mountains. It was completed by the summer of 1883 at a cost of $10–15,000 – approximately £190,000–280,000 by modern values. The Glessners named their new summer home The Rocks; among themselves it was 'the Big House'. According to the *Littleton Gazette*, it was 'the finest summer residence in the mountains', with 'one of the finest and most extensive views of any house in the mountains'.[6] It would become one of the most important places in the Glessners' lives for many decades to come.

Scott then designed a carriage barn with a granite foundation and wood-shingle siding, which was completed in 1884. He designed many buildings and structures for The Rocks, including an apiary for Frances Macbeth's beekeeping and several gazebo-like summerhouses that dotted the estate, connected by walking trails.[7] For young Fanny, he created something truly special: her own two-room log-cabin playhouse, complete with a kitchen with a working wood-burning stove.

In the neighbouring villages of Littleton and Bethlehem, there were distinct class differences between townsfolk who had lived in the area for generations and wealthier newcomers such as the Glessners who purchased summer homes at the higher, more picturesque elevations. 'Up the hill' referred to the seasonal residents; those who lived there year round were 'down the hill'. Locals couldn't understand why somebody would prefer to build a grand house way up in the mountains, in the middle of nowhere, far from town amenities. Sensing their curiosity, Frances Macbeth invited local residents to visit The Rocks and meet the family. She made elaborate preparations for her guests, having a huge black fruitcake sent from Delmonico's restaurant in New York and stocking her cellar with fine French wines.[8]

One day, a mountain wagon drawn by four horses brought about sixteen guests from the Twin Mountain House to call on the Glessners. Frances had the wine and fruitcake brought out and served.[9] Fanny recalled later in life that 'Each lady looked at the cake and with turned up nose said, "No thank you" until one lady braver than the others took both cake and wine and then said, "Better take some, Mrs Devoe, it's pretty good."'

The visitors peppered the Glessners with questions. *Don't you get lonely up here? Do you get anything to eat up here?* 'We were always so glad to see them go and so annoyed when they came,' Fanny said.

For a while, visiting The Rocks became something to do, to go and see what the Glessners were up to. Wagonloads of locals and seasonal visitors came around at random intervals, much to the family's annoyance. Matters came to a head one day when a wagon full of tourists pulled up to the kitchen window and ordered a pitcher of lemonade. The cook, in no subtle terms, refused. Fanny took great pleasure in telling the story to her parents, who had a pair of formal stone gateposts installed (the gate was never closed) with a sign that read THE PUBLIC IS REQUESTED NOT TO ENTER THESE GROUNDS.

Around this time, the Glessners began to think about having a home designed and built for them in Chicago. They wanted a house that reflected their tastes and style and in its way contributed to the architectural renaissance of post-fire Chicago. Having looked at several neighbourhoods, they settled on acquiring a plot of land on the southwest corner of Prairie Avenue and 18th Street, near the city's South Side.

Some of the finest homes in Chicago were on Prairie
Avenue. The street was lined with magnificent mansions
framed by manicured lawns and sculpted gardens, with
majestically sweeping staircases leading to porches or grand
entrances.[10]

John Jacob wanted an architect of note for his new home.[11]
Henry Hobson Richardson,[12] along with Louis Sullivan and
Frank Lloyd Wright, was one of the leaders in the field.
After graduating from Harvard, he went to Paris in 1860
to attend the famed École des Beaux-Arts – only the second
American to attend the École's architectural division.

The style that Richardson developed for his designs, like
Isaac Scott's with its allusions to medieval elements, was so
distinctive that it is known as Richardsonian Romanesque.
Characteristics common to Richardson's buildings include
thick walls, semicircular stone arches and clusters of squat
columns.

Glessner regarded Richardson highly but had been
informed by friends that he only undertook monumental
buildings – Boston's Trinity Church, the Buffalo State
Asylum for the Insane and Albany's City Hall, among
others. Glessner decided to contact the architect anyway,
telling him that he'd heard he didn't do private residences.

'I'll plan anything a man wants, from a cathedral to a
chicken coop,' Richardson replied. 'That's the way I make
my living.'[13]

Richardson visited the Glessners' Washington Street
residence to gain a sense of the family's circumstances. He
and John Jacob sat in the library to discuss the latter's needs
and wants for his new home. On the mantel was a small
photograph of a historic building at Abingdon Abbey in
Oxfordshire, England.

'Do you like that?' Richardson asked, gesturing to the
photo.

'Yes,' Glessner replied.

'Well, give it to me,' Richardson said. 'I'll make that the keynote of your house.'

Later, driving to view the Prairie Avenue site, Richardson sat in silence in the carriage. After several minutes, he blurted out, 'Have you the courage to build the house without windows on the street front?'

'Yes,' Glessner said without hesitation, knowing that he could tear up the plans if they were not to his satisfaction.

The men agreed to discuss plans for the house during dinner at the Glessners' the following night.

Frances Macbeth painted a vivid portrait of Richardson in her journal, describing him as 'the largest man I have ever seen'. Concerned about resting his girth on the Glessners' fine furniture, he insisted on sitting on a piano stool during his visit.[14]

'He parts his hair in the middle,' Frances Macbeth wrote. 'He stutters and spatters – breathes very heavily – and aside from his profession is not what I would call an interesting man.'

After dinner was served, Richardson took a scrap of paper and began sketching in pencil. He drew a large L shape, marked the location of entrances and filled the shape with boxes to represent rooms. Within minutes, he had designed the first floor of the house, almost exactly as it was ultimately built.

'He was the most versatile, interesting, ready, capable and confident of artists, the most genial and agreeable of companions,' Glessner said of him. 'He delighted in difficult problems.'

Richardson's plan was a stark departure from typical residential architecture of the time. It was certainly unlike any other home on Prairie Avenue. Rather than framing a welcoming front garden, the north and east exterior walls were almost at the pavement property line. Rows of rusticated Wellesley granite blocks in contrasting colours emphasized the building's horizontal lines. The long side of the house, on 18th Street, had a few narrow windows on the first floor and a service entrance sheltered by a semicircular arch. The main entrance, on Prairie Avenue, was understated, almost plain; there was no staircase, no veranda: just a modest street-level door of heavy oak. Stylized columns supported another semicircular arch, smaller than the service entrance. With only small square windows at street level, the public was presented with broad, flat, relatively unornamented walls.

From the outside, the house looked institutional, like a prison or hospital. What the public couldn't see was that it wrapped around a large private courtyard. All the landscaped spaces were within the courtyard, away from public view, giving the family their own private oasis in the city.

Just inside the front door, a 3.5m (12ft) wide staircase led to a foyer large enough to be a hotel lobby. There was enough room in the 1,700m² (18,000sq.ft) house for a formal dinner with more than a hundred guests, which the family eventually hosted many times.[15]

Richardson placed the main family rooms in the interior of the house, facing the courtyard. Windows on the southern side bathed the living spaces with warm light. Most of the rooms had two or more entryways, allowing household staff to move discreetly through the house. A hallway along the north side, used primarily by staff, insulated the family from street noise and Chicago's bitter winter winds.

Railroad-car maker and immensely wealthy industrialist George Pullman, who lived diagonally across the street in one of the largest and grandest homes in the neighbourhood, said, 'I don't know what I have ever done to have that thing staring at me in the face every time I go out of my door.'

A newspaper cutting from 10 July 1886 made note of the unusual addition to the avenue:

Prairie Ave. is a social street and also a gossipy one and it does not suit the neighbours that this newcomer should exclude all possibility of watching his windows and finding out what may be going on within doors... that this house is going up in spite of disapproval has thrown the neighbourhood into a state of stupefaction.[16]

The Prairie Avenue residence was the last design Richardson completed. Three weeks after finishing the plans, he died of kidney disease at the age of forty-eight. His assistants completed every project that was underway at the time of his death, including the Glessners' home, and gave the entirety of the $85,000 in commissions to his widow.[17]

'The house responds [to all the demands put upon it],' Glessner wrote in a collection of photographs and remembrances, *The House at 1800 Prairie Avenue*. 'It seems available for almost any social function. Large companies have been entertained in it comfortably and easily... Music and dramatic readings have been given to hundreds of persons, and receptions to more than 400 at one time, without any feeling of crush, confusion or heat. Elaborate course dinners have been served in its rooms to more than 100 guests at a time, the cooking all done in our own kitchen and by our own cook. Twice the full Chicago Orchestra had dined there, and once the Commercial Club.' The expansive house was the clearest manifestation of Glessner's rapid journey to the heights of Chicago society.[18]

On Frances Macbeth's birthday or other special occasions, orchestra conductor Theodore Thomas would sneak two dozen or more musicians into the house, unbeknown to her until the soft strains of music floated from the front hall during dinner. For the Glessners' twenty-fifth wedding anniversary, the entire orchestra came quietly through the 18th Street servants' entrance and up the rear stairs to surprise the family with an impromptu concert.[19]

Despite the fatigue and discomfort of chronic health problems, for which she was prescribed 'Cannabis indicie (Indian hemp)'[20] – a form of medicinal marijuana – Frances Macbeth maintained a busy social schedule. She was a board member of the Decorative Arts Society and the highbrow Fortnightly Club. In addition to the lessons in languages and literature, she applied her silversmithing lessons to refine her skills in jewellery-making.

She was also a voracious reader, completing two or three substantial books a week. In 1894, she established a gathering that became one of the most desirable in their social circle, the Monday Morning Reading Class.[21]

Membership in the class was by Frances's invitation. Every season, she created a members' roster with up to ninety names. With the exception of her sister, Helen Macbeth, and the class's paid professional reader, Anne E Trimingham, members were all married women, many of them the wives of the faculty of the newly formed University of Chicago. Almost all lived on the city's South Side.

The classes began every Monday at 10.30am with an hour of serious reading by Trimingham or a lecture by an invited guest, then an hour of lighter, more amusing works or a musical performance by one or more members of the Chicago Symphony Orchestra. On the first Monday of each month, the class was followed by a luncheon.

Many members of the reading class sewed or knitted during the readings. During World War I, they knitted gloves and sweaters for men fighting overseas. After the war, they made blankets and garments for infants at Cook County Hospital. 'The ladies' fingers were busy with sewing and other womanly occupation,' John Jacob recalled. 'And when the reading stopped, doubtless their tongues grew active in womanly conversation.'[22]

Invitation to the reading class was highly sought after. 'All of Prairie Avenue was present,' the newspaper social page reported, noting a gathering of 'smartly arranged women in glossy furs, becoming hats, and the latest importation in work bags over their arms'.[23] The classes met weekly in the library of the Glessners' home from November to May for more than three decades until, in the 1930s, Frances's poor health forced the club to close.

The Glessners' wealth ensured that Fanny and George wanted for nothing. The children were provided with every advantage: lessons in horse riding, dance, music and art with private tutors. Due to George's severe hay fever, a doctor advised that he not be subjected to 'the nervous strain of school where he would meet the competition of others'.[24] Instead, George and Fanny were educated at home by some of the finest private instructors for hire in Chicago. Their Prairie Avenue home had a schoolroom immediately inside the front door, allowing the children to go in and out without tracking dirt through other parts of the house.

'Over the thresholds of this house has passed a regular procession of teachers for you – in literature, languages, classical and modern, mathematics, chemistry, art and the whole gamut of the humanities and the practical, considerably beyond the curricula of the high schools,' John Jacob wrote in *The House at 1800 Prairie Avenue*.[25] 'Whether this plan of education was wise or not may be questioned. Of this I am sure, that it gave to each of you a great fund of general information, a power of observation and of reasoning, an ability and desire for study, and to be thoroughly proficient in what you might undertake. If ever there was a royal road for that, you had it, whatever its defects may have been in other respects.'

Fanny was every bit the achiever she had been groomed to be. In addition to all the classes she took, from the time she could hold a needle and thread in her tiny fingers as a toddler, she practised sewing, knitting, crochet and other forms of needlework. She became fluent in German, French and Latin. Her father noted that, even at a young age, Fanny was a good conversationalist, accustomed to spending most of her time in the company of adults.

Every summer, brother and sister escaped the heat of Chicago and enjoyed the freedom of their time at The Rocks.

'Never shall I forget the effect when, stepping off our [rail] car in Littleton, I drew the first full breath of good clean country air,' Fanny wrote in a letter much later in life. 'George and I were so happy to be there that we thought we couldn't live till we got home.'[26]

'That first night at the Big House was always something never to be forgotten – so cool, so clean, so quiet,' she continued. 'George and I would settle down in our beds so deliciously comfortable we could hardly get to sleep, and wake up in the morning to bright sunshine and getting up to be sure that everything was still there.'

Fanny used the wood-burning stove in her cabin to make jams and preserves for the household. On at least one occasion, she used it to make a full-course meal.

Days were spent swimming or exploring in the White Mountains or hiking around Franconia Notch, location of the iconic 'Old Man of the Mountain' formation that is a New Hampshire state symbol, and a 250m (800ft) long natural gorge called the Flume, where granite walls rose to a height of 21–27m (70–90ft).

Whether in Chicago or at The Rocks, evenings were whiled away with cards, word games or elaborate *tableaux vivants* – 'living pictures' – using improvised costumes and props to represent works of art or figures from the theatre or classical literature.[27]

At The Rocks, Isaac Scott built an 11m (35ft) tower with a small platform at the top, which the family called an observatory. Its elevation allowed a grand overview of the property and the villages of Littleton and Bethlehem below in the distance. George and Scott made it a daily ritual to climb the observatory at sunset and light a candle at the top, the flame a faint beacon in the darkness.

Scott was close to both children, teaching them drawing and woodcarving, but he had a particular bond with Fanny. During the summers at The Rocks, he became one of her constant companions and often accompanied the family on walks to observe wildlife.

'We have been most interested in the lovely birds,' Frances Macbeth wrote in her journal. 'There are hundreds of them and of many varieties – bluebirds, king birds, robins, song swallows, goldfinches, swallows, chippies, etc. We do not consider the day complete without finding a nest.'[28]

* * *

Fanny developed an interest in medicine at an early age. As a child, she was fascinated with mummies and the anatomical drawings of sixteenth-century anatomist Andreas Vesalius. This interest took a personal turn in May 1887 when, at the age of nine, she developed a serious illness while travelling by train from Chicago to The Rocks: fever, sore throat and vomiting.

Breaking the journey in New York City, Frances Macbeth took her daughter to a doctor, who diagnosed tonsillitis and recommended that she consult a surgeon. An operation was not a matter to be taken lightly in those days. Before the advent of antibiotics, analgesics and aseptic surgical methods, even a minor procedure could easily develop into a harrowing, life-threatening ordeal.

The first consultation was with a surgeon by the name of Dr Vanderfolk. Frances Macbeth recorded in her journal that he said there was nothing to be done but remove her tonsils; he would paint them with cocaine and snip them off.[29]

Fortunately for Fanny, her mother got a second opinion from another surgeon, Dr Lincoln, who was recommended as one of the best in the city. He said he would do the surgery using ether as an anaesthetic agent. Frances opted for Dr Lincoln's approach.

The surgery was done on the afternoon of 12 May. Dr Lincoln, assisted by a Dr Porter who administered the ether, performed it in the Glessners' hotel room. Fanny 'was very brave and good', her mother reported. 'Only once did she hesitate.'

Fanny sat in an armchair with a sheet pinned around her neck. Dr Porter dripped ether onto a cloth-covered mask over her mouth and nose. The operation proceeded uneventfully. Fanny woke briefly as the ether wore off, suffering great pain in her throat and ears, then slept for hours.

There is no way of knowing what substances might have been given to a nine-year-old girl in such circumstances at that time. Drugs and patent medicines were unregulated. There was no requirement for a drug to be proven safe or effective. A patent remedy might contain opium, morphine, heroin or cocaine.

Dr Lincoln gave the Glessners a prescription for an unspecified drug, but there was no need to have it filled. Fanny recovered, without the benefit of modern medicine, over a period of weeks. After two months, she was back to normal. Once fully recovered, Fanny wrote a poem in gratitude to her doctor:

D is for Doctor Lincoln
Of whom Fanny is constantly thinkoln
If he will come to The Rocks
We will don our best frocks
A white one, a blue one, a pink oln—

My dear doctor
It is very hard to find a rhyme for your name—
But I had to make a verse for you
So I have done my best all the same
And this is all that I can do.

Your little friend
Fanny[30]

At The Rocks, Fanny began to accompany local doctors on their rounds, visiting patients convalescing at home. Watching the doctors' ministrations filled her with awe. They were always wise and knowledgeable, kind and comforting. Sometimes, the doctor actively recruited Fanny to assist with procedures and minor operations. She began to use her cabin kitchen to make remedies – broths, nutritive wine jelly – for the patients.[31]

'But cooking and surgery were not the only interests in a home where mother and aunt were both domestic and artistic; such activities as fine sewing, embroidery, knitting, crocheting, painting and even working in handmade jewellery were as natural as breathing,' Fanny later recalled in an unpublished memoir.[32]

* * *

In 1890, George began his undergraduate education at Harvard University with the goal of taking a law degree. He became fast friends with a medical student, George Burgess Magrath. The two Georges, as Fanny called them, were inseparable. They even shared a birthday: 2 October.

Born in 1870, the only son of Reverend John Thomas and Sarah Jane Magrath, George Magrath sang in the choir at his father's church and at an early age became the church

organist. This skill was very useful to him as he worked
his way through medical school as an organist. Through
adulthood, he sang with The Handel and Haydn Society,
The Boston Cecilia chorus and The Harvard Alumni Chorus.
His vocal self-awareness and training would later lend
considerable gravitas to his bearing on the witness stand.

One thing seemingly absent from Magrath's character was
a romantic interest in women. He confirmed his bachelor
status in an alumni directory published by Harvard College.
'I am unmarried and expect to remain so,' he reported to
former classmates.[33] A newspaper profile published later
in his career noted what might be considered Magrath's
alternative lifestyle in genteel euphemisms. 'Yes, he's a
bachelor, not yet old enough to be called "confirmed",' a
reporter wrote. 'He appears to be one of those who "would
rather live in Bohemia than any other place".'[34]

* * *

In June 1893, Fanny, fifteen years old at the time, rode the
Ferris wheel with the two Georges at the World's Columbian
Exposition, the first world's fair to be held in Chicago.
Situated on 690 acres of the southside waterfront, the fair
was an opportunity to display the city's recovery from the
great fire of 1871.[35]

The Glessners visited the Exposition several times. Because
John Jacob had served on a steering committee of prominent
businessmen that had brought the event to the city, the family
had special access to the grounds during construction and
for the duration of the fair, and attended the grand opening
ceremony presided over by President Grover Cleveland.[36]

Fanny and her parents toured the fairground before
the opening, accompanied by Daniel Burnham, the fair's
director of works. Their tour included a trip on the lagoon
in an open motorboat, which floated past the Women's

Building, an impressive two-storey neoclassical structure near the Midway Plaisance.

The 7,500m² (80,000sq.ft) Italian Renaissance building was designed by twenty-one-year-old Sophia Hayden, the first female graduate of the architecture programme at the Massachusetts Institute of Technology and the first woman to design a prominent public building in America. It contained the largest and most ambitious exhibition of women's art ever undertaken until then, and the fair marked the first time women had created public art. At the time, women were thought to be unable to use the ladders and scaffolding necessary to work on sculpture and large-scale paintings. Critics and patrons were thus naturally curious about the art female creatives could produce.

Hayden and her building were intensely scrutinized. Other builders wondered aloud whether a woman could navigate a muddy construction site in a dress and high-heeled shoes. Critics and the public projected their own biases onto Hayden's design, assigning feminine qualities to her architecture. They said the building was somehow less assertive, more reticent and demure than buildings designed by men.

The clearest difference between Hayden's building and others at the fair was how much the architects were paid. Hayden earned $1,000 for her first commission. Men who designed comparable buildings at the exposition commanded ten times that sum for their work.

There was also much discussion in the Glessner household about the World's Congress of Representative Women, a week-long convention held in May in conjunction with the World's Columbian Exposition. The congress was the largest gathering to date of prominent women from across the spectrum of advocacy and activism. Nearly 500, including representatives from twenty-seven countries, delivered lectures and took part in panel discussions during the event, while more than 150,000 participants attended sessions. The writer Maud Howe Elliott was a guest at the Glessners' home for a fortnight. During the week of the women's congress, she was joined by her mother, Julia Ward Howe, renowned as the author of the patriotic 'Battle Hymn of the Republic'.

It is likely that, in another part of the exposition – the France pavilion – Fanny and George encountered an exhibit from the Paris police department and a curious bearded man, Alphonse Bertillon. George, a keen amateur photographer, would certainly have been intrigued by Bertillon's odd photographic equipment.

A reliable way of identifying criminals had been a long-standing problem. Names could be changed and signatures faked. Appearances could be altered. Even when police departments began using photography, creating rogues' galleries of criminals, the images were often useless for identification. Photos were of poor quality, overexposed or blurred, or just a wide shot of the whole body that made identifiable features hard to see. Police needed to know who they had in custody, so that wanted men couldn't run away from their misdeeds.

Bertillon, the son of a noted French statistician and anthropologist, believed that no two people were *exactly* alike. He devised a system of recording five primary measurements – the length and width of the head, the length of the middle finger, the length of the left foot and the length of the forearm from the elbow to the extended middle finger. He then created a record that included these measurements, descriptions of physical characteristics such as hair and eye colour, and standardized photographs – a clear close-up portrait of the face and a second image of the subject in profile. The profile photograph was particularly important, Bertillon contended, since the profile changed less dramatically with age, weight gain and facial hair.

Bertillon called his system *anthropometry*, the measurement of humans. It became known as *bertillonage* or the Bertillon system, and was adopted by police departments throughout Europe and the United States.[37] In preparation for the Columbian Exposition, Chicago police compiled a massive database of known criminals and recent parolees from across the country – the largest collection of bertillonage records in the United States.

One name missing from the rogues' gallery was H H Holmes – a physician, an entrepreneur, a devious liar, a skilled swindler and con man, and a sadistic murderer from the stuff of nightmares.[38] Holmes was responsible for dozens of – by some accounts as many as 200 – murders in Chicago around the time of the exposition, including many young women and children. He built a hotel with false walls and hidden rooms that became known as the 'Murder Castle'. Despite his having been in the hands of police numerous times in cities throughout the United States, authorities were completely unaware of his most serious crimes until long after the exposition ended and Holmes left Chicago.

At the time, there was no effective system to identify wanted criminals and little communication between police departments across the country. Bertillonage was far from ideal. It could only be applied to adults, since the measurements of children continue to change until they stop growing. More problematically, the system required calipers and other measuring equipment that tended to bend and misalign. It was difficult and unreliable and was abandoned when fingerprinting emerged in the early 1900s. All that remains of bertillonage today are the photos – the classic mugshot.

* * *

Upon graduation from Harvard in 1894, George Glessner spent the summer at The Rocks, intending to return in the autumn to begin law school. 'Before summer was out, however, I changed my plans, and went to work with my father's company,' he reported to Harvard classmates. 'I began at the bottom as a filing clerk, and for a time had good prospects of staying there, but owing to a fortunate combination of circumstances [I] have been appointed to the position of assistant manager. I find the work much more interesting than I expected, but also more engrossing.'[39]

George remained with Warder, Bushnell & Glessner through its merger into International Harvester, ultimately rising to the position of manager in the firm's Utility Division. He was involved in a number of organizations popular with businessmen of means, including the Chicago Club and the University Club, and was a member of the board of trustees of the Art Institute of Chicago.

His friend Magrath stayed at Harvard as a pathology assistant after graduating from medical school. He taught medical students and was a consulting pathologist for several hospitals in the Boston area.

Fanny 'came of age' in 1896. As befitting her arrival into young adulthood, she was subsequently called Frances more often than Fanny. The occasion of her birthday was noted in her mother's journal: 'On Wednesday, Frances was eighteen years old. We had eighteen carnations, eighteen lilies of the valley, eighteen candles and a fine cake on the breakfast table. We gave her a lovely watch and chatelaine.'[40]

The Glessners celebrated their daughter's milestone by sending her abroad with her Aunt Helen. In May 1896, the two women departed on the steamer *Etruria* for London, where they stayed for several months. Their excursion then included Norway, the Netherlands, Germany and France. They returned after being away for more than a year, in July 1897.

Within months, Frances began 'keeping company' with a thirty-year-old attorney, Blewett Lee, having been introduced by Dwight Lawrence, Blewett's legal partner and a Harvard classmate of George. Blewett visited the Glessners often during the latter months of 1897, having dinner with the family and taking Frances out for carriage rides.

A native of Columbus, Mississippi, Blewett was the only child of Stephen Dill Lee and Regina Lilly Harrison Lee. Stephen Dill Lee was a venerated former Confederate military leader who subsequently served in the Mississippi state senate and was the first president of the Agricultural and Mechanical College of the State of Mississippi at Starkville, now known as Mississippi State University. Some regard him as the father of industrial education in the South.[41]

Blewett graduated in the first class of the Mississippi Agricultural and Mechanical College, attended the University of Virginia for two years, then received his law degree from Harvard. After clerking for US Supreme Court Associate Justice Horace Gray for a year, he settled in Atlanta to practise law, but found the business difficult to break into and not particularly lucrative.

Family legend credited him with a remarkable missed opportunity. One day, he was visited by a man who asked the lawyer to draft the paperwork to incorporate a company. The client planned on producing a beverage based on a secret formula. He didn't have much money, so he offered Lee either shares in the new company or twenty-five dollars in cash. Blewett sipped the beverage, thought it tasted awful and insisted on the money. The man was Asa Candler and the company was Coca-Cola.[42]

Unsuccessful in Atlanta, Blewett moved to Chicago to teach law at Northwestern University. To supplement his income, he formed a practice partnership with Dwight Lawrence, who had flunked out of Harvard Law School but had extensive connections in the business and social worlds. This worked well for Blewett, since he knew the law but had no connections in Chicago.

His engagement to Frances Glessner was announced in late December 1897.

A notion persists that the young Frances didn't go to university because one or both of her parents forbade it. There is no evidence for this. John Jacob and Frances Macbeth Glessner were loving, supportive parents who doubtless would have helped their daughter fulfil her dreams. As a young woman of affluence, however, it was not considered likely for Frances to be concerned about a career or higher education. She wasn't expected to work outside the home. She would never have to earn a living but could look forward to a comfortable life of leisure and wealth.

Later in life, Frances told a reporter that she might have enjoyed being a nurse or going to medical school, but when she was young that sort of thing 'just wasn't done'. The truth is a little more complicated. Frances could have gone to university, even to medical school, if that had been what she really wanted.

To be sure, the medical field was an unusual choice for women at the time. It was a common belief that medicine was too indecent for a woman's delicate sensibilities and that women shouldn't know about the inner workings of the human body. By the end of the 1800s, however, many women were practising medicine in the United States, and there were several women's medical schools. Thanks to the efforts of five prominent Baltimore women who raised $500,000 – over £9 million in today's terms – to establish the Johns Hopkins School of Medicine in that city, three of the eighteen students in its first class in 1893 were women.[43]

Sarah Hackett Stevenson, the first woman accepted into membership of the American Medical Association, was a long-time friend of Frances Macbeth and often spent holidays with the Glessners, so the concept of a female medical doctor wasn't unfamiliar to them.[44]

The younger Frances had options, but not the one that she really desired. There was only one university that she wanted to attend, only one medical degree worth pursuing, and that was beyond her grasp: Harvard Medical School did not accept women as students.

Nevertheless, Frances maintained an affinity with the university. After all, it was still Harvard: purportedly the best and the brightest, the elite of New England bluebloods. In time, her feelings for Harvard would become more complicated, but it would be several decades before the university became an important part of her life again.

Frances was a month shy of her twentieth birthday when she married Blewett Lee, who was ten years her senior. 'We would rather have her a little older,' her mother wrote in her journal, 'but Mr Lee is so nearly everything in the world that is good and perfect that we cannot find it in our hearts to interfere with their complete happiness.'[45]

The wedding took place at 5pm on Wednesday 9 February 1898, in the Glessners' Prairie Avenue residence. Men moved the grand piano to the second floor and removed all the furniture from the parlour and hall. The floors were covered with muslin and the parlour draped with lilies, wild smilax and white orchids. Frances wore a satin gown with a deep, narrow flounce of double rose Venetian needle lace (*point de Venise*) and a tulle veil, and carried a bouquet of lilies of the valley.

The ceremony was conducted by Reverend Philip H Mowry, who had officiated at John Jacob and Frances Macbeth's wedding in 1870. The Chicago Symphony Orchestra played August Soderman's 'Swedish Wedding March' and 'Call Me Thine Own' from Fromental Halévy's opera *L'Eclair* for the procession, and Mendelssohn's 'Wedding March' after the ceremony.

At nine in the evening, Frances changed into her travelling clothes as the carriage waited to take the newlyweds to the train station. Then, according to Frances Macbeth's journal, '… they – the two – went out alone together, never to enter the home in the same way again.'[46]

CHAPTER 3

Marriage and the Aftermath

1898–1918

The newly wedded couple embarked on an excursion by rail to honeymoon at Blewett Lee's ancestral home in Mississippi, stopping along the way in St Louis, Missouri.[1] The marriage seemed blissful. Frances appeared to be the perfect bride, dutifully fulfilling the roles expected of her, and quickly became pregnant with their first child.

'I have never seen two young people more happily married,' Stephen D Lee wrote to Frances's parents after their visit.

On returning to Chicago, the Lees stayed at the fashionable Metropole Hotel on Michigan Avenue for several months, before taking an apartment at Indiana Avenue and Twenty-First Street, four blocks from her parents' Prairie Avenue home.

Despite the happy outward appearances, friction soon emerged in the marriage. As individuals, Frances and Blewett had quite different constitutions. He was a church-going nondenominational Christian, while for most of her life Frances was not religious. She enjoyed hiking and spending time outdoors; he preferred reading and other quiet intellectual domestic pursuits. She was a northerner, raised in a progressive and cultured family; he was the son of a revered Confederate figure who espoused the supremacy of white males above all others.[2]

Blewett was unable to feign enthusiasm for his wife's interest in needlework and crafts. Frances was prone to bursts of creative energy, sometimes seizing on an idea and working all day and into the night. It is quite likely that she felt unappreciated and unfulfilled in her marriage.

Neither Frances nor Blewett was used to the everyday adaptations and accommodations that are necessary for a successful union. He was an only child, while she was an only daughter who had not socialized in a school setting. Both of them had grown set in their ways.

As a Glessner, Frances had also become accustomed to a certain style of living, which her parents expected would be maintained for her. Blewett's salary could not afford this lifestyle, so the couple depended on her parents' continuing financial support. The Glessners' subsidy was gratefully accepted, but no doubt gnawed at both Frances and Blewett for different reasons. Relying on the assistance of his in-laws might easily have undermined Blewett's masculinity and his confidence as a breadwinner for the family. Frances resented the strings implicit in her acceptance of her parents' money, the insinuation of their presence and control in her life. She was also frustrated that she did not enjoy the independence and autonomy she thought would come with adulthood.

The birth of Frances and Blewett's first child, John Glessner Lee, on 5 December 1898, came barely ten months into their marriage. 'The Doctor said several times that he had never seen a more heroic girl or a quarter piece of stoicism than she showed all day,' Frances Macbeth noted in her journal. 'She made no outcry or complaint.'[3]

Even so, the young bride did not have an easy time after John's birth. 'She has been quite nervous,' her mother wrote. 'Saturday I was three times at Frances's house. I found her in tears several times. Yesterday she told me she doesn't like her nurse, that she is not obliging or agreeable, neither sympathetic nor gentle. I talked with the nurse and tried to impress her and make things better.'[4]

By the time the couple's second child, Frances Lee, was born in 1903, John Jacob Glessner had built matching homes for his children a block away from his own – at 1700 and 1706 Prairie Avenue. The stately three-storey houses were symmetrical, with the home where George and his wife Alice lived with their children a mirror image of the Lee family home next door.

Shortly after the birth of their daughter, Blewett Lee moved out of the family home. The specific issues leading to the couple's separation were not recorded, but deep temperamental and cultural differences are likely to have driven a wedge between husband and wife. Blewett remained on good terms with his in-laws during the separation, while the Glessners never wavered in their affection for him and remained sympathetic to the difficulties of having to deal with what, at the time, seemed to be a 'headstrong' woman.

Blewett rented an apartment at Prairie Avenue and Twenty-Second Street, directly above the apartment of his wife's aunts, Helen and Anna. He visited his children every day, arriving after work at 5pm on the dot; he read them the Bible or Joel Chandler Harris's Uncle Remus stories – the children delighted in his drawling rendition of Brer Fox and Brer Rabbit – and left forty minutes later.

The Lees reconciled briefly in 1905, during which period their third child, Martha, was conceived. Not long after Martha's birth in the autumn of 1906, however, Blewett moved out for good. He was hurt by the separation but never spoke ill of his children's mother, as his son John recalled later in life. Frances, on the other hand, was 'extremely outspoken and partisan' about Blewett.[5]

* * *

Meanwhile, attending to the family's interests in New Hampshire placed increasing demands on George Glessner, particularly as his parents grew older and spent less time there; the estate at The Rocks became more sophisticated and required more upkeep too. The fresh air remained a welcome respite from his hay fever, while being at The Rocks also allowed him to work on civil engineering projects that he enjoyed, such as building the generating station that provided the property with electricity.

The Rocks had a complete woodworking shop, equipment for milling and forging metal, and any tool that George could want. He had a staff of eighty people at his disposal, many of whom lived in one of the twenty buildings scattered throughout the property. George built his own home on the estate, which was named The Ledge.

In 1907, Alice and George, along with their three children, relocated from Chicago to reside full time at The Ledge. George acquired majority ownership of the Bethlehem Electrical Company, which provided electrical power to the community, and served as managing director of the affiliated Lisbon Light and Power Company. He also served as the Bethlehem town auditor for three years and, in 1912, was elected to the state House of Representatives, where he served two terms. In addition, he was engaged in a variety of civic roles, including as a trustee of the Littleton Savings Bank and as president of the Littleton Hospital Association, an organization founded by his father that built a modern fifteen-bed community hospital in 1907.

On 27 December 1903, John Jacob Glessner gave $125,000 – not far short of £3 million in today's money – in International Harvester stock to his daughter Frances and $100,000 of stock to her brother, in addition to the $25,000 in stock George had received upon graduation from Harvard. Dividends from these gifts would provide a comfortable income for both of Glessner's children for the rest of their lives.[6]

Three days later, several of Frances Lee's friends and their children were among more than 2,000 people in the Iroquois Theatre in Chicago for a performance of *Mr. Blue Beard*, a musical featuring Dan McAvoy and Eddie Foy. Located on Randolph Street between State and Dearborn, the newly constructed Iroquois was advertised as 'Absolutely Fireproof'.

Designed with a capacity of 1,600 people on three levels of seating, the venue was sold out for the 30 December performance. Hundreds more watched from the 'standing room' at the back of the theatre and an additional 300 were working as performers or crew.[7]

At the beginning of the second act, sparks from an arc light ignited a nearby muslin curtain. The fire quickly spread, filling the theatre with thick smoke as panic broke out. More than 600 people died, many of them women and children. That evening, Frances and her children visited her parents' home as word of the tragedy filtered through the community. Among the missing, presumed dead, were many of their friends and neighbours, including a number of children.

'It has all been a most horrible sickening thing, a most terrible disgrace in a civilized city,' Frances Macbeth wrote.[8]

The exact number of fatalities is unknown, since some victims were carried away from the scene and unaccounted for, and many of the dead were burned beyond recognition and had to be identified by jewellery or other personal belongings. The Iroquois Theatre fire remains the deadliest single-building fire in United States history.

On the evening of the fire, George Glessner went to the theatre to help recover bodies.[9] At her parents' home, Frances held her children close. Such a wrenching tragedy could happen to anybody, she thought. How horrible to lose a child or for a child to lose a parent or sibling, never to see them again – not even in a casket. Most heartbreaking were the bodies that would never be identified.

* * *

Back in New Hampshire, Frances purchased a property with a rustic hunter's cabin on Forest Lake, about an hour's drive away from The Rocks. She called this property Camp Lee, and it was her refuge away from her parents. During the summers, she and her children spent three or four days roughing it there; Frances cooked over a fire while the children went fishing or swimming.

The days at Camp Lee 'were the happiest times of my childhood', John recalled later. The family made up long adventure stories to tell each other and invented their own games. Frances was cheerful during these sojourns away from The Rocks, and when relaxed made for amusing company. 'Once she undertook to sing opera, all the parts, with gestures,' John said. '[My sister] Frances and I nearly died of laughter.'[10]

No longer inhibited by Blewett, Frances Lee's creative energies flourished. She produced needlepoints, sewed outfits for herself and her children, and devised elaborate centrepieces for the family dining table. In 1912, she undertook an ambitious project to create the entire Chicago Symphony Orchestra in miniature as a gift for her mother.

The Glessners had continued their association with the orchestra and maintained close relationships with the conductor, Frederick Stock, and many of the musicians. On more than one occasion, the full symphony orchestra played in the spacious courtyard at Prairie Avenue.

Frances Macbeth was so fond of music that she once expressed the fanciful desire to have the orchestra at her house every day. The idea germinated in her daughter's

mind to make her mother's wish come true. The younger
Frances imagined a miniature orchestra: all ninety musicians
in formal performance clothing, with their instruments.
Miniature men – the orchestra was exclusively male –
and miniature instruments weren't enough to satisfy her
obsession with detail. Each figure in the orchestra would
be finished to appear as close as possible to his real-life
counterpart.[11]

Frances chose to use a familiar 1:12 scale that is standard
for miniature doll's houses, with 2.5cm representing 30cm
(1in representing 1ft). She sat in her parents' box at the
Symphony Hall during rehearsals, sketching details of each
musician in pencil on porcelain bisque heads – hairline and
facial hair, the bushiness of eyebrows. Many members of
the orchestra posed for her sketches and assisted in the
construction of the miniature. In her home workshop,
Frances replicated the hair, moustaches and beards by
applying slip, a clay slurry, to the heads before refiring them
in a kiln. Painting with colour-matched enamel completed
the transformation.

She bought ninety identical wooden doll's-house straight-
back chairs and acquired a complete set of miniature musical
instruments. Some of these she purchased from dealers and
speciality suppliers if they appeared realistic and were in
the correct dimensions, but instruments not precisely to
scale were unacceptable. She hired a craftsman to make the
brass instruments and carved the reeds for the woodwinds
herself. The reed instruments, along with the bows of the
string section and other parts, were made from wooden
candy boxes and other cleverly repurposed household items.
Harpist Enrico Tramonti introduced her to a company that
made her a 15cm (6in) harp, complete with carrying case.

In appreciation for the Glessners' patronage, conductor
Frederick Stock wrote out by hand – working under
a magnifying glass and using sheets of paper the size of

postage stamps – a page of one of Frances Macbeth's favourite works, Arthur J Mundy's 'The Drum Major of Schneider's Band'. Each musician had the correct score for his instrument sitting on his stand.

Frances also sewed formal evening dress for each figure. The musicians wore white shirts with pearl buttons and detachable paper wing collars, black single-breasted waistcoats and matching evening coats. Stock, his arms raised, was dressed in a swallowtail evening coat. As a nod to her mother's practice of sending carnation boutonnières to the orchestra before performances, each figure had a perfectly formed fabric carnation, 4mm (⅙in) across, pinned to the right lapel.

Frances hired a stage carpenter to build a tiered platform nearly 2.4m (8ft) long. The miniature Stock was surrounded by musicians on a five-level stage. Six potted palms behind the orchestra decorated the display, along with roses in tasteful pink vases on either side of the conductor.

Frances presented the orchestra to her mother on 1 January 1913, on the occasion of the latter's sixty-fifth birthday. John Jacob Glessner described the event in his wife's diary, keeping it up to date when she was too ill to write herself:

New Year's was Frances' birthday and that afternoon Frances Lee gave her the wonderful 'little orchestra' – the full orchestra stage and full ninety men and their instruments, doll-size, all worked out in exquisite detail, and most of it done by Frances's own fingers... Nothing could be more complete or perfectly done, or more interesting.[12]

Little did anyone in the family know that, in the future, Frances's life's work would involve the creation of an entirely different kind of miniature.

Two weeks later, the entire orchestra was invited

to the Glessner home for dinner and to see Frances's finished creation. As was his custom with daily events that occurred in the home, John Jacob Glessner documented the occasion:

> Every member of the organization except three was present, making, with the fifteen or sixteen other guests, 105 or 106 who sat down for dinner that was prepared in this house... There was a punch at the close and toasts and songs and the musical programme before that was fine and humorous. The men were much interested in the 'little orchestra', and in seeing themselves as others see them, and went back again and again to the room over the parlour where it was, and Frances Lee was fully satisfied with their appreciation.[13]

Frances's next artistic endeavour was a homage to the celebrated Flonzaley Quartet. Formed in New York City in 1902 by Swiss-American banker Edward J de Coppet to accompany his amateur-pianist wife, the group was named after de Coppet's summer villa near Lausanne, Switzerland. Its members – Adolfo Betti on first violin, Alfred Pochon on second violin, Ugo Ara on viola and Iwan d'Archambeau on violoncello – were supported so that they would not have to tutor or do any other work and were free to devote themselves full time to playing music together.[14]

The Flonzaley Quartet rose to prominence after its first public concert in 1905, which led to performances in major cities in Europe and the United States. It was the finest and best-known string quartet of the time, a critical and commercial success; it was also the first string ensemble to record and issue music under its own name, allowing it to cultivate a following.

Frances's model of the quartet was constructed in the same 1:12 scale as her miniature Chicago Symphony

Orchestra and used the same bisque heads, but these proved to be better replicas. She took what she had learned working on the miniature orchestra to improve her techniques. All she needed were good, detailed observations of the physical appearance and distinguishing characteristics of each of the four musicians.

Her son John, now aged fifteen, accompanied her to hear the quartet perform. 'We went to concerts together, and sat on opposite sides of the house,' he recalled. 'We made elaborate notes on how the men sat and what they wore... Mr Betti's vest...how Mr Pochon put his feet... d'Archambeau's gold watch chain and how it hung...and last, but by no means least, Ugo Ara, who played the viola, a little Italian man with a magnificent Assyrian beard, how he managed his viola amongst the profusion of shrubbery.'

Betti and Pochon were depicted in dark evening coats and pinstriped trousers. D'Archambeau wore grey flannel trousers, waistcoat and bow tie, the gold chain of his watch slung across his midriff. On the right, wearing a long black coat, Ara held his bow poised over his viola. All four men wore white shirts with detachable paper collars and black shoes. Wires running under the clothing held limbs posed in place.

The instruments were perfect miniature replicas, and the tiny 10cm (4in) violoncello even worked, after a fashion. 'You could actually play the 'cello,' John Lee wrote. 'It emitted a faint squeak, but no sound would come from the smaller instruments, despite the care in making the bridge and strings and other parts.'

The model was presented to the musicians during their 1914 cross-country US tour. Frances Lee invited the quartet for dinner at her home. She sat at one side of the long, narrow table across from her father, between Pochon and d'Archambeau. John Jacob Glessner was placed between Betti and Ara. Aside from Frances's children, the dinner was also attended by three men connected with the Chicago Symphony Orchestra – conductor Frederick Stock, harpist Enrico Tramonti and assistant manager and treasurer Henry Voegeli – and their wives.

The figures were hidden within a large floral centrepiece in the middle of the table. 'After dinner, the floral piece was removed with a flourish, and there, not two feet from their noses, was this model of themselves playing!' John Lee recalled. 'The effect was extraordinary. For a moment nobody spoke, and then all four members of the quartet burst out in voluble language. Nobody listened. But each one of them pointed with delight to the eccentricities of the other three. I still remember Mr Betti, with a magnifying glass, peering over the shoulder of his own miniature, trying to read the music on the music rack.'

Once again, Stock had painstakingly handwritten the music on sheets of paper 2cm (less than an inch) tall. He had written an original composition mimicking the style of Austrian expressionist Arnold Schoenberg which, as a subtle musical joke, was not humanly possible to perform.

The quartet asked Frances for a photograph as a remembrance of the occasion. She gave them the models to keep.

* * *

Producing exquisite miniatures was no diversion from the unsatisfactory state of Frances's marriage. It became obvious that the relationship was beyond repair, and she wanted a divorce. At the time, one of the few acceptable grounds for divorce was desertion. Had Blewett been asked if he would return to the family home, he would have responded affirmatively. It was Frances who didn't want him.

In June 1914, after five years of separation, Blewett finally agreed to a divorce. At the hearing, Frances said that she had adequate financial means for herself and the children, who would remain in her custody. Afterwards, she destroyed every photograph in which she appeared with her ex-husband. No known photos exist of Frances and Blewett together.

The period after the divorce was 'an unhappy time for all', their son John recalled.[15] 'There was much family bitterness stemming from the divorce.' Frances was never on easy terms with her parents or her brother's family again. She felt that they were sympathetic to Blewett and not supportive of her needs, and that she was being blamed for the marriage's failure.

Isolated at home with her children, Frances whiled away her hours by sewing all of her children's clothing. 'During these troubled times FGL [Frances Glessner Lee] produced monumental amounts of needlework and played endless hours of solitaire,' John said, adding that his mother's dark moods were punctuated by flurries of activity: during summers at The Rocks, for example, she would recruit her children for a candy-making binge.[16]

'When a candy-making spree was started, the furniture was all pushed against the walls, and two alcohol pressure stoves brought down from the attic,' John recalled. 'White enamel kettles appeared from elsewhere, along with long candy thermometers, wooden stirring paddles, and a lot of miscellaneous equipment, including several professional candy-maker's [recipe] books.'

Frances and the children made chocolate creams, caramels, fudge, peanut brittle and taffy. Her equipment included a candy-maker's hook for pulling taffy and a marble slab she had obtained from a tombstone carver.

Whatever she was involved in, Frances allowed herself to be consumed by her work. Projects became all-absorbing, and she often worked all day and half the night for weeks at a time.

* * *

When the United States entered World War I in 1917, Frances took an interest in Naval Station Great Lakes, the US Navy's boot camp near northern Chicago. During the course of the war, about 125,000 sailors trained at the base.

Frances entertained sailors from Great Lakes at her Prairie Avenue home. In particular, she sought to invite musicians, whether enlisted men or officers. On Sundays, sailors were welcomed to dinner for an evening of entertainment and socializing, with talks and music provided by members of the Chicago Symphony Orchestra. Frances kept detailed notes on each guest: the dates of his visits, a physical description, whether gifts or correspondence were exchanged, home town, family situation and preferred beverage. If a sailor was a well-behaved and gracious guest, one of the boys she liked best, she pasted a gold star by his name.[17] She also gave servicemen stamped self-addressed envelopes so that they could keep in touch with her when they moved on. Many men wrote her letters and sent photographs. She rewarded those considerate enough to write by sending a package of cookies in return.

* * *

In March 1918, Chicago newspaper society pages announced an unusual performance at the Chicago Art Institute called the Finger Tip Theater. The announcement promised interpretative dancing from around the world, a circus performance, acrobatic stunts and tricks by trained animals.[18]

'The performance will be given on a stage 2 x 3 feet [60cm x 90cm], with a proscenium arch 19 inches [48cm] high,' the announcement said. 'Living performers only; no manikins.'

The Finger Tip Theater was scheduled to perform at 3pm for ten performances over a two-week period. Proceeds from the show were destined for the Fatherless Children of France fund, to help the children of soldiers killed in the war.

Curiosity was piqued about how living performers could appear on such a small stage. 'The auditorium will seat about fifty people, and the stage will be so tiny that everyone is wondering what or who the living performers that are advertised will be,' wrote the *Chicago Daily Tribune*'s society columnist. 'So whether dwarfs or trained fleas or white mice, one is left to wonder.'[19]

Finger Tip Theater premiered on the afternoon of 19 March. The sold-out audience included Hattie Pullman, wife of railroad magnate George Pullman; Grace Murray Meeker, wife of the Armour meatpacking company general manager; John Jacob and Frances Macbeth Glessner; and many more of Chicago's elite.

The stage was set up in the doorway between two galleries of the Art Institute. Drapes of black muslin framed the proscenium, giving the audience no clue as to what lay behind it. Bronze figures of a hunter goddess and her prey stood on newel posts flanking the sides of the stage.

The first item on the programme was 'Scourge de Djeverghitleft Ballet Russe', poetically performed by Madame Karsanoma. Also Charlotte Russe, the Matchless, the Champion Glace Skater of the World, was assisted by Axel Erickson, late Skater-in-Chief to the King of Scandinavia. The programme also included the dazzling flame dancer Luciola, and Mlle Sallpoffska and her Arabian Charger, Perpetuum Mobile; and it featured the Smallest Show on Earth, the Amalgamated and Consolidated Circus Company of Kalamazoo and Oshkosh, with Elmer, the smallest trained pachyderm in captivity, and sensational slack-wire artist Signor Centrifugo.

When the show began, according to *The Chicago Herald*, the audience was delighted to find that the performers were 'none other than the clever fore- and middle fingers of Mrs Frances Glessner Lee, who originated the new art'.

Lee – as we shall now begin to call her – had sewn costumes and dance outfits for her fingers, with little fingertip ballet slippers and a ruffled frill around her knuckles. Each act included exquisitely detailed sets and decorations. 'If one has an imagination that will shrink and shrink (which we all undoubtedly have),' continued the enraptured newspaper report, 'one can see on this miniature stage the most complete panoramas and thrilling dances one could possibly desire.'[20]

'There seemed to be no limit to Mrs Lee's ingenuity and versatility and the tiny scenes, which were perfect to the smallest detail,' said the *Chicago Tribune*'s society and entertainment columnist.[21]

Finger Tip Theater raised about $1,000 for the Fatherless Children of France, equivalent to more than £12,500 in present-day terms. On 30 March, the *Tribune* printed a letter written by Lee, thanking the Art Institute members for their generosity in providing the room and paying for the lighting and other expenses, allowing all the proceeds to go to charity. 'I am glad to have given my small efforts to this cause, and am grateful to you for your kind notices,' the letter said.[22]

But Lee wanted to do more than provide dinner and entertainment for sailors or host another benefit for a worthy cause. While working on Finger Tip Theater, she had felt the tug of a higher calling, a drive to do something with her life that was more meaningful and permanent: something in the service of others, something that might change lives for the better.

'I didn't do a lick of work to deserve what I have,' she once told a reporter. 'Therefore, I feel I have been left with an obligation to do something that will benefit everybody. I feel that I must justify my reason for being here.'[23]

The end of World War I in November 1918 would give her that opportunity. Thousands of young servicemen returned from overseas, many still suffering from the shellshock of battle. They found themselves far from home, unsure whether they wanted to return to the rural farms and towns they had left as younger, less experienced men, unsure what to do next with their lives. Servicemen's homes cropped up in major cities, providing a place for returning troops to decompress and reintegrate into society. In Boston, the Massachusetts Branch for Women of the Special Aid Society for American Preparedness opened a servicemen's refuge in Beacon Hill; it was called Wendell House in honour of Mrs Barrett Wendell, president of the Massachusetts Branch for Women, whose husband was chairman of the English faculty at Harvard. The house occupied two adjoining buildings on Mount Vernon Street, within blocks of Boston Common.

It was here that, at the age of forty, Frances Lee began the first job of her life. While her daughters, aged fifteen and twelve, remained under the care of their governess in Chicago, she moved to Boston, where twenty-year-old John was attending the Massachusetts Institute of Technology. The Chicago social pages noted Lee's departure for postwar service in Boston. She attended a concert of the Chicago Symphony Orchestra and 'said au revoirs to all friends present "till the last man's out of uniform".'[24]

Lee lived at Wendell House full time, serving as house mother and supervising the hostesses and service staff. Unlike other similar establishments, Wendell House was intended to feel like a private home rather than a dormitory or club. Lee furnished the building with carefully selected used furniture to give it a lived-in feel so that the men would step into a comfortable, familiar domestic environment.

Wendell House had a capacity of about a hundred residents, although men occasionally slept on camp beds or couches when necessary. A private room cost fifty cents a night, a bed in a dormitory room thirty-five cents. The house provided showers, laundry, a writing room, a reading room and a gymnasium. Breakfast was also available for a modest cost.

Writing to the Monday Morning Reading Class in Chicago, Lee said that the servicemen appreciated her efforts: 'The boys all say, "Well, ma'am, this is the only place we have ever struck that is just like *home*." They settle down as contentedly as cats.'[25]

Within five months, 1,212 servicemen had passed through Wendell House. It helped them get back home, find work or figure out the next chapter of their lives. With the troops now returning to civilian society, Lee faced the prospect of figuring out her own next chapter.

Over the years, she had continued to get updates about her old friend Magrath from her brother's frequent visits to Boston. 'All this time [my] interest in medicine did not lapse,' she wrote in an unpublished memoir. 'George Glessner accompanied George Magrath countless times on his cases, always bringing home a living detective story, all the more fascinating because it was true.'

CHAPTER 4

The Crime Doctor

1922–7

George Burgess Magrath was exasperated. According to Massachusetts law, medical examiners in the state did not have independent authority to investigate deaths. They worked at the discretion of district attorneys, although an autopsy could also be ordered in writing by the mayor or the district selectmen – local elected officials. Medical examiners were limited to investigating 'dead bodies of such persons only as are supposed to have come to their death by violence'.[1] Neither the law nor the courts ever defined what was meant by *supposed* or *violence*.

The problem was that medical examiners relied on the ability of police and prosecutors to recognize when a victim had died by violence. But what did the word mean? Was poisoning a form of violence? Was drowning violence? Did an infant suffocated in its crib suffer death by violence?

By the time the signs of violence were recognized, the deceased was often already in the funeral parlour. The indications could be as subtle as the puncture of a hypodermic needle or the pinpoint red spots of petechiae on the inside of the eyelid, suggesting strangulation. There might have been nothing externally visible at all.

It's the nature of murder that perpetrators try to cover up their deeds, attempt to alter facts to throw suspicion off their trail. A murder could be staged to look like an accident or a suicide. The signs of violence could be obscured by leaving a body on railroad tracks for a train to mutilate, by setting a body and building on fire, or by leaving a body buried in the woods to skeletonize.

Police, coroners and even many medical examiners were reluctant to examine a body that was in an advanced state of decomposition or burned beyond recognition, under the erroneous belief that any meaningful evidence was gone. These were also the most unpleasant cases, an additional incentive to keep at a distance and dispose of the body quickly. As often as not, police and district attorneys 'supposed' incorrectly, letting an unknown number of suspicious cases go undetected and calling in the medical examiner when most of the important evidence had already been altered or destroyed.

'We should do our own supposing,' George Magrath said in a talk to members of the Massachusetts Medico-Legal Society. 'Certainly if we wait for outward evidences of injury irrespective of the mode in which it was sustained, if we wait for proof that an individual has been shot, stabbed or run over, from the appearance of the body we shall miss a good many investigations which ought to be made, when death is due to causes other than natural.'[2]

Magrath never cared for the usual practice of clinical medicine. He was more interested in the broader perspectives of public health, serving at the start of his career as an assistant to the state's secretary of health, in charge of epidemiology and vital statistics for Massachusetts. Then in 1907, when Magrath was thirty-seven, Governor Curtis Guild Jr appointed him to a two-year term as medical examiner for Suffolk County, a jurisdiction that included Boston.

Boston's medical examiner office, the first in the nation, was established in 1877. Magrath was the second person to hold the job, succeeding a medical doctor named Francis A Harris. Magrath was the first medical examiner in the United States with training in pathology: the study of the causes and effects of disease. In a very real sense, he was America's first forensic pathologist. He had also been appointed as an instructor at Harvard Medical School, giving weekly one-hour lectures on legal medicine to third-year students as an elective course.

When he took on the medical examiner job, Magrath inherited an office in shambles. There was no archive of old case files, no systematic organization of records, no memoranda of practices and procedures. His official vehicle was his predecessor's horse-drawn carriage. Magrath asked for – and eventually received – a motorized ambulance to transport the bodies of the dead. The county's morgue on North Grove Street, behind the Charles Street Jail, was in poor condition. Even with improvements suggested by Magrath, the facility was barely adequate.

Most seriously, Magrath also discovered that his office lacked funding for basic necessities. For the first fifteen months of his tenure, the state legislature failed to appropriate money for the medical examiner's office. It wasn't until 1908 that state lawmakers provided funds for a telephone, printed stationery and the wages for assistants. Magrath's salary was a modest $3,000 a year.

Suffolk County had four medical examiners in total. Dr Timothy Leary, a pathologist at Tufts University Medical School, just north of Boston, was appointed in 1908. By agreement, he and Magrath divided the jurisdiction in half, with Magrath in charge of the northern division, Leary in charge of the southern and two associate medical examiners to assist them. Magrath and Leary often worked together on cases.

In addition to the lack of systems and of funding, Magrath found scant material on legal medicine. There were a few textbooks and journals but nothing like the literature that was available in Europe, where the field of legal medicine was much more developed.

No medical school in the United States offered the training Magrath believed was necessary preparation for the responsibilities of a medical examiner. Medical school had trained him in pathology. But legal medicine, what would later come to be called forensic pathology, was focused on patterns of fatal injuries, poisoning, postmortem changes and other subjects that were outside the usual teachings of medicine.

Before undertaking the job, Magrath spent more than a year in Europe to immerse himself in legal medicine. In London and Paris he observed their systems of death investigation, regarded as the most advanced in the world. He learned about inspecting death scenes, examining bodies, performing the autopsy procedure and microscopic tissue pathology. Most importantly, he learned to withhold judgement until all of the circumstances and facts were known. Upon his return, he incorporated the principles and practices learned from Europe's brightest legal medical minds into his work as medical examiner and into Harvard's medical school curriculum. He expressed his view of the responsibilities ahead:

> The duties of this office consist chiefly in the investigation of deaths due to injury of any sort and those which are sudden or unexplained; they necessarily include service from time to time in court... In doing my work I have sought to apply to the branch of state medicine, which my office represents, the result of the generous type of scientific medical education which it was my good fortune to receive... The general standard of medical jurisprudence in this country is none too high and it is my aim to help raise its level by applying to my own work the

principles and the methods of modern scientific medicine
and by impressing on the student the importance of the
responsibility of the physician in all matters wherein
medicine is brought into the service of the law.[3]

Magrath carried a leather-bound loose-leaf field book to
document cases he investigated as Suffolk County medical
examiner. He kept notes on each case in a code understood
only by himself and his secretary so that, if the book fell
into the wrong hands, no derogatory information would
be disclosed about a deceased person. Inside the cover he
inscribed a quotation by Paul Brouardel, pathologist and
member of the Académie nationale de médecine, France's
leading authority on legal medicine. Brouardel's words
became Magrath's fundamental guiding principle:

> If the law has made you a witness, remain a man of
> science; you have no victim to avenge, no guilty person
> to convict, and no innocent person to save. You must
> bear testimony within the limits of science.[4]

On duty twenty-four hours a day, Magrath was a well-
recognized figure on the streets of Boston, motoring around
in the same clattering 1907 Model T that served him for
the duration of his career. The car, which Magrath named
'Suffolk Sue', was equipped with a fire-engine bell to clear
traffic and a small, round MEDICAL EXAMINER medallion
mounted on the grille.

By nature, Magrath was mild-mannered and even-
tempered. 'He was always cheerful and genial, kindly and
tolerant,' Frances Lee said. 'He never sat in judgement on
anyone. I never saw him angry or impatient.' He was just
like Suffolk Sue's number plate – 181 – which read the
same backwards or forwards or upside down. 'Like his car
licence, "always the same",' Lee said.[5]

Physically, Magrath was a striking figure – tall, with broad shoulders muscled from years of rowing on the Charles River and an unruly shock of flaming red hair. He favoured flowing ties and a dark-green waistcoat, wide-brimmed hats and an ever-present curve-stemmed tobacco pipe. He intentionally cultivated an air of eccentricity: for example, by letting it be known that he ate only one ample meal a day, at midnight.

Magrath told his Harvard colleague, toxicologist William F Boos, that being conspicuous was a large part of professional advancement. 'You ought to set about to impress yourself on 'em more,' Magrath said to Boos. 'It helps.'[6]

At the scene of a death, however, any semblance of showmanship disappeared. Magrath's investigations were meticulous and thorough, applying keen scientific judgement to the tasks at hand. He often pointed out clues overlooked by police and suggested productive lines of investigation.

In the autopsy room, Magrath fell into a mood of deep concentration the moment a body was wheeled in on a hospital trolley. One eyewitness wrote that he had 'the controlled frenzy of the explorer... More than most men, he had the chance and the genius to explore the mysteries which each of us carries within the envelope of the skin... He gave the same careful attention to a repelling "floater" taken from the harbour, as the well-preserved man of distinction who'd happen to drop dead on Tremont Street.'[7]

On the witness stand, Magrath was confident and unshakable. With a baritone voice burnished by choral practice, he answered questions in a clipped, direct manner, keeping to facts he knew to a reasonable degree of medical certainty, based on scientific evidence and not drifting into speculation or conjecture. 'His statements were the model of precision,' Boos said.[8]

Courtroom sketches of Magrath show him with his face cast downwards, eyes closed or obscured behind spectacles.

He looks as if he might be sleeping, but in fact he is deep in thought, listening to a question or formulating his response. Framed by his wild mane of hair, on the witness stand Magrath was 'like a lion resting', one observer noted.[9]

Outside court, Magrath declined to talk to reporters about cases still unresolved or under investigation. The proper place for matters of legal medicine was the courtroom, he believed, not the pages of newspapers. He sometimes talked about closed cases years after the fact, spinning yarns for crime reporters about some of his infamous investigations, but never before a case was concluded with a conviction or acquittal.

If he had one fatal flaw, it was his weakness for alcohol. He never drank to the point of stuporous belligerence, but consumed on a daily basis to maintain a steady state of intoxication. He drank to calm his nerves at the end of the day. He drank to erase the unspeakable horrors to which his occupation forced him to bear witness. He drank to chase the demons that lurked in the recesses of his mind. Although the man dissected human bodies for a living, he 'went into something approaching eclipse at the death of those close to him', a contemporary said.[10]

Some of Magrath's duties must have been deeply upsetting, such as the requirement to witness the execution of condemned prisoners and pronounce their deaths. After executions, friends would meet him outside the state prison to 'get three drinks into him quickly'.[11]

Those who knew Magrath said it was his superior intellect, integrity and a fastidious eye for detail that made him particularly well suited for legal medicine. For every measurement he took, he measured twice. So as not to influence an investigation with misbegotten hunches, he forced himself to keep an open mind until he knew all the facts and had considered all the circumstances; he then applied judgement and common sense in a relentless pursuit of the truth.

'As a medical examiner he was pre-eminent, finding in that profession the niche into which he exactly fitted,' Lee said of her friend. 'His meticulous accuracy, his exact adherence to the truth, and his immeasurable patience and skill in determining what was the truth made his advice and judgement much sought after.'[12]

At the time of his appointment as medical examiner, Magrath lived in a renovated dwelling at 274 Boylston Street, overlooking the swan boats in the Boston Public Garden. With no suitable office space available, Magrath based the medical examiner's office in Boylston Street, which was its official address for the next thirty years.

The room behind his office was Magrath's living space, the walls lined with shelves groaning with books. He had a 2m (7ft) long ship's bunk with a reading light at one end, a steamer chair by a fireplace and a telephone at the bedside so he could respond quickly in an emergency. To the rear of this room was a combined bathroom and kitchenette, with cabinets and a gas stove.

He ate most of his meals at St Botolph Club, a gentleman's club situated conveniently around the corner in a mansion at 7 Newberry Street, to the west of the Public Garden. St Botolph was a gathering place for men who appreciated the arts, sciences and humanities. Magrath's old school friend George Glessner was also a member, as were H H Richardson, who had designed the Glessners' Chicago home, and many other Harvard men of substance. Magrath was at St Botolph so often that he used the club as his residential mailing address.

On a typical day, after working late in the evening at the morgue or the scene of a death, Magrath telephoned the chef at St Botolph just as he was about to close down for the night and gave his order for dinner – clams and spaghetti or beef steak barely charred and served blood-rare. He showed up at midnight for his meal, socialized and told stories for a while, then returned home to read until the wee hours of the morning.

Magrath made a name for himself by applying the rigorous methods of medical science to the investigation of death. Newspaper stories about his high-profile cases added to his prestige as a Sherlockian 'crime doctor'. In time, he was asked to consult on cases by police departments throughout Massachusetts and other New England states.

And always, every day and every night as he did his work, Magrath used science to learn as much about the facts of a death as was humanly possible. He believed that death merited the most rigorous critical analysis and that the archaic coroner system should be abandoned for one that allowed a rational basis for determining the causes of death.

One of the prominent cases that cemented the value of the medical examiner system was the death of Avis Linnell.[13] Linnell was a nineteen-year-old choral singer from Hyannis, living at Boston's Young Women's Christian Association. Shortly after 7pm on the evening of 14 October 1911, residents of the YWCA heard sounds of distress from within the shared bathroom, which was locked from the inside. They forced open the bathroom door to find Linnell sitting in a chair, her feet immersed in a tub half-filled with warm water, gasping for breath and groaning in agony. The matron sent for a doctor immediately. Linnell was moved to a bed, but by the time the doctor arrived she was dead.

The matron had the presence of mind to close the bathroom door and leave the room as it was until the police and the medical examiner arrived. Magrath was out of town on a rare holiday, so Timothy Leary responded to the call to inspect the bathroom and the body. Linnell was taken to the morgue for an autopsy.

During the minutes before she died, Linnell had told witnesses at the YWCA that she had had lunch that day with her fiancé, thirty-five-year-old Reverend Clarence Richeson, a pastor in Cambridge. The matron asked one of the girls to telephone Richeson and notify him of her death. At first, he denied knowing Linnell. Then he said, 'Why are you telling me this?'

Leary's autopsy revealed that Linnell was about three months pregnant. The lining of her stomach was deeply discoloured, with streaks of red radiating over the gastric mucosa – the mucous membrane that lines the stomach – which indicated poisoning by cyanide. Leary retained Linnell's organs for Magrath to examine on his return.

Magrath agreed with Leary's diagnosis and prepared specimens of the gastric mucosa for examination under the microscope and laboratory testing for the presence of cyanide. The tests confirmed their suspicion.

The police were ready to close the case as a suicide. Obviously, they said, she took the cyanide herself. Nobody was in the bathroom with her, and the door was locked from the inside. Perhaps the shame of her delicate condition had led her to end her life.

Leary disagreed. For one thing, Linnell had had a change of clothing in the bathroom to wear after her bath. She also had a harness and sanitary napkin even though she was pregnant and hadn't menstruated in several months. It appeared as though she expected to begin menstruating: she may have been attempting to induce an abortion. Leary was certain that Linnell had expected to leave that bathroom alive and insisted that the police keep digging.

Police interviewed Richeson but were unable to connect him to the cyanide that killed Linnell. Richeson was a serial philanderer who had left a trail of fraud and broken hearts stretching from Boston to Kansas City. He may have been a cad, but did that make him a killer?

Newspapers latched on to the tragic death of the young singer. Reading about the case, William Hahn, the owner of a drugstore in Newton Center, just outside Boston, contacted police to inform them that Richeson had been in his shop four days before Linnell's death. Hahn knew Richeson, a regular customer. He said that, on 10 October, Richeson had told him he had a dog at home that was going to have puppies. 'She is whining around the house and is a nuisance,' Hahn said Richeson told him. 'I want to get rid of her.'

Hahn sold Richeson potassium cyanide – enough to kill ten people. 'It is as quick as lightning, but it is very dangerous,' he warned his customer.[14]

Richeson didn't own a dog.

When confronted with Hahn's statements, Richeson confessed to poisoning Linnell. He had wanted to leave her and marry a wealthy socialite, but Linnell's pregnancy had thrown a spanner into his plans. Richeson gave Linnell the cyanide, telling her that it was a medicine that would induce an abortion.

Two weeks before he was to stand trial for her murder, Richeson stood before a judge and admitted that he had intentionally killed Linnell. He was sentenced to death. Magrath was a witness when Richeson was executed on 21 May 1912.

'There was no primary suspicion of foul play,' Magrath pointed out. 'It was only when the postmortem examination disclosed a condition in the stomach suggesting poisoning by potassium cyanide that death from causes other than natural was suggested.

'The further discovery of a physical condition compatible with suicide strongly suggested this motive of death,' he continued. 'Only the care and diligence of Medical Examiner Leary, who had charge of the case, led to a further investigation by the police resulting in the conviction of Richeson.'[15]

If Boston had been operating under a coroner system and without the benefit of standardized practices such as autopsies, Magrath knew, Richeson would more than likely have got away with murder.

Two similar cases. One death, almost mistaken for a suicide, resulted in a man being sent to the electric chair. Another death seemed highly suspicious, but Magrath's investigation revealed a natural cause. Either case could have turned out very differently. In another era, in another place, one person may have been prosecuted for a crime he did not commit while another got away with murder. Scientific investigations cleared the innocent and convicted the guilty.

* * *

Not a political creature by nature, George Magrath did his work and kept his mouth shut. His unwillingness to compromise and his single-minded adherence to the facts as established within the bounds of science occasionally made things difficult for others. It should come as no surprise that he made enemies along the way. The police couldn't count on him to see things their way. Lawyers were unable to get him to say what they wanted in court. Magrath wasn't on one team or another. His only loyalties were to the deceased.

However, Magrath did have one key ally: Suffolk County district attorney Joseph C Pelletier, who was elected to office in 1906 and served until 1922. Pelletier relied on Magrath's judgement and trusted him to testify truthfully in simple terms that were easy for a jury to understand.

Some parties in the Boston political machinery wanted to replace Magrath with a medical examiner who might be more malleable to their interests. Magrath's first seven-year term of office was scheduled to expire in January 1914. As this date approached, he became the target of concerted attacks on his work and his character in an attempt to thwart his reappointment by the governor. His opponents hoped to install a crony who could be relied upon to play ball with local politicians.

In February 1913, a politically connected attorney filed a lawsuit on behalf of a woman who claimed that the medical examiner had mutilated her husband by performing an autopsy without her permission. The husband, John A Brimfield, had been a patient in the psychopathic department of Boston State Hospital for an unspecified brain disease.[16] According to the lawsuit filed by Berenice Brimfield, in which she sought the considerable sum of $10,000 in damages, her husband had died on 7 January from natural causes. When asked about an autopsy, she had refused to give permission.

The body, Mrs Brimfield alleged, had been delivered to the medical examiner without her consent. She claimed that Magrath 'sacrilegiously cut, hacked, hewed and mutilated the body', removing and keeping the brain and leaving the dead man's tongue in his abdomen. 'She alleges the condition of the body would offend a stranger, to say nothing of an afflicted and bereaved wife,' read an account in *The Boston Globe*.[17]

A few months later, as the Brimfield lawsuit inched along, the stakes were raised in a separate incident, when a group of morgue employees ill-advisedly plotted to frame Magrath with larceny.[18] On 17 June 1913, a man named Thomas O'Brien dropped dead while painting the Bay State Trust Company building. His body was taken to the North Grove Street morgue, where assistant superintendent George Miller and autopsy assistant Frederick Green found more than $350 in his waistcoat pocket. Another worker, Thomas Kingston, and the undertaker's assistant who brought the body to the morgue also saw the money.

Three hundred and fifty dollars was a substantial sum – a decent month's salary at the time. Miller and Green kept about $230, then sealed the rest and O'Brien's other personal effects in a regulation manila office envelope – essentially an evidence envelope that also served as a receipt to prove that objects had a continuous chain of custody. Green, Miller and Kingston agreed to pin the theft on Magrath. It would be the word of three people against one, after all. How could it fail?

A couple of days later, O'Brien's nephew, a police officer, went to the morgue to identify the body and collect his uncle's personal effects. It didn't take long for him to notice a discrepancy between the amount of money in the envelope and the amount that the undertaker's assistant told him had been removed from the body. When notified that money was missing, Magrath called the police and referred the matter to the district attorney.

By coincidence, around the same time Governor David I Walsh began receiving letters complaining of shocking goings-on at the North Grove Street morgue – thefts from the dead, a medical examiner who mutilated bodies, all sorts of horrible things. Walsh announced that he would not reappoint Magrath or name a successor while these issues remained a cloud over the medical examiner's office.[19]

Fifteen police reporters representing every newspaper in Boston urged Walsh to reconsider. Coming together of their own accord, they told the governor that they acted out of a sense of duty to warn that failure to reappoint Magrath would be a serious blow to the best interests of the people of Massachusetts.

After Magrath's appointment expired in January 1914, his position was in limbo. But although not officially on the job, he was determined to continue working until he was reappointed or replaced, and so went on with his duties as usual.

Magrath was represented in the Brimfield lawsuit by Joseph Pelletier, the district attorney. Testifying in his own defence, Magrath explained that the postmortem examination he had performed on Brimfield was a standard procedure, the same that was followed in every full autopsy. He insisted that the investigation had been done in pursuance of written authority from the district attorney and in accordance with the law. An examination of the brain had been necessary to determine whether Brimfield's death or the condition for which he was institutionalized was related in any way to an injury, either recently or in the past. It wasn't uncommon for patients in facilities to experience falls that resulted in head injury or even to be struck by other patients. The brain was retained, as was routine in these cases, for fixation of the tissue and examination of slides under a microscope.

Yes, Magrath said, Mr Brimfield had died of natural causes. But that couldn't have been known for sure until the postmortem examination was completed. In his closing argument, Pelletier told the jury that if Magrath was guilty, then he was too, because the medical examiner was working under his direction. The jury returned a verdict in Magrath's favour.[20]

Weeks later, the plot by Green, Miller and Kingston backfired in spectacular fashion.[21] As it turned out, Magrath had been busy on 17 June, the day Thomas O'Brien had died and Magrath was supposedly stealing money from his body. He had attended the Harvard–Yale baseball game, sitting in the front row to be accessible in case of an emergency. After the game, on his way to the morgue, his attention had been drawn to a large fire in east Boston. He drove to the fire in case there were fatalities and he was needed. Later, he attended a dinner with Harvard alumni, and it was three in the morning by the time he reached the North Grove Street morgue.

When Magrath arrived to examine O'Brien, he learned that the body had already been searched and the deceased's property sealed in an envelope. This was a violation of procedures and was noted as unusual by others, including

Magrath's secretary. Magrath's rule was that bodies were not to be searched until he issued the order. The medical examiner should always inspect the untouched body first, before a search for valuables and property, to avoid affecting the body in any way and to ensure that the collection of personal effects was witnessed.

Green was forced to admit that he had made entries in the logbook, searched the body and sealed the evidence envelope before Magrath arrived at the morgue. Magrath could not possibly have taken money from O'Brien's body. The last person to touch O'Brien's money was, in fact, Green himself. His own handwriting sealed his fate.

Green, Miller and Kingston were arrested and charged with larceny and conspiracy. They were sentenced to fifteen months in prison.[22] Governor Walsh reappointed Magrath to another seven-year term as medical examiner for Suffolk County.

* * *

A year after his reappointment, Magrath was asked to help New York City reform its notorious coroner system, which was hopelessly corrupt, a detriment to public health and a hindrance to the administration of criminal justice.

New York City's coroners were the worst of all worlds. 'The coroner is not a medical man and is thus incompetent to determine causes of death,' *The New York Globe* noted in a 1914 editorial. 'He is not a lawyer and thus does not know how to gather evidence and to examine witnesses; he has had no experience in criminal investigation and is an injury rather than a help to following up clues.'[23]

Reform of the system was inspired by the sudden collapse and death of an elderly citizen at The Century Association, one of Manhattan's exclusive clubs. Even though the death was clearly due to natural causes, the coroner refused to sign the death certificate unless the body was taken to the funeral parlour he recommended (and from which he was presumably receiving kickbacks). Members of The Century Association were outraged and demanded action from Mayor John Purroy Mitchel, who appointed his commissioner of accounts, Leonard Wallstein, to investigate.[24]

Magrath told Wallstein's committee he was certain that in at least one case, a coroner's physician had covered up a murder – either on purpose or unwittingly through incompetence. A man by the name of Eugene Hochette had been found dead at New York's Hotel Delaware in March 1913 with a single gunshot wound to the head. Dr Timothy Lehane, the coroner's physician, certified the death as suicide and permitted the cremation of the body the next day without an autopsy.[25] Before this, however, two pathologists had had an opportunity to examine Hochette – Dr Charles Norris, director of laboratories at New York's Bellevue Hospital, and Dr Douglas Symmers, pathologist of Bellevue Medical College. Both noted the absence of powder burns around the gunshot wound in Hochette's head. When a gun is fired, burning gunpowder produces stippling and soot on the skin up to a distance of about 60–90cm (2–3ft). This wound was caused by a gun held at a greater distance and could not have been fired by the deceased.

Magrath agreed with Norris and Symmers. 'I should say,' he said, 'that the diagnosis of the coroner's physician was not supported by evidence.'[26]

Magrath urged state lawmakers to abolish the office of coroner and replace it with a system of medical examiners. Testifying before members of the state legislature, he said that a properly written law would be 'a nearly perfect instrument, and that under its provisions New York City would be provided with an opportunity not only to protect its citizens but to contribute incalculably to the advancement of medicine as applied to crime and casualty'.[27]

State lawmakers drafted a bill to establish a medical examiner office in New York City. The statute eliminated the office of coroner, prohibited inquests and took away the legal and judicial aspects of death investigation. The legal part of the coroner's job, placing charges in cases of homicides and criminal negligence, would be taken over by prosecutors, while magistrates would assume the judicial duty of setting bail.

Under the new law, which came into force on 1 January 1918, the chief medical examiner was authorized to conduct an autopsy in cases of sudden, unnatural or suspicious death without the need for an order from a prosecutor. He was independent of the district attorney and the police, elevated as an equal to provide the medical expertise in forensic investigation. He was required to be a competent physician, expert in legal medicine, and would be chosen based on the civil service exam and not as part of any political process. His only duty would be to the deceased.

Magrath was asked to apply for the position, but he was disinclined to leave Boston. Charles Norris, who had trained in pathology and anatomy in Europe, was appointed instead. He immediately began improving forensic investigation in New York City, including hiring key personnel such as Alexander Gettler, who established a chemistry laboratory to perform tests for poisons and drugs. In time, New York City's chief medical examiner's office became a model of a modern forensic medical centre, working some of the most sensational cases of the twentieth century and becoming the birthplace of American forensic toxicology.[28]

* * *

The evening of 7 November 1916 was unseasonably warm. At 5.30pm, Bostonians were hurrying home or to Newspaper Row, the stretch of Washington Street that housed several of the city's newspapers and the place where many people got up-to-the-minute news.

Streetcar Number 393 was headed inbound down Summer Street, fully loaded with fifty to sixty passengers. As the streetcar barrelled along, driver Gerald Walsh realized – too late – that the drawbridge over the Fort Point Channel was open. He pulled the brake, locking the wheels as the car crashed through iron gates that blocked the street, then slid 8m (25ft) down the tracks to the edge of the canal, where it teetered, seeming to hang momentarily. The car's rear platform lifted into the air until it plunged over the side and sank in 9m (30ft) of water.

'The rear end seemed to catch on the edge for an instant so the car tilted almost straight up and down. Then it shot downward toward the water,' said tugboat captain William G Williams, who witnessed the incident. 'The crash was followed by a deathlike stillness. I expected to hear shrieks and shouts, but not a sound of human voice did I hear. Everything was very quiet.'[29]

Fifteen people who had been standing on the rear platform of Number 393 were able to jump off before the car dropped into the water. An unknown number remained in the packed streetcar, which sank to the bottom of the channel.

It was a disaster of unprecedented scale and complexity, compounded by large crowds gathering to watch the unfolding tragedy. By 9pm, thousands of people thronged along the canal at the approach to the bridge. Police repeatedly charged at the crowd with batons drawn to push them back from the edge of the water.

Magrath was responsible for identifying and examining bodies recovered from the canal. Mayor James Curley ordered that the bodies be recovered out of view of the public, to deny gawkers and press photographers the ghastly and undignified sight of casualties being fished from the water. The bodies were moved underwater by a team of six divers, who tied ropes to them, enabling them to be dragged unseen to the police boat moored a distance away from the scene. In one of the boat's cabins, Magrath set up a temporary morgue and carried out a preliminary assessment. The bodies were then transferred to another police boat, ferried to Constitution Wharf and taken from there by ambulance to the North Grove Street morgue for identification and postmortem examination.

A total of forty-six bodies were recovered from the submerged streetcar, making this the deadliest disaster in Boston history. Magrath's thoughts about the incident were never recorded, but the scale of the tragedy was unlike anything he had ever seen and must have left him stunned and exhausted.

Less than three years later, on 15 January 1919, Boston was struck again by an unusual catastrophe. On the Purity Distilling Company wharf at the city's North End, an old waterfront neighbourhood where the Charles River emptied into the harbour, stood a tank of molasses. The tank, five storeys high and 27m (90ft) across, held over 10 million litres (2.3 million gallons) of molasses destined to be fermented into ethanol.[30] What the neighbours didn't know was that the tank, only three years old, had been poorly designed, had never been pressure-tested and was constructed with substandard materials. It was so badly built that children ate chunks of hardened molasses that had leaked through the seams.

At 12.30 on that January afternoon, 150 paving-yard employees were taking their lunch break when they felt a low rumbling. Suddenly, rivets popped like gunfire, and the tank blew apart, releasing 12 million kilograms (26 million pounds) of molasses in an 8m (25ft) tall wave moving at 56kph (35mph) and destroying everything in its path. A section of the tank blew out two supports of the nearby elevated train line, causing it to collapse to the ground and nearly derail a streetcar.

The freight shed and paving yard were instantly reduced to kindling, covering workers with molasses and debris before they had a chance to escape. Trucks, motorcars and horse-drawn wagons were swept along by the relentless tsunami of molasses. The firehouse was pushed off its foundation, killing one fireman and injuring two more. Another fireman was knocked into Boston Harbour; he survived, but a ten-year-old boy pinned beneath an overturned railroad car was not so lucky. More than a dozen injured horses were mired in molasses and eventually had to be shot to end their suffering.

Magrath was one of the first to respond to the scene. He helped set up a field hospital and temporary morgue in a nearby building. Wearing hip-high rubber wading boots, he surveyed a scene of unimaginable devastation. Every structure within 120m (400ft) of where the molasses tank had stood was demolished. Buildings were splintered, and steel beams and sheet metal lay in twisted piles. More than two blocks – tens of thousands of square metres of a busy city neighbourhood – were coated with molasses up to several centimetres thick.

Bodies recovered at the scene looked 'as though covered in heavy oil skins', Magrath said. 'Their faces, of course, were covered with molasses, eyes and ears, mouths and noses filled.'[31] He examined the bodies as quickly as they arrived at the morgue. 'The task of finding out who they were and what had happened to them began by washing the clothing and bodies with sodium bicarbonate and hot water.'

Autopsies showed that several of the victims had been crushed or fatally injured by debris. Some were horribly mutilated, their chests caved in and limbs twisted. Many had suffocated, molasses filling their airways and lungs; they had drowned in molasses. Twenty-one people died in the disaster, and about 150 were injured. Despite all his training and the thousands of cases he had examined up to that point, nothing had prepared Magrath for the devastation wrought by a common storage tank.

* * *

Magrath became involved in the most controversial case of his career on 15 April 1920. Two employees of the Slater-Morrill Shoe Company in South Braintree, Massachusetts, were robbed and shot to death while carrying the company's $15,700 payroll into the factory.[32]

Magrath performed the autopsies on Alessandro Berardelli, a thirty-four-year-old security guard, and forty-four-year-old Frederick A Parmenter, an unarmed paymaster. The men were fathers with two children each. Berardelli had been shot four times and Parmenter twice. Magrath measured the path of each wound, using his fingers to retrieve the .32-calibre projectiles, never grasping with metal instruments that might scratch the bullet and obscure rifling marks.

As he recovered each projectile, Magrath used a surgical needle to scratch a Roman numeral on the base of the bullet – the one surface without significant markings. He numbered the bullets individually, in sequence, so that he could verify his mark and describe in court the damage caused by the projectile.

Police charged Italian-American anarchists Nicola Sacco and Bartolomeo Vanzetti with the homicides of Berardelli and Parmenter. The men were swept up in postwar hostility against foreigners and radicals, and the case became a cause célèbre throughout the country.

Sacco, a shoemaker and security guard, and Vanzetti, a fish peddler, denied involvement in the crime. Neither of them had a criminal history, but both had been carrying handguns when they were picked up for questioning by police: Sacco had a Colt automatic pistol he said was necessary for his job as a security guard; Vanzetti's gun was a .38-calibre Harrington & Richardson revolver he said was to protect himself while carrying cash he earned selling fish.

The case against the two men was built on a profusion of confusing witness statements and ambiguous ballistic evidence. Both had alibis for the day of the crime. Vanzetti had peddled fish to customers all day. Sacco also accounted for his whereabouts. Still, five eyewitnesses placed them at the scene of the crime.

Prosecutors claimed that the revolver found on Vanzetti had been taken from Berardelli, the slain guard, but the link was never positively established. Others have suggested that Berardelli didn't even have his gun with him on the day of the robbery.

Witnesses said that Berardelli had been shot twice, then two more times while he was lying prone on the ground. The bullets Magrath recovered were consistent with these statements, with two wounds in the back having been inflicted by a person standing over the body. Magrath described one projectile, which he had etched with the Roman numeral III, as the fatal bullet. It had pierced Berardelli's right lung, severing the pulmonary artery.

To Magrath's eye, nearly all the bullets recovered from Berardelli looked the same, and none of them could have been fired by the .38-calibre weapon found in Vanzetti's possession. But bullet III, the fatal bullet, was different. The other five had markings with a right twist produced as the bullet spun down the gun barrel. Bullet III had a left twist, consistent with Sacco's automatic pistol.

The ballistic evidence was less than conclusive, but still sufficient for a jury whose prejudices had been inflamed by the prosecutors' depiction of the accused as disloyal radical foreigners. Additionally, Sacco and Vanzetti did themselves grievous harm when they lied to police during their initial questioning, believing they were being detained for their political beliefs. Months earlier, the US Department of Justice had initiated a programme of mass arrests and deportation of immigrants suspected of being communists or communist sympathizers. Sacco and Vanzetti knew of two friends who had already been deported and thought they were about to be next.

The lies they told police about their politics came back to haunt them at trial. Prosecutors argued that the lies were evidence of 'consciousness of guilt'. Innocent men, they told the jury, had no reason to lie.

Sacco and Vanzetti were found guilty and sentenced to death. After several years of appeals, they were executed at Charlestown State Prison in Boston on 21 August 1927. Magrath was present to witness their execution and declare the men dead.

The prosecution remains one of the most contentious criminal cases of the twentieth century. The evidence is still debated and contested. Some believe the men were guilty as charged. Others contend that the execution of Sacco and Vanzetti was one of the great miscarriages of the American criminal justice system.

CHAPTER 5

Kindred Spirits

1929

During the early 1900s, Prairie Avenue began to decline as the character of the neighbourhood around it changed. The area's proximity to the city's business and transportation hubs, once so desirable to Chicago's elite, became more valuable to commercial interests.[1] One by one, the grand mansions of Prairie Avenue and nearby streets were razed for large commercial buildings, apartments and parking lots. Wealthy residents fled to more pastoral environs in suburban communities.

About two dozen Prairie Avenue homes were converted to furnished rooms for rent, some housing as many as forty-five people. The mansion of local department-store magnate Marshall Field Jr at 1919 South Prairie was converted into the Gatlin Institute, a hospital for the treatment of alcohol and drug addiction. No longer an exclusive address, Prairie Avenue became overrun with transients and the unfortunate. By 1920, the elderly Glessners were among only twenty-six original Prairie Avenue settlers who still lived on the street.

At this time, Frances Glessner Lee was spending most of her time in Boston and at The Rocks and had little need for the Chicago home her parents had purchased for her after her marriage. The residence at 1700 Prairie Avenue was sold in 1921.

In September 1926, Lee's uncle, George B Glessner, died at the age of eighty-one. John Jacob's only surviving brother, he had been an officer in Warder, Bushnell & Glessner and subsequently International Harvester. In his will, the childless millionaire left $250,000 in cash and securities – comparable to about £2.7 million in present-day terms – to his only niece, Frances Glessner Lee.

Lee's son John had received his master's degree in mechanical engineering from Massachusetts Institute of Technology in 1922. He went to work in the aviation industry, designing aeroplanes. In 1926, he married MIT classmate Percy Maxim of Hartford, Connecticut. John and Percy, who was named for her father, Hiram Percy Maxim, made their home in Connecticut, where John worked for the United Aircraft Corporation.

The following year, in June 1927, Lee's twenty-one-year-old daughter Martha married Charles Foster Batchelder, a Harvard-educated engineer who had been hired by Lee's brother George to divert an unused water reservoir he had acquired for use on The Rocks estate. The Batchelders set up residence in Augusta, Maine. A year later Lee's other daughter, Frances, married Chicago attorney and entrepreneur Marion Thurston 'Bud' Martin, an entrepreneur and aspiring businessman.

With her children successfully launched into their own lives, Lee needed a place to stay in Chicago for those occasions when she was visiting her parents or taking care of business in the city. In 1928, she purchased a twelve-room apartment in a high-end building at 1448 Lake Shore Drive for $55,000 – over £600,000 in today's money.

In the first days of January 1929, George Glessner began feeling ill at his home on The Rocks estate, with pain in the lower abdomen, fever and a general malaise. He was diagnosed with acute appendicitis and admitted to a hospital in Concord. Surgery to remove the inflamed appendix was successful. However, during his recovery, George developed pneumonia and died. He was fifty-seven years old.

The period after her brother's death was a low point for Lee. She was as distant as ever from her extended family; her children were grown and having children of their own. With little to occupy her time, Lee felt melancholy, alone and unmoored.

To compound matters, she had to go to Boston for medical care at Massachusetts General Hospital. The nature of her condition is unknown but evidently involved a surgical procedure that required a lengthy convalescence in Phillips House, the hospital's deluxe private-care facility. An eight-storey building located on Charles Street near Beacon Hill, Phillips House had been an innovative concept when it opened in 1917. Wealthy people avoided the open wards typical of hospitals at the time, preferring to have procedures done in their home, a private home offering nursing care, or in a hotel room, just as when Lee had had her tonsils removed as a child. Medical care had come a long way since then. Patients who were able to afford it no longer needed to have surgical instruments disinfected on the kitchen stove, but could receive care with the latest in anaesthesia, aseptic surgery and modern technology. Phillips House offered tastefully furnished private rooms. A fenced-in rooftop and verandas on the north end of the building allowed patients plenty of sunshine and fresh air during their stay.[2]

Lee, fifty-one years old at the time, was a patient at Phillips House for an extended period in 1929. By coincidence, her old friend George Magrath was hospitalized there at the same time. He had a severe infection and inflammation affecting both of his hands: a consequence of circulatory problems caused by his failing liver and repeated exposure to formaldehyde and strong disinfectants. It was the third time he had been admitted for care at Phillips House for his crippled hands. The condition was very serious and could potentially have led to amputation.

Lee and Magrath rekindled their friendship during their convalescence. They whiled away the endless hours talking, often sitting together on rocking chairs on the veranda overlooking the river. They reminisced about long-ago days: life at The Rocks, the 1893 World's Columbian Exposition, youthful memories. They talked about music, art and literature. And they talked about Magrath's career as a medical examiner. Lee found Magrath's work endlessly fascinating. His stories were so much more interesting than the usual conversations in her social circles. Magrath was concerned with weighty subjects, subjects that mattered: life and death, crime and justice. The world was an unpredictable and often violent place, Lee knew. Magrath helped make order out of chaos, satisfying the most basic human drive to understand why death happened.

He told vivid, engaging stories filled with drama, pathos and occasional morbidly dark humour. There was the case of an elderly man found dead in his sixth-floor room in a Boston hotel, sitting in a Morris chair beside an open window. He was discovered when hotel staff checked on guests after a fire on the fourth floor. It was a small fire, confined to one room, and didn't create enough smoke to asphyxiate the old man. Near the body was a small metal container with the residue of an unknown substance.[3]

Magrath learned that the man had been a retired chemist. He had a morbid fear of fire, having nearly been burned to death as a youth. To avoid that fate, he always carried a small vial of aconite – a fast-acting poison derived from a plant commonly known as wolf's bane – in case of an emergency. When he smelled the smoke and saw flame licking out the window, he was certain his end had come. He consumed the aconite, preferring to die by poison than by flames or smoke inhalation, although he was never actually at risk from the fire.

Another of Magrath's oft-told stories was about the murder of Florence Small. Her husband, Frederick Small, thought that he had devised the perfect crime. And he almost did.[4] 'I consider this one of the most remarkable of all my cases,' said Magrath, who had been called in to help the New Hampshire State Police with the investigation.[5]

On 28 September 1916, the body of thirty-seven-year-old Florence Small was found in the debris of a fire that destroyed her home in Ossipee, New Hampshire. She had been burned beyond recognition, some of her bones exposed to such intense heat that they were calcified and crumbling.

When the fire erupted, Frederick Small was not at home but miles away, attending a film in Boston with friends. A hired driver who took him to the railway station said he saw him say goodbye through the open door when leaving his house, but did not see Mrs Small or hear her reply. The fire broke out seven hours later. Certain things about Small's behaviour aroused the suspicion of police. The couple had recently taken out a life-insurance policy, paying the surviving spouse $20,000 – a generous £400,000 in modern terms. Only one premium payment had been made.

When Magrath asked Small his preference for a funeral parlour to receive his wife's body after the postmortem, he replied, 'Is there enough left of the body to require a casket?'

Frederick Small's penny-pinching ways ultimately proved to be his undoing. The Smalls' cottage was not well maintained. The cellar was prone to flooding and at the time of the fire was filled with several feet of standing water. The bed on which Florence Small had been lying burned through the bedroom floor, dropping her body into the cellar and preserving its remains so that evidence remained in the bone and deeper tissues.

During the postmortem examination, Magrath found that Florence had a cord tightly wrapped around her neck. Her skull was fractured, and she had also been shot in the head with a .32-calibre bullet. More evidence was sifted from the ruins left from the fire – a .38-calibre revolver, a sparkplug, some wire and a charred alarm clock. Magrath noted something curious: a cast-iron stove with bits of fused metallic material on its surface.

The small defects, Magrath noted, 'showed the stove had been subjected to a shower of molten steel... Neither cast-iron nor steel fuses in the heat of an ordinary house fire.'[6]

He looked around for something that could cause such intense heat and found evidence of thermite – a grey flammable powder used to weld steel. He theorized that somebody had scattered thermite all over Florence Small's body, the bed and the bedroom floor and rigged an alarm clock to ignite the material.

Small denied responsibility for his wife's murder. He claimed that she had been alive when he left the house. She was assaulted by a lumberjack, he said. Few believed his version of events, and Small was charged with murder.

During the trial, prosecutors pulled a dramatic stunt. Without Frederick Small's knowledge, the district attorney had obtained a court order directing Magrath to decapitate Florence and preserve her dissected head as evidence. Before the head was introduced as an exhibit in court, the judge suggested that women leave the courtroom. Some did, but eight remained among the spectators craning to see the grisly evidence. Frederick Small sat in the courtroom sobbing, his face in his hands, while Magrath described the injuries inflicted upon his wife.

Magrath testified that Florence had been struck on the head at least seven times, but the skull fractures that resulted were not severe enough to be lethal. She had been shot through the forehead while lying supine, by somebody standing over her. That injury would have been fatal, but she had already been strangled to death by the cord around her neck.

Magrath explained to the jury how he'd reached his conclusions by pointing out evidence on the skull and specimens of the victim's tissue preserved in formaldehyde. Magrath showed the jury a piece of Florence Small's airway, a pink rectangle of tissue. When a person inhales air thick with smoke, soot is deposited on the airway. Florence's was clean and perfectly normal, proving that she had not been breathing when the fire started.

Magrath also pointed out injuries to the trachea, to the horseshoe-shaped hyoid bone in the neck, and to the strap muscles: evidence of strangulation. Enough of the mucous membrane inside Florence's eyelids survived the fire to identify petechiae, the tiny pinpoint haemorrhages that are also characteristic of strangulation. He explained how the bevelling of the bullet hole in her forehead and the pattern of stippling on her skin produced by the burning gunpowder indicated the position and distance of the person who had fired the shot. Everybody knows that when you cut your skin, blood flows immediately. The bullet wound through the skin of Florence's forehead did not bleed as the skull fractures did, so that injury occurred after death.

The medical evidence showed that events happened in this order: Florence Small was beaten, fatally strangled, shot, then set on fire.

Next, the prosecution introduced more evidence: the frame of the bed on which Florence died and the cast-iron stove – that had been shrouded behind a curtain and revealed with dramatic effect. Everybody in the courtroom turned to look, except one person: Frederick Small. He kept his face covered with a handkerchief.

'An innocent man would have been curious what was about to be shown,' Magrath said, 'but Small was guilty and he knew.'[7] Frederick Small was convicted of murder and executed on 15 January 1918. Magrath attended his execution.

With each story, Lee gained a deeper appreciation of Magrath's pursuit of the truth to clear the innocent and convict the guilty. One day during their convalescence, he discussed the difficulty of explaining evidence to a jury. Trying to describe the place of a death was challenging. Since the scene itself no longer existed, jurors developed an image in their mind that may or may not be correct.

'I'm still trying to find something better than a diagram and a photograph to show a jury the exact spot where the body was found in proper relation to the stairs, the stove or the window,' he said. 'That's the hardest thing in the world to get across.'[8]

Lee thought a moment, remembering the miniature orchestra and quartet she had made years earlier. 'What if you had a small model of a room, drawn in the correct scale, and a doll or dummy dressed exactly like the victim and all the other details in the correct place?' she asked. 'Would that help?'

Magrath tapped his pipe. 'A model?' he said. 'Could I use it in court? Half the time, they won't even let me introduce photographs. Let me think about it a while.'

Useful as a model might have been, Lee didn't return to the idea of replicating death scenes in miniature for several years.

As Magrath saw it, the legal-medicine education he had received in Europe was a great gift that he had a duty to use. He felt obligated to the profession and also to the deceased – not just to those who died in his bailiwick, but to all. Every person, he felt, was entitled to a thorough, scientific and impartial death investigation, should it be necessary.

As part of his mission, he wanted to promote awareness of medical examiners, the duties they fulfilled and how they differed from coroners. Progress wouldn't occur unless people knew that there were better ways of doing things – not just the general public, although they were probably the most important, but also lawmakers, police, prosecutors and the courts. Legislators needed to understand the importance of instituting medical examiner systems and making them work more effectively. Lawyers and judges needed to be educated about the nature of medical evidence. District attorneys needed to give medical examiners a freer hand to decide which cases required an open autopsy.

Additionally, the police needed to know what to do – and what not to do – at the scene of a violent or suspicious death. Most were not equipped to be thrown into a situation in which scientific and medical evidence was paramount. What they did in those first critical moments could make or break a case. Who knew how many people had slipped away from justice due to poor police work or had been convicted based on a confession obtained by third-degree coercion while scientific evidence went unexamined?

And the public? If people knew the sorts of things that went on behind the scenes, they would demand change. Greater education would lead to a deeper understanding of the need for thorough and proper inquiries into deaths.

By 1929, when Magrath was recuperating in Phillips House with Lee, in the more than half a century since Boston had introduced medical examiners in 1877, only two other major cities had followed suit: New York in 1917 and Newark, New Jersey, in 1927. In Essex County, New Jersey, serving the greater Newark area, the change had come about in the wake of the botched investigation of the murders of Episcopalian priest Edward Wheeler Hall and Eleanor Reinhardt Mills, a singer in his choir and also his mistress. The crime scene was unsecured for several hours. Onlookers trampled the scene and touched the bodies, ruining any evidence that may have existed.

Newspaper photos showed a crowd of men standing around the bodies, stripping a nearby crabapple tree of bark to keep as souvenirs. Hall's wife, two of her brothers and a cousin were charged with the murders but were subsequently found not guilty. The case remains officially unsolved to this day.[9]

Magrath's view was that it shouldn't take a scandal like this to shock people into implementing reform. But in many cases that seemed to be the only thing that could get the job done.

* * *

During their time at Phillips House, Magrath gave Lee a printed copy of a landmark study published by the National Research Council (NRC) in 1928, entitled 'The Coroner and the Medical Examiner'. It had been funded by The Rockefeller Foundation, an organization with a long-standing interest in improving medical education and the criminal justice system.[10]

The study compared the two cities with medical examiners at the time – Boston and New York City – to three cities with coroners: Chicago, San Francisco and New Orleans. It was unsparing in its criticism of the coroner system. Aside from the familiar litany of malfeasance attributed to coroners, the study found that medical examiners were more reliable and less expensive. It called the coroner system 'an anachronistic institution which has conclusively demonstrated its incapacity to perform the functions customarily required of it', and concluded that it should be abolished.

The report recommended that the medical duties of the coroner be vested in a medical examiner and the nonmedical duties taken over by the appropriate prosecuting and judicial officers. Medical schools were singled out for their failure to train students adequately in the area of legal medicine. Few doctors were prepared to work competently as medical examiners.

'In not a single school is there a course in which the student may be systematically instructed in those duties which he may be called upon to perform in connection with conditions which may arise as the result of crime or accident,' the report said. 'There must be a demand for properly trained men, there must be opportunities which would make the medical graduate wish to elect a career as medical examiner, and there must be facilities for obtaining the thorough training which would fit him for such a career.'

* * *

During another conversation at Phillips House, Magrath's outlook turned dark.

'You know, I won't be around here much longer, and when I die all this dies with me,' he said to Lee, referring to the documents that comprised his life's work. 'I suppose as soon as I'm gone, all my notes and slides and books and stuff will go to the junk pile.' [11]

Lee looked at him. 'What would you like to have done with all your material?' she asked.

'If I had my way, I'd have it used as the foundation of a department of legal medicine,' he said. 'You know, there isn't any such thing in the whole United States. A complete academic department, engaged in education, research, training...'

'Wait, I'll get some paper and we will make a rough outline,' Lee said.

'I'd have first a new modern research laboratory,' Magrath said, 'then a library, with my books and notes as a starter, and a complete file of lantern slides and motion-picture films for use in instruction. We should need a competent staff of instructors to lecture on the medical angle of the law to doctors, lawyers, dentists, insurance men, coroners, medical examiners, undertakers and the police.'

Lee wrote page after page of notes.

When he was finished, Magrath puffed his pipe thoughtfully. 'It's just a dream,' he said. 'I've thought about it for years, but there's no way it can be done.'

On another occasion during their convalescence, Magrath made an innocuous, offhand remark, a trifling observation that resonated with Lee in unexpected and unpredictable ways, and changed the course of her life.

'I have always contended that the organs of the human body were the most decorative things in the world, and would make wonderfully effective murals for a medical school or doctors' club,' Magrath said.

The beauty of human organs?

'The idea appealed to me at once,' Lee wrote later.

Her thoughts began to whirr. It was as if a switch had been flipped in her mind. Those extemporaneous thoughts of Magrath's were a seed, an idea that took root and gained a life of its own. They sent Lee on a years-long quest to prove him right: that the organs of the human body are indeed beautiful. Perhaps one or two panels depicting a 'mix and tangle of bones and glands and organs' that could be hung over a mantel or doorway. Or perhaps something... different.

As ideas began to formulate in her mind, Lee said to Magrath, 'I want to look for myself. Soon, when we get out of here, I want you to show me the beauty of human internal organs.'

CHAPTER 6

The Medical School

1931–1936

Draped in a cotton surgical gown, Lee stood next to
Magrath at the side of the autopsy table in the North
Grove Street morgue. The autopsy room was as clean and
starkly white as a hospital operating room. To the right
were steeply banked seats of the amphitheatre where medical
students usually sat. That day, the seats were empty. On the
left were a bank of windows and cabinets of instruments.
At the far end were the double doors of the lift leading to
the refrigerating room downstairs.[1]

In the middle of the room, beneath a bright overhead
light, the body of a man found dead in his nightclothes lay
face up on a stainless-steel table. The man looked awkwardly
posed, arms raised aloft in rigor, like a department-store
mannequin. A jarring stench permeated the room, redolent
of rotting seafood combined with manure. Lee held a
perfumed handkerchief to her face.

Magrath pointed out a purplish mottling of the skin on
the posterior side of the dead man's forearm. He explained
its significance to Lee as he had many times in lectures. It
was *livor mortis,* or lividity. This discoloration of the skin
results when blood is no longer circulating under pressure.
When the heart stops beating, blood pools by the force of
gravity in the space of dependent areas of the body. Lividity

appears on whatever surface of the body is lowest, except for where the capillary beds are compressed, such as if a body is resting on the ground.

Magrath pulled up the deceased's shirt sleeve to show a patch of paleness in the discoloration at the elbow. 'You can see where the skin was under some pressure,' he said, 'at the points of the hips and shoulder blades on which the body rests its weight. You can see how the arms and legs were folded, the imprint of a belt around the waist. You can see where something was pressed against the skin. Many times, I've seen the outline of a weapon.'

'Lividity becomes apparent around two hours after death,' Magrath continued. 'The size of the patches increases over a period of hours and reaches maximum intensity around eight to twelve hours after death. For the first six hours after death, lividity can be redistributed. That is, if the lividity is on a person's anterior body and you roll them over, it can shift to the posterior side. For the first twelve hours, the lividity will blanch; if you press on it, the skin turns pale. After twelve hours or so, lividity is fixed. It won't blanch, and it won't redistribute. The intensity of *livor mortis* gradually fades in time.

'*Livor mortis* is a scientific fact as certain as the sun will rise in the east tomorrow morning. It is a simple matter of physics. If a person is found dead on his back with lividity on his anterior body, he could not have died that way. That is a scientific impossibility. There has to be an explanation. Either somebody placed the victim there or rolled him over.

'Now, another person might look at lividity and not see any particular significance to it,' Magrath acknowledged. 'Even medical doctors. They don't teach a lot about postmortem changes to medical students. They think it's just a diffuse discoloration without any specific meaning. But nothing could be further from the truth. Proper assessment of lividity can provide a wealth of information:

an approximation of how long they have been dead, the position in which a person died, whether the body was moved after death, whether any objects were touching the body, and so on.'

Once a body had been taken to the emergency ward or undertaker, all those facts were lost forever. Examining a body the day after death was a day too late. This was one of the reasons why Magrath insisted that it was so important for the medical examiner to observe the body in situ. The medical examiner should be involved before the police – for lack of knowing any better – spoiled the evidence that might be present at the scene of a death.

With the aid of a laboratory assistant, the deceased's clothing was removed and a cotton towel draped across his hips to maintain modesty. Magrath proceeded with his external examination, looking closely at the deceased's skin and scalp from head to toe. Any defect of the skin – a wound or contusion, any sort of mark – was noted, and a yardstick was used to measure its distance from the midline of the body and from the head or heel. Magrath dictated his findings to his secretary, who was sitting off to one side, taking notes. Lee looked on, fascinated.

The external examination completed, Magrath placed a wooden block beneath the deceased's neck to elevate the chest and extend his head backwards. He drew a scalpel blade diagonally across the dead man's chest to the tip of the sternum or breastbone. He next sliced from the other shoulder, then down the midline from the sternum to the pubic bone, the deep incisions forming a Y on the torso.

Lee watched as Magrath cut through the layers of skin and muscle, caught off guard by the absence of bleeding and the orange-yellow colour of human adipose tissue, so different in appearance to the fat of beef or pork or even chicken. Magrath then used a small saw to cut the ribcage from the sternum, lifting the flat breastbone from its place.

With the abdominal and thoracic cavities exposed, Lee looked in wonder at the organs, many of them familiar from illustrations she had seen in medical books and the drawings of Vesalius. The lungs, their surface smooth and glistening, cradled the heart, perfectly nestled together. Viscera, some pale and some starkly coloured, snaked around the abdomen. Everything was pristine, as carefully arranged as a floral centrepiece. It was…breathtakingly beautiful.

This person had once been a living machine of infinite complexity. Each one of these parts had worked together, flawlessly, for years, until something damaged the human machinery beyond repair. With his specialized knowledge and the laboratory tools at his disposal, Magrath would find out what happened.

Lee recalled the words of William Shakespeare, from a speech of Hamlet's: 'What a piece of work is a man.'

Reaching into the body's thoracic cavity, Magrath began to dissect the tissues of the neck, the carotid arteries and jugular veins, severing the oesophagus, and removing the trachea with the tongue still attached above the epiglottis. Working his way downwards, he cut the diaphragm and the few vessels and suspending ligaments holding the organs in place. In the lower abdomen, Magrath sliced through the urethra and rectum.

Using his arms, Magrath lifted the organs out en masse and placed them on the dissecting table. Lee peered into the hollowed-out body, looked at the smooth, shiny lining of the chest and the thick bones of the vertebral column.

Magrath felt for the mastoid process – the bump behind the ear – and drew his scalpel in an arc over the top of the head to the other side. He used the scalpel to work the scalp away from the skull, pulling the skin and hair far forwards over the face until the skullcap was completely exposed.

Using a bone saw with a broad, flat blade, he scored around the circumference of the skull. He then used a chisel, tapped with a hammer, to separate the bowl-like skullcap. When the bone had been removed, the brain was revealed, encased in its milky meningeal membranes. Magrath worked the tip of his scalpel around the skull opening to cut the cranial nerves, lifting the frontal lobes to access the optic nerves and finally severing the brain stem from the spinal cord.

The organs, spread out on the dissecting table, were then examined individually. Magrath dictated a description of the appearance of each organ as he felt it between his fingers. Each was measured and weighed, then sliced like a loaf of bread to inspect the tissues inside and out. Magrath set aside a specimen from each organ, dropping it in a jar of formaldehyde for later examination under a microscope.

When Magrath had completed the postmortem examination, the tissues and organs were returned to the body. The assistant reattached the skull, pulled the scalp back into place and closed the Y incision with a rough baseball stitch using heavy thread.

Lee watched as the hospital trolley was rolled towards the lift that would take the body back to the refrigerator room.

* * *

Back home at The Rocks, ruminating on the recommendations in the 'The Coroner and the Medical Examiner' report and on everything she had learned from Magrath, Lee identified three areas that required development in order for American society truly to embrace modernity in its investigations of unexpected death. Medicine, the law and the police all desperately needed reform in order to establish a functioning discipline of legal medicine.

'Legal medicine may be likened to a three-legged stool, the three legs being medicine, the law and the police,' she once said. 'If any one of these is weak, the stool will collapse.'[2]

For medical examiners to replace coroners throughout the country, hundreds more like Magrath would need to be trained. State lawmakers needed to be persuaded to abolish inquests and the office of coroner and adopt a medical examiner system. And states with medical examiners needed laws to be reformed in order to give them greater autonomy and independent authority, putting them in charge and protecting them from political and public pressure.

The police were another essential component. A police officer was often the first to arrive at the scene of a death and sometimes the only person present. Those first few minutes could make or break an investigation, and law-enforcement officers needed to be trained how to avoid compromising a crime scene.

This, Lee decided, was the path she would take through the door Magrath had opened for her. She would spend the rest of her life developing the three-legged stool of legal medicine. But she would need to figure out a way to do so that would be acceptable for a woman of her social status, perhaps by drawing upon the connections and resources her upbringing had afforded. However it needed to happen, Lee, with her unbridled curiosity and exacting personality, would get it done.

* * *

During his early years as an instructor at Harvard Medical School, Magrath had been given an annual stipend of $250 by the university – a meagre £5,500 in today's terms. During World War I, for reasons that were never explained, that stipend ceased. Magrath continued with his lectures to medical students from Harvard, Tufts and Boston universities on an unpaid basis, in addition to performing his duties as a medical examiner.[3]

In 1918, Magrath wrote to Dr Edward Bradford, dean of Harvard's medical school, explaining that he had been teaching pathology at the university for twenty years, and that the task had only increased in complexity and workload in recent years with legal medicine as an emerging discipline. Magrath had developed an entire systematic course on legal medicine for third-year students that had been well attended in its inaugural year; he planned to follow this up with instruction in the morgue in the fourth year of medical school.

'The subject of legal medicine as I attempt to present it includes many matters relative to various branches of medicine which, for one reason or another, escape attention in the courses of instruction given therein,' Magrath wrote, 'matters of importance to the practitioner of medicine concerning which it should be certain that every man who received a degree from Harvard University should have some instruction.'

All of Magrath's time and the material he acquired to teach medical students were coming out of his own pocket. 'I...feel sure that you believe me entitled to some advance in academic rank and to compensation for my services,' he said.

Among his colleagues, Magrath wasn't considered a typical medical-school faculty member. He gave lectures and provided practical experience for medical students at the morgue, but he didn't do research and, during his tenure as medical examiner, had never published a paper for a scientific journal about his cases.

There is no record that Magrath's request for compensation was acted upon at the time, but he continued teaching and developing a curriculum to teach legal medicine, in addition to his established pathology courses.

After becoming interested in legal medicine, Lee saw an opportunity to support Magrath and Harvard Medical

School, both causes that were dear to her heart. Harvard, after all, was the alma mater of her brother and many other men close to her, even though it had been beyond her grasp as a young woman.

In March 1931, she approached the university president, A Lawrence Lowell, with a proposal to commemorate Magrath's twenty-fifth year as medical examiner. She wanted to give Harvard $4,500 a year, two-thirds of which was earmarked for the salary of a professor of legal medicine and the remaining third for honoraria and travel expenses for outside lecturers on the subject. 'It is my desire that Dr George Burgess Magrath shall occupy this professorship with the title of full professor, which I believe I am correct in assuming to be your intention in this matter,' she wrote to Lowell.[4]

She also said that she intended to leave Harvard $250,000 – over £3 million in modern terms – in her will to support her initiative in perpetuity. 'My intentions are to create a Department or Chair of Legal Medicine which will bear the name of Dr George Burgess Magrath when it is proper,' she wrote. Lee's gift included one key condition – that she serve as Magrath's teaching assistant.

Lowell responded to Lee's proposal in a letter dated 4 May 1931: 'Your wishes will be carried out and I look for there being a great benefit both to our Medical School and to the country,' he wrote. 'They touch the public interest at many points – medical, legal and social.'[5]

Lee asked for Lowell's complicity in a ruse to persuade Magrath to take a much-needed holiday, with a European trip. Except for the times he was forced to seek treatment at Phillips House, it had been years since Magrath had been away from work for an extended period. A change in scenery might also help curtail his drinking, which continued to be a problem.[6] Lee asked Lowell to tell Magrath that, through a fortunate oversight, there were fellowship funds available to send him to Europe for a period of unstructured study. If Magrath accepted the offer, she would provide Harvard with $3,000 to pay for his trip.

Magrath didn't take the bait. 'He really does not feel that he can get away until midsummer,' Lowell reported to Lee. 'He has not, or pretends [not] to have, any suspicion where the gift comes from.'[7]

The subterfuge was one of the many ways Lee took an interest in the wellbeing of her friend. In an era without modern rights to privacy, she was kept informed about Magrath's health and drinking habits by his personal physician, their mutual friend Dr Roger Lee (no relation), a prominent Boston internist who later served as president of the American Medical Association. She also set up a joint bank account with Magrath and kept the balance flush with thousands of dollars at his disposal, should he ever need them.

Friends and acquaintances openly speculated on the close relationship between Lee and Magrath. At times Lee bordered on the coquettish, referring to herself in unpublished writing for Magrath as 'Ye Saucy Scrybe'. Yet in their correspondence, neither ever used terms of endearment. Lee always called him Dr Magrath, while to Magrath she was Mrs Frances G Lee. Their relationship was based on mutual respect and common interests, particularly music, art and now legal medicine. While there was clearly great affection between the two, there is no evidence that their relationship was intimate. If Lee did carry a torch for Magrath, it remained unrequited.

* * *

With her children gone, Lee now divided her time between her cottage at The Rocks and Chicago, which she visited frequently to see her ageing parents. After a long illness, her mother, Frances Macbeth, died in October 1932 at the age of eighty-four. John Jacob remained in the Prairie Avenue home, living alone.

Around this time, Magrath introduced Lee to Ludvig Hektoen and Oscar Schultz, both of whom had been involved in the National Research Council report comparing coroner and medical examiner systems. The men were also active members of the Institute of Medicine of Chicago, a private organization dedicated to improving medical science and public health. The institute was engaged in efforts to abolish the coroner system in Chicago and replace it with medical examiners. Progress came at a glacial pace, partly because of a requirement to amend the state constitution from which the coroner's authority was drawn.

'I am not sure that our objective should be a change limited to Cook County, or to counties with a certain population, or to the entire state,' Schultz wrote in a letter to Lee. 'Personally, I would prefer to advocate a state-wide examiner system.'[8]

Suggesting a change to the investigation of sudden and suspicious deaths invariably stirred controversy. Politicians were reluctant to give up to the state something that had traditionally been under local control. Undertakers, coroner physicians and others with a stake in death investigation held their own opinions.

'Our fight is going to be a long and uphill one, because in most of the counties of the state the office [of coroner] is held to be of so little importance that the inertia against change is difficult to overcome,' Schultz wrote to Lee. 'In Cook County the office has sufficient spoils to make the politicians desire to hold on to it. And the politicians, after all, are the ones who tell us what we shall or shall not have.'[9]

It became clear that winning over hearts and minds regarding the superiority of the medical examiner system would be a very slow process. Everybody wanted something, and their vested interests were often at odds. Creating change would require diplomacy, tact and a great deal of time.

Diplomacy and tact, Lee thought to herself, recalling the social skills she had acquired in her parents' home in Chicago. *I've been doing that my whole life.*

Lee was appointed to an advisory membership of the Institute of Medicine's Committee on Medicolegal Problems. She asked Schultz for advice on arranging an exhibit of the Massachusetts Medical Examiners' Society at the annual meeting of the American Medical Association, which was based in Chicago. They shared a mission to bring awareness of medical examiners to wider audiences.[10]

Under the sponsorship of the Institute of Medicine, Schultz created a large exhibit for the Century of Progress International Exposition, the Chicago World's Fair of 1933–4. Through text and images, the 12m (40ft) display explained the curious history of the coroner system and challenged viewers to consider whether scenarios depicted in the images might be homicide, suicide or accident. 'Death demands scientific investigation,' the exhibit stated in block letters. Schultz's display marked the first time that the discipline which would come to be known as forensic medicine was presented to a public audience.

Meanwhile, Lee's self-directed education in legal medicine resulted in a massive collection of literature: books and medical journals from the historical to the contemporary. Among her acquisitions were rare and valuable works such as the 1473 text of *Liber de Venenis* (*The Book of Poisons and Venoms*) by thirteenth-century Italian physician Petrus de Abano (Pietro d'Abano) and the only complete set in the world of the nine-volume treatise completed in 1779 by German public-health pioneer Johann Peter Frank. Her collection also included a 1512 printing of *De Proprietatibus Rerum* (*On the Properties of Things*) by Bartholomaeus Anglicus and a 1498 edition of *Stultifera Navis* (*Ship of Fools*) by Sebastian Brant, both of which contained exceptional illustrations of postmortem examinations. She also sought esoterica and crime-related curiosities, such as the memoirs of Charles Guiteau, written in his own hand while awaiting execution for the assassination of President James Garfield.

By 1934, Lee had acquired about a thousand volumes. She intended to donate the entire collection to establish the George Burgess Magrath Library of Legal Medicine at Harvard Medical School, but Harvard first had to create an appropriate place for the library, and time was of the essence. Lee wanted several rooms on the third floor of Building E-1 allocated for the Department of Legal Medicine, with one room renovated with bookcases and furniture – and painted a colour she selected – for the library. She wanted everything to be finished in time for the dedication of the library, but she also had another reason for urgency: she was due to have surgery for an unknown ailment, possibly breast cancer.

Fearing that her death was imminent, Lee wanted to make sure that arrangements were in place to support the work she and Magrath had begun. 'I have this morning executed a new Will in which I have given to Harvard, one million dollars for the continuation of the Department of Legal Medicine,' she wrote to the new university president James Bryant Conant. 'I confess it is my hope that in my lifetime I may yet provide a bit more.'[11]

After much negotiation between the medical school dean and department chairmen – and the relocation of mice used for experimentation – four adjacent rooms on the third floor of Building E-1 were reserved for the Department of Legal Medicine. One room would be the library, another outfitted as a laboratory and two used for office space.

Dr David Edsall, who at the time was dean of the medical school, wrote a letter to Dr J Howard Mueller, chairman of the Department of Bacteriology, explaining why rooms were being commandeered for the Department of Legal Medicine. 'The donor of money for Legal Medicine threatens to give more money – all told, quite a large amount – but more particularly wished to have definite arrangements made in a hurry as to what we should be willing to do before she went into a hospital for a major operation which she thought possibly might terminate her life,' Edsall said.

Lee's gift was predicated on her serving as curator for the library – if she survived the operation – so she could continue to add to the collection as she saw appropriate. The orders from Conant that filtered down through the hierarchy were to defer to Lee in every way possible.

The new library contained all of Lee's rare volumes, as well as one of only three complete sets in existence of the Journal of the Massachusetts Medico-Legal Society and complete bound volumes of all the European criminology and legal medicine periodicals. The Magrath Library of Legal Medicine was the largest of its kind in the world.

Conant was among the luminaries present when the library was dedicated on 24 May 1934. Magrath, hobbled by illness, was unable to attend.

'By his vigorous personality and the skilful discharge of his duties [Magrath] has played an important part in demonstrating the superiority of the system of medical examiners as compared with the old coroner system,' Conant said at the dedication.

Lee spoke on the same occasion:

For many years I have hoped that I might do something in my lifetime that should be of significant value to the communitity. I was sincerely glad to find that my opportunity to serve lay here at Harvard Medical School. You are possibly all familiar with the objective in mind. My wish is to build up here a department of legal medicine second to none other, but I firmly believe that its growth must be gradual in order to be sure. The plan is destined to be a manifold development, only a small part of which is as yet under way... I am grateful for this opportunity to pay a tribute to your colleague, my old-time friend Dr Magrath, a man who practically created this profession, and whose life has been devoted to perfecting it.[12]

* * *

It was around this time that Magrath introduced Lee by letter to Dr Alan Gregg, director of the Medical Sciences Division of the Rockefeller Foundation.[13] Gregg oversaw a broad portfolio of research and pilot projects in the areas of public health, psychiatry, basic sciences and medical education. He had been involved in the construction, in Cleveland, Ohio, of the Institute of Pathology at Western Reserve University, one of the first pathology facilities in the United States to follow the European model. The institute, which served all the affiliated hospitals in the Cleveland area and the university's School of Dentistry, developed into prominence under the directorship of groundbreaking experimental pathologist Dr Howard T Karsner.

Lee asked Gregg about developments in legal medicine since the Rockefeller Foundation had funded Schultz's survey for the National Research Council almost a decade earlier. How much progress had been made in the recommendations listed in the report?

None at all, Gregg admitted. The report was gathering dust in a file drawer. Not a single major jurisdiction in the country had adopted the medical examiner system since then.

Lee sought Gregg's assistance in developing a fellowship programme to train doctors to specialize in legal medicine, much as the Rockefeller Foundation had done with psychiatry and other areas of medicine.[14] No medical school on the American side of the Atlantic had such a programme. With the support of the Rockefeller Foundation, Harvard's Department of Legal Medicine would urgently address this lack of manpower.

Lee shared a proposal she had written, entitled 'Skeleton Plan for Department of Legal Medicine'. An entire field of study was fully formed in her nine typed pages: teaching staff to lecture to third-year medical students, a fellowship programme to train specialists in legal medicine, and courses for coroners, coroners' physicians and medical examiners. The proposal outlined a complete academic department involved in education, research and public service – well beyond the scope of the resources that had so far been established for legal medicine at Harvard. The department would have a toxicologist with a well-furnished laboratory, a photography and X-ray unit, and a library with an extensive collection of books, photographs and instructional material.[15]

'It is sketched on rather broad lines, but in some places I have been able to go into detail, while in others I am still fairly indefinite,' Lee wrote to Gregg about her plan. 'Of course, as I learn more, some changes will occur.' Lee said that she was willing to endow $250,000 to Harvard to establish a department of legal medicine: a 'factory' to produce forensic pathologists to work as medical examiners.

What Lee was suggesting was nothing less than creating an entirely new field of medical practice from the ground up. The ultimate goal of her vision was to develop the department into an institute of legal medicine to conduct all forensic death investigations in Massachusetts, and to serve as a resource for police departments across the country.

'Told her we were interested in doing something in this field and said that we laid particular emphasis on getting good young men to go into the field as a career and getting training for it,' Gregg dictated for his diary.[16]

According to Gregg, Lee said that she could 'induce Dr Magrath to take such a beginner' – a young doctor with an inclination towards legal medicine to train in a fellowship programme – and that she could present any difficult task to Magrath and, given time, could convince him of it. She intended to develop a programme and work with Magrath as long as he was able to serve.

Lee was a force to be reckoned with, and Gregg was impressed by her determination. 'Mrs Lee bids fair to be the Lucretia Mott of legal medicine,' he wrote in a memo to his assistant after a visit, referring to a great abolitionist and women's rights campaigner of an earlier generation. 'The next time she comes I want you to see her to get the full flavour of her practical and pertinacious mind.'[17]

* * *

In 1932, New York University had announced, in its medical school catalogue, the formation of a new department of legal medicine.[18] Dr Charles Norris, the head of laboratories at Bellevue and chief medical examiner for New York City, served as chairman of the department until his death from heart failure in 1935. Other members of staff included renowned toxicologist Alexander Gettler; Milton Helpern, a future chief medical examiner for New York, who came to be known as 'Sherlock Holmes with a microscope'; and Harrison Stanford Martland, the medical examiner from Newark. Members of the NYU faculty provided undergraduate courses to medical students and postgraduate courses in forensic medicine, pathology, toxicology and serology.

The Rockefeller Foundation could have chosen to develop a fellowship programme at the Department of Legal Medicine at NYU, but it believed in investing its resources where they had the best chance of success and the widest impact. Largely because of Lee's financial support and personal involvement, the foundation chose Harvard. Ultimately, NYU developed its legal medicine programme anyway, but Lee's influence ensured that the earliest incarnation of the field came out of Harvard.

* * *

Around the time she was discussing the establishment of the Department of Legal Medicine, in 1934, Lee made gifts to her daughters, Frances Martin and Martha Batchelder, of 350 shares each of International Harvester preferred stock. The dividends would provide the women with an income of about $2,450 annually – around £35,000 today. Lee had been giving her daughters the same amount in cash for many years but thought that capital would provide them with greater financial security. Recalling her own divorce, she understood the importance of women having an independent source of income.[19]

'I know from experience the comfort it is to possess your capital yourself,' Lee wrote to her daughters. 'It is with pride and happiness and love that I transfer to you this part of my capital.'

At about the same time, Frances Martin and her husband Bud adopted a baby girl, Suzanne. Within months, however, the thirty-two-year-old Frances contracted pneumonia; she died on 19 June 1935. There is no record of how Frances Lee reacted to her daughter's death. She always supported Suzanne, who is mentioned in her will, but Lee and Bud seem to have drifted apart over the years – there is no mention of visits with him and Suzanne in any of Lee's correspondence.

* * *

By the time Magrath was named a professor of legal medicine in 1932, his liver had become cirrhotic, scarred from repeated insults. Others had also noted a change in his physical appearance. In his early sixties, he appeared a much older man. He walked with an unsteady gait, his skin seeming to hang on his body. His friend and physician Roger Lee continued to keep Lee informed about his health.

'George seemed very pleasant. After the first [greetings], this sort of false heartiness disappeared and we had a very pleasant talk,' he wrote. 'At present he makes a very good appearance, but I think there is a good deal of weakness behind that appearance.'[20]

The doctor was trying to manage Magrath's irregular schedule and frequent use of alcohol, prescribing him a barbiturate to help him sleep at night. 'Our reports about George are that he still maintains his nocturnal habits and he does not seem very different,' he told Lee on another occasion.[21]

In the autumn of 1935, deteriorating health forced Magrath to resign as medical examiner. He continued with his teaching activities at Harvard as long as he was able and remained involved in choral groups and rowing organizations.

Lee's financial generosity to Magrath eclipsed even the joint bank account she had opened and kept stocked with funds for him. After his retirement, she bought him a Packard, a substantially larger and more comfortable automobile than the Model T, Suffolk Sue, that had served him for so many years. She also paid the fees to store the car in a garage.

Magrath's state pension from Massachusetts provided him with a meagre $2,250 a year, while the pension available to him from Harvard for his years of service amounted to less than $150 a year. Lee told the dean of the medical school, Dr Sidney Burwell, that $2,400 a year was not enough for Magrath to live on. Burwell spoke with Magrath and agreed that he needed another $100 a month to support his customary lifestyle.[22] Lee proposed that she would provide $600 a year if Harvard matched it; her portion was to be paid to Magrath through the university 'without bringing her into the picture', Burwell wrote in a memorandum of the conversation.[23] 'I think some action should be taken in the case of a man who has really devoted a lot of time to the university since he was first taken on as a teacher in 1898 and who has received a substantial salary for only a few years,' Burwell wrote in a separate memo.[24] Harvard agreed to the unusual arrangement, with Lee secretly helping to support Magrath.

* * *

In May 1935, Lee paid a social call on John Edgar Hoover, the youthful director of the recently renamed Federal Bureau of Investigation, in order to bring the discipline of legal medicine to his attention.

The FBI is a descendant of the National Bureau of Criminal Identification (NBCI), a centralized collection of photographs and bertillonage data that was established in 1896. Initially based in Chicago, the NBCI, also known as the National Bureau of Identification, was relocated to Washington, DC, in 1902. The database didn't include fingerprints until 1924, when the NBCI was absorbed by the Bureau of Investigation, a unit of the US Department of Justice.[25]

For most of J Edgar Hoover's tenure, the Bureau of Investigation was primarily involved in enforcing Prohibition laws, eradicating organized crime and investigating bank robberies. The agency's mission then changed dramatically in March 1932 when the twenty-month-old son of aviator Charles Lindbergh and his wife, Anne Morrow Lindbergh, was kidnapped from their New Jersey home. Lindbergh, who had flown solo across the Atlantic five years earlier, was one of the most famous men in America.

In response to the abduction and subsequent murder of Charles Augustus Lindbergh Jr, Congress passed the Federal Kidnapping Act, giving the Bureau of Investigation authority over the investigation of kidnappings.[26] Forensic evidence discovered by the FBI – tool marks on a plank of wood used in a homemade ladder found at the crime scene – was instrumental in convicting the alleged kidnapper, Bruno Richard Hauptmann.

The scientific expertise acquired during the investigation of the Lindbergh baby case formed the basis for the agency's technical laboratory, established about six months after the kidnapping. Now officially known as the FBI Scientific Crime Detection Laboratory, it was not the first crime lab in the country; that distinction belongs to the Los Angeles Police Department, where a crime lab was formed in 1923. But the FBI went on to become the best known and most sophisticated crime lab in the US, and one of the foremost in the world.

Bearing a letter of introduction from Magrath, Lee charmed her way into a meeting with Hoover on the afternoon of 16 May. At the time of her visit, Hoover was involved in starting a national police training centre, the forerunner of the FBI National Academy. He was not particularly receptive to the opinions of women. When he became director of the Bureau of Investigation in 1924, he had fired all the female agents and prohibited the hiring of any women for those positions.[27]

Nonetheless, Hoover met with Lee after she toured the building and had her fingerprints taken for the agency's civil identification files. According to a memorandum written by H H Clegg, assistant director for the investigations division, Lee described her plans for a department of legal medicine at Harvard and encouraged Hoover to train FBI special agents in forensic medicine, correctly pointing out that the agency's expertise was lacking in the medical aspects of investigations. She mentioned the National Research Council report and said that the agency could fill a role as a national resource for legal medicine.[28]

Lee indicated that the FBI's lack of expertise in legal medicine could be critical in investigations involving a suspicious or violent death. In an effort to establish a collaborative relationship, she let Hoover know that expertise to assist the FBI with investigations involving fatalities was available in Boston. 'She indicated that she would desire some help and advice from time to time,' Clegg wrote.

L C Schilder, in charge of the agency's fingerprint division, wrote a memorandum for what would become a file the FBI maintained on Lee. 'This lady is interested in the establishment of a department of legal medicine in connection with the Harvard Medical School,' he noted. 'She impressed me as being most intelligent, alert and aggressive and I believe that she will apply herself to her plans very energetically.'[29]

* * *

Lee's father, John Jacob Glessner, died a week short of his ninety-third birthday, on 20 January 1936. The Glessners had been one of the last residential holdouts as their beloved Prairie Avenue neighbourhood was enveloped by commercial buildings. In 1924, they had deeded their home to the American Institute of Architects (AIA), with the condition that John Jacob and Frances Macbeth could remain there for the rest of their lives. The deed also included a stipulation that a photograph of the house's architect, H H Richardson, remain permanently in its library.[30]

On 7 April 1936, Lee and her sister-in-law, George Glessner's widow Alice, hosted a reunion of the Monday

Morning Reading Class for one last visit to the landmark residence before its ownership was transferred to the AIA. The *Chicago Daily Tribune*'s society page noted the passing of a group which, a generation earlier, 'was considered one of the most exclusive and fashionable in Chicago'.[31]

However, within months of receiving the house, the AIA learned that remodelling it for their purposes would cost $10,000 to $25,000. The sum could not be raised, and the architects voted to return the property to the Glessner estate. Eventually, Lee and Alice donated it to the Armour Institute of Technology for use as a vocational aptitude testing centre.[32]

* * *

Following his retirement, Magrath turned his attention to the papers and records he had collected over the course of his three decades as medical examiner, including high-profile cases such as the Sacco and Vanzetti investigation. Perhaps, at last, he would have time to publish something about his work. He hoped to write a book. The obstacle in his way was Dr William Brickley, his successor as medical examiner for the Northern District of Suffolk County. Brickley was of the opinion that the official records belonged to the medical examiner's office and were not Magrath's personal property.

Lee resolved the impasse. She proposed to Sidney Burwell that Brickley be appointed an instructor in the Department of Legal Medicine. He would be called upon to give two or three lectures a year and would have students to assist with postmortem examinations. Lee would provide a reasonable compensation out of her own pocket. However, she said, the appointment should not be made unless all case records, lantern slides, negatives, photographs, microscope slides and other material accumulated during Magrath's career were deposited in the Department of Legal Medicine.

'If Dr Magrath is to write his book, which is the ardent hope of his friends, it will be imperative that he have this, the sum of his life's work, ready at his hand in his medical school quarters,' Lee said to Burwell.[33]

Brickley agreed. From then on, he and Dr Timothy Leary, medical examiner for the Southern District of Suffolk County, became members of staff at Harvard, with their salaries paid by Lee.

CHAPTER 7

The Three-legged Stool

1936–1940

On 23 May 1936, Lee sent a formal proposal for a department of legal medicine to Sidney Burwell, dean of the medical school. Instead of being a department in name only with a staff of one – Magrath – it would be a full, well-equipped academic department, involved in teaching and research, and would produce a steady supply of qualified medical examiners.

Lee indicated that she intended to give Harvard a total of $250,000 in the form of stocks, bonds and cash. By her calculations, dividends from the stock would produce about $15,000 a year to support the department, supplemented by funds provided by Harvard.[1] She also wrote that she would leave Harvard an additional $250,000 in her will for the department's ongoing support. Privately, her plans were grander. A contemporaneous will, drafted but not executed, allocated $1 million – perhaps £15 million today – for Harvard.

In her proposal, Lee offered to pay Magrath's personal salary until his retirement from the department, as well as continue paying for a part-time secretary and a librarian. Her gift had two stipulations: 'First, that it shall remain anonymous until I release you from this provision, and second, that the name of Dr George Burgess Magrath shall be attached to [the department] in perpetuity, in whatever manner your good taste shall dictate.'

She also requested that she remain actively involved in the department. 'It would give me pleasure to reserve unto myself the privilege of adding more volumes to the library, from time to time, and possibly giving some item of necessary equipment when a specific need for such shall arise,' she wrote.

Magrath was approaching his sixty-fifth year of life and his health was declining rapidly: he had increasing difficulty with mobility and with his mental faculties, and had been hospitalized repeatedly at Phillips House. Lee knew that the productive time her friend had left was running out. She told Burwell and Alan Gregg that no more money would be forthcoming for Harvard unless the medical school made a good-faith effort and invested the resources necessary to develop the Department of Legal Medicine.[2]

The ultimatum worked. Burwell convened a committee to consider the prospect of legal medicine at Harvard, chaired by Dr S Burt Wolbach, the medical school's chief of the Department of Pathology. At their first meeting, the committee unanimously agreed that there were opportunities for pioneering work in legal medicine. The scale of the task seemed overwhelming, as it included the recruitment of specialized teaching staff, the creation of new laboratories and finding enough space for everything in the existing medical school buildings. If the Department of Legal Medicine were developed in accordance with Lee's plans, it was likely that it would eventually need its own building on the Harvard campus.[3]

Wolbach wrote to Gregg, soliciting his support. 'It is my unfortunate luck to be the chairman of a committee to consider the future of legal medicine in Harvard University,' he wrote. 'You, of course, know the reason, which is a very good chance of securing [a] considerable endowment from

Mrs Lee, possibly even as much as a million dollars. The problem of the committee, however, is to satisfy Mrs Lee and construct and arrive at an organization suitable for a university.'[4]

A department or institute of legal medicine at Harvard could provide a public service to communities across Massachusetts and influence the field throughout the nation. However great the potential, Wolbach expressed doubts about the amount of work involved in developing a new practice of medicine. 'Even with a million-dollar endowment, the problem seems hopeless,' he said.

At the committee's second meeting, on 11 December 1936, the panel concluded that its efforts to search for a successor to Magrath 'gave no promise of securing a person with all the necessary qualifications... In all probability it will be necessary to select a young person and provide him with the means for travel and study abroad.'[5] So this is what they set out to do. There's no evidence that Magrath had any say in the choice of his successor.

* * *

In 1937, Alan Richards Moritz was a bright and ambitious young pathologist looking to make a name for himself. A native of Nebraska, he spent a year studying in Vienna before going to Cleveland, Ohio, for his residency in pathology at Lakeside Hospital. By the age of thirty-eight, he was pathologist-in-charge at University Hospitals of Cleveland and associate professor of pathology at Western Reserve University's illustrious Pathology Institute, working as the right-hand man for director Dr Howard Karsner.

Moritz felt that his career had hit a wall of sorts. His dream job – director of the Pathology Institute – seemed out of reach. Karsner, although approaching sixty, didn't show any signs of retiring, and the institute's deputy director,

Dr Harry Goldblatt, was young enough to serve for many years as Karsner's successor. 'I was third man on the totem pole,' Moritz said. 'It would be a long time before I got the job I wanted, which is the one that Dr Karsner had.'[6]

Moritz's name appeared on a short list of candidates to develop a department of legal medicine at Harvard. At the time, no pathologist in the United States had the background and expertise necessary for the task, so Burwell and his advisory committee decided to find the best pathologist available and have him trained in legal medicine.

A background in pathology was a good foundation for a medical examiner, but legal medicine required specialized knowledge that was not taught in other areas of medical practice. Training in the effects of trauma – blunt-force injuries, stabs and bullet wounds, crushing injuries, drownings and fire victims, asphyxia and poisonings – was a key element of the discipline of legal medicine that was often brushed over in the traditional medical school curriculum. To a doctor, a laceration was a wound to stitch up and heal; it was not necessary to know how to identify the direction in which it had been made. Medical school classes didn't include how to tell whether a gunshot wound was self-inflicted, assess postmortem changes and stages of decomposition, or examine skeletal remains.

Moritz was intrigued by the prospect of a career pivot into legal medicine. It was still a fairly new field and presented the opportunity to break new ground. With Lee's resources backing the programme, Harvard could do something no medical school had done before.

'There were several schools where it was called a "department" of legal medicine, but there was just a man who gave occasional lectures and had some part-time interest,' Moritz said. Harvard 'was the only medical school in America that was really giving legal medicine the attention it deserved'.[7]

He visited Harvard in February 1937 to meet with Burwell and Lee. 'I knew little or nothing about the legal aspects of the frontiers between law and medicine,' he recalled. 'Harvard was aware of this, and so was the Rockefeller Foundation.'[8] Nonetheless, Moritz was offered the job.

The prospect of creating a department of legal medicine at Harvard was tempting. 'The more I have considered it, the more attractive such a development has appeared,' Moritz wrote to Burwell after their meeting. 'I know of no better place in America to undertake pioneer work in medicine than at Harvard, where so much of the progress of American medicine has received its impetus.' Still, he had to think about making such a major decision. Without some assurances from Harvard, moving his family to another city in order to start a new department from scratch was a huge risk. 'I have some accomplishment and a large investment of time and work in the field of pathology and I would be gambling with my future to leave the field of general pathology – to give up a good position in a good medical school – to spend two years' study abroad and then be faced with the insecure tenure of an associate professorship, an income considerably lower than my present one and no assurance of a budget adequate to build up a department,' Moritz wrote to Burwell. 'In short, I believe that such an offer indicates a lack of confidence in me or the lack of a means or desire to establish a new department as I feel that it should be established, and under these circumstances I cannot consider the offer.'[9]

With a full professorship and a pledge to provide adequate financial support to develop the department, an agreement was struck for Moritz to take the job.

Lee's first impression of Moritz was tepid, although his competence as a pathologist was not in question. He was an accomplished researcher, most recently involved in studies of vascular disease. Most who met him were impressed by his knowledge of pathology and his engaging personal qualities, but Lee felt he lacked a political sensibility. She wondered how he would hold up in the crucible of public pressure in which medical examiners often found themselves.

In short order, however, Lee warmed to her new colleague, and they would soon form an enduring partnership.

* * *

Moritz was made a professor of legal medicine and chairman of the department at Harvard on 1 September 1937 and departed almost immediately for a two-year travelling fellowship to survey legal-medicine practices in the major cities of Europe. In his absence, the activities of the department were halted. No doctors were trained, as Magrath's crippled hands limited his ability to teach. Moritz faced the task of recreating a department from scratch.

His fellowship began in the UK, with six months of study with Dr John Glaister, Professor of Forensic Medicine and Public Health at the Glasgow Royal Infirmary Medical School, and Dr Sydney Smith, Professor of Forensic Medicine at the University of Edinburgh. Both highly regarded forensic scientists, Smith and Glaister had been involved in the investigation of Dr Buck Ruxton, who was convicted of the 1935 murders of his common-law wife, Isabella, and her housemaid, Mary Jane Rogerson. The bodies of the two women had been dismembered and mutilated to remove fingerprints and facial characteristics to hinder their identification. It was the first time forensic photography had been used as evidence in a murder trial.

It didn't take long for Moritz to arrive at some fundamental conclusions about his new field of study. 'Last summer I had a hazy idea about the organization and function of a department of legal medicine,' he wrote to Burwell. 'Although I have been studying for less than two months and that entire period here in Glasgow, I have come to some conclusions which I do not believe will be modified by additional experience.'[10]

One obvious conclusion was that a department of legal medicine would need a steady supply of material: dead bodies. It would be difficult to teach postmortem examination without a body to examine. Neither Moritz nor Harvard had any official affiliation with a medical examiner's office, so some sort of relationship needed to be made with existing agencies that could provide such material.

Another thing Moritz found was a lack of consensus on the scope of medico-legal practice. In some places, legal medicine encompassed industrial hygiene, which today would be regarded as workplace safety or occupational medicine. Some authorities in Europe and the United States considered legal medicine to include the study of the psychological and behavioural aspects of crime. These days, questions about insanity and criminal responsibility are within the purview of forensic psychiatry, not forensic medicine. Some departments of legal medicine were involved in all scientific aspects of criminal investigation: they performed autopsies and had toxicology and blood-typing laboratories and also did fingerprinting, ballistics and analysis of trace evidence.

'I have forced myself to dig into many of the heterogeneous activities that constitute the practice of legal medicine,' Moritz wrote to Wolbach, the chairman of pathology at Harvard Medical School. 'These have ranged from fingerprint classification on through to juvenile delinquency. The result of this is that I am more firmly convinced than ever that the centralization of the practice of legal medicine robs the practitioner of his usefulness by making him a jack-of-all-trades.'[11]

So what exactly was, or should be, the practice of legal medicine in the United States? Moritz began to formulate his thoughts in a letter to Lee:

My greatest problem to date has been to arrive at some more or less definite idea as to what a department of legal medicine at Harvard University should be. It is pathology because the determination of the cause of death is of fundamental importance. It differs from the ordinary practice of pathology in that in addition to facts of medical importance, all medical evidence likely to be of importance to the law must be ascertained... The pathological diagnoses of multiple wounds to the scalp, a comminuted, compound fracture of the skull and laceration of the brain would meet the ordinary medical requirements in a given case. The medico-legal expert might add to such a diagnosis the opinion that the decedent was under the influence of alcohol at the time of his death, that he had been dead for between four and twelve hours, that he had not died where his body was found, that his death represented homicide rather than suicide, that he was killed by being struck by a heavy blunt instrument and that the assailant was a woman whose hair was dyed black and whose skin had been deeply scratched by the decedent.

The medical legal expert should function as a medical examiner representing the state and as such should investigate all cases of violent, suspicious or sudden death as completely as the circumstances warrant. He should be responsible for the examination of medical exhibits for the police and he should investigate all cases of death in which the state may be responsible for compensation of the estate of the decedent. He should be the adviser to and the witness for the court in the medical aspects of litigation before it. [12]

A warm rapport blossomed through the correspondence between Lee and Moritz while the latter was in Europe. They exchanged letters several times a week, sharing news and updates about developments in the Department of Legal Medicine. Lee had big plans to push forward in Moritz's absence. Having recovered from her medical scare, she oversaw the cleaning and renovations of the offices and continued to aggressively acquire books for the Magrath Library.

Lee wrote to book dealers across the East Coast in search of any text or periodical that might be remotely relevant to criminology or forensic medicine. Moritz suggested contemporary works. Lee also arranged for books that were only available in foreign languages to be translated into English. On more than one occasion, the medical school library expressed the desire to incorporate the Magrath Library into its larger collection so that all reference materials would be available in one building on the Harvard campus. Lee was adamantly opposed to her collection being subsumed in this way.

'I had a letter from Miss Holt, librarian at the Harvard Medical School,' she wrote to Moritz. 'Miss Holt is anxious to take our departmental library completely in charge, even to move it over to her own quarters and I am, of course, against that... Be forewarned so that our library will not be taken away from us.'[13]

Lee had strong feelings about the books she had invested so much money and effort in acquiring. She didn't even want any to be borrowed from the Magrath Library. Her collection included many rare and valuable volumes and irreplaceable original documents, and she found the idea of a missing volume intolerable. 'Without wishing to be arbitrary, I greatly prefer that no books should go out from the premises of the library to any other premises, or to any other person, under any circumstances or at any time,' she told Burwell.[14]

As a compromise with Miss Holt, three complete sets of catalogue cards were created: one for the Magrath Library, one for the main medical library and one for Lee to keep at home at The Rocks. Lee reimbursed Harvard $66 for the cost of duplicating the card catalogue for her.

* * *

In the autumn of 1938, Lee's thoughts turned to the world's fair that was being planned for New York from 1939 to 1940.[15] She saw the upcoming event as a chance to educate the public about the modern medical examiner system and asked Dr Thomas Gonzales, who had succeeded Charles Norris as chief medical examiner for New York City, whether his agency intended to have an exhibit at the fair.[16]

Gonzales responded that an exhibit in the New York City Building was planned to portray the work of the medical examiner's office. Another exhibit, which was still in the formative stage, was planned for the Public Health and Medicine Building, to depict various aspects of crime prevention and crime detection.[17] Lee relayed the information to Moritz in Edinburgh; he replied, 'I am anxious that the great advertising possibilities in the New York fair be taken advantage of for the benefit of legal medicine'.[18]

Moritz suggested that the exhibit planned for the Public Health and Medicine Building could include a series of panels illustrating common situations in which a medical examiner's expertise was needed. Each panel would have a drawing – 'calculated to be dramatic without being shocking' – and a short description of the hypothetical case, including:

- An automobile accident involving two cars, the driver of one of which dies during the accident. Did the accident occur because of some incapacity on the part of the dead driver? Did that driver die because of disease or because of the accident?
- Death from gunshot wound. Was it suicide or homicide?

- Death from carbon monoxide poisoning. Was it suicide or accident predisposed by some disease or intoxication?
- Found dead in the water. Was it accident or homicide?
- Death in suspicious circumstances. Was it due to natural causes, poison or unrecognized mechanical injury?
- Unaccounted-for death. Was death predisposed to or caused by some accident or special type of injury sustained during employment?

There was little Moritz could do from overseas to help with the project. He asked Lee to look into an exhibit for the fair. 'If you think that nothing will be done unless we do it, I think that we had better get busy despite the handicap of my being on this side of the Atlantic,' he wrote.

Lee knew that public support was essential in order to change laws and make other improvements that would bring about medical examiners throughout the country, and she recommended making outreach efforts to interest writers in legal medicine.

'She suggests various methods of events in the lay appreciation of the importance of the field of legal medicine, including getting the support of Courtney Ryley Cooper, a professional writer, who might prepare an article for *The Saturday Evening Post* or some other journal in this field,' Burwell noted after a conversation with Lee.[19]

* * *

On a December afternoon in 1938, Magrath happened upon an old friend, Robert Fulton Blake, a fellow oarsman and 1899 graduate of Harvard. Blake informed Magrath that an elderly mutual friend of theirs had recently died of a sudden heart attack. Magrath was saddened but philosophical.

'That's the way to go, when the time comes,' he said. 'I wonder who will be next?'[20]

Within twenty-four hours, on 11 December 1938, Magrath died. He was sixty-eight years old.

Lee described the circumstances of his death to Moritz, who had met Magrath only briefly before his departure for Europe:

> Since you saw him, his health has been failing but he had not ceased his ordinary activities. On the day of his death he was planning to go, as usual, to one of his musical rehearsals, and was stricken while in the bathtub. Help came to him promptly. He complained of a violent headache over his eyes, soon lapsed into unconsciousness from which he did not rouse. It was only a matter of some eight hours. The postmortem findings proved cause of death to be cerebral hemorrhage.[21]

Lee felt a deep sense of loss at the death of her mentor and dear friend. He may have died not knowing the extent to which his comment about the beauty of internal organs, all those years ago at Phillips House, had inspired her.

'I read voraciously for weeks – nay, *years* – in more than a dozen libraries, besides accumulating a small but peculiarly effective library of my own,' she said. 'I have worked in museums, have employed special photographers, have gathered material wherever it was to be found. It was necessary to study a little of everything – anatomy and physiology (neither one entirely strange to me), the history of medicine, many volumes on book-making and bookbinding, on illuminated manuscripts and lettering, lives of the saints – books on art, on precious stones, on colour, on symbolism, on music, on botany, on fish – accounts of savages, their beliefs and customs, histories of ancient religions and cultures – Egyptian, Assyrian, Chaldean, Babylonian, Greek, Roman – on up through the Middle

Ages in Europe and the Indian civilizations in the Americas to the present time and place.'[22]

Over a period of several years, at the same time as she was establishing the Department of Legal Medicine, Lee also wrote a book. She produced an extraordinary 400-page manuscript intended as a gift for Magrath – written, illustrated and lettered in her own hand – entitled 'An Anatomography in Picture, Verse and Music'.[23]

Anatomography, Lee explained in an accompanying letter, was 'a coined word of home minting, therefore presumably counterfeit', intended to mean 'a graphic anatomy'. Her book was a tribute to the beauty of the human body, as expressed in verse and images.[24]

The book told a story through an epic poem, a series of quatrains in the metre of *The Rubáiyát of Omar Khayyám*, about 'an Indian deity, without rhyme or reason, sent from the far West to punish the Indian God of the East Wind in Boston, where, meeting with treachery, he is murdered in the Public Garden and his body is taken to your Northern Mortuary,' she said in her letter. 'His son comes to identify and claim the remains, which are buried in due Indian style. They disappear, only to reappear again in part in the tanks at the Harvard Medical School, where they were gathered and described.'

Lee's book was meant to be read in a particular way, not like an ordinary book. Each two-page spread was intended to be regarded as a whole. The ideal method was to read the heading on the right-hand page, if there was one, then the Shakespearean quotations on the left page. Next, the reader was directed to a marginal note and a corresponding quatrain. In her letter to Magrath, Lee said such marginal notes had been employed as a sort of index in ancient texts.

Just open up the abdomen and find   Ye Knotty
Contortions of Intestines, velvet lined   Problem
By sheathing, fan-shaped mesentery moored
In systematic chaos intertwined

Dear lovely Lungs, all spotted blue and black,   Ye Aire Castles
Your dingy substance wrapped in pleural sac,
I could not live without you, and I strive
To guard you from pneumoniac attack

The Tibia and Fibula take part   Ye Connecting
In lifting up the human head and heart.   Links
Without them continuity is lost,
The head and feet would simply come apart

The Skin, of which we humans have so much   Ye Tactile
Is full of pores sebaceous glands and such,   Tactics
Seductive, silken-smooth and softly sweet –
Oh man, confess! some Skin you love to touch!

Every organ and tissue in the human body was represented in *Anatomography*, except for some vertebrae, the patella, the parathyroid gland, the adrenal glands and the genitalia. The art Lee selected for her book was rich with symbolism, classical references and images with particular significance to Magrath and herself.

'What training in draughtsmanship and design I have had came in childhood from our dear mutual friend Isaac Ellwood Scott, one of the gentlest and most lovable natures I have ever known,' she wrote. 'I am sure you will recognize lines throughout these pages that could have been inspired only by him.'

She hired photographers to document aspects of Magrath's life – such as the Union Boat Club on the Charles River, St Botolph and the refrigerator cabinets in the North Grove Street morgue – to include in the book. Layers of meaning were hidden within every image. For her design elements she chose certain foliage, flowers and animals, particularly fish, which she used as her 'signature'. The seaweed illustrated on one page, for example, is *Chorda filum*, commonly known as dead man's rope. The oak leaves recurring through the manuscript represent strength and independence. Charon, the mythological ferryman who transports the newly deceased across the underworld rivers Styx and Acheron, is depicted, Lee said, because he was one of the earliest oarsmen. Disguised as flowers ornamenting one page are fingerprints – Magrath's and her own.

The book's end pages, beginning with the egg case of the Port Jackson shark (because Magrath was born in Jackson, Michigan) and ending with a fish skeleton, were meant to represent the beginning and the end, birth and death. As a whole, Lee's manuscript is a reflection on the great mysteries of life and death, immortality and the passage of the soul.

'Like everything else I have ever done, this was blundered into,' Lee wrote in her letter to Magrath explaining her manuscript. 'It has been all-absorbing and intensely interesting work, and has led me down many heretofore untrodden paths.'

Working on *Anatomography* had been therapeutic for Lee, who had been at a low point in her life when she began it. It was as though a veil had been lifted, a light illuminated and a path found to go forward. Where it would lead, she had no way of knowing. But in it and in working to establish a department of legal medicine at Harvard she had found a renewed sense of purpose: a subject in which to sink her intellectual teeth.

There is no evidence that Lee ever gave the *Anatomography* manuscript or the letter to Magrath. Maybe she felt the book was immoderate, or maybe she never finished working on it.

* * *

Lee persuaded Moritz to retain Parker Glass, a Massachusetts native who had been Magrath's part-time secretary at the medical examiner's office, to serve as his assistant at Harvard. To keep him employed during Moritz's fellowship in Europe, Lee arranged for Glass to receive training at the Hickox Secretarial School, where he honed his skills in dictation, filing and medical shorthand.

Glass felt a responsibility to continue Magrath's work after his death. 'Although our work for Doctor [Magrath], and what he started, will never be finished, what we took over last December will have been carried out to the best of our ability,' he wrote to Lee. 'Even from my little share in the task, I find satisfaction. How much more you must find after all the years of protection you have given him.'[25]

With the installation of a properly trained forensic pathologist in Moritz, Lee saw an opportunity to reform and modernize death investigation in Massachusetts by changing the law to give medical examiners independent authority. She summarized her thoughts in a letter to Sidney Burwell shortly after Magrath's death. 'It is a good time to start to revamp the Medical Examiner system in Massachusetts,' she wrote. 'Massachusetts has always led in medico-legal matters, but New York and Essex County, New Jersey, are ahead of her now and even some of the midwestern states are coming to the front.'[26]

Lee suggested the creation of a statewide system with a centralized medical examiner's office in Boston where autopsies would be performed. The headquarters would also have a centralized toxicology and ballistic laboratory to serve investigations throughout the state. She declared that the medical examiner's office should be located at Harvard and that one person – ideally Moritz – should be appointed as chief medical examiner for the state, with two assistants and two associates.[27]

Having the medical examiner's office in close affiliation

with Harvard Medical School would solve the problem of providing a supply of bodies for students and fellows in the Department of Legal Medicine as well. The duties, pay and activities of the existing part-time medical examiners in various districts around the state would be unaltered, but they would have free access to expertise in Boston.

It was perhaps not a perfect system, but it was a move in the right direction. More importantly, Lee's plan navigated a path that minimized the ruffling of political feathers. 'This need not be any more expensive than it is now, would occasion no loss of prestige, nor would it reduce the number of appointive offices for political purposes,' she said to Burwell.

Lee urged Burwell to join her in visiting Governor Leverett Saltonstall and Paul Dever, the attorney general, to push for the statewide system. 'Since legislation is required, it must be started now,' she said.

Burwell was disinclined to join the fight at that moment, and nothing resulted from Lee's visionary proposal. Massachusetts didn't adopt a statewide medical examiner system until 1983.[28]

* * *

Moritz's fellowship tour included visits to the UK, Denmark, Germany, Austria, Switzerland, France and Egypt. He gained first-hand legal-medicine experience in Edinburgh, Glasgow, London, Paris, Marseilles, Berlin, Hamburg, Bonn, Munich, Vienna and Graz. He was also pleasantly surprised by what he learned at the Federal Institute in Cairo, where he expected to find poorly trained staff working under primitive conditions. Instead, he found a well-equipped centralized facility that conducted all the postmortem examinations in the kingdom. The facility was kept busy: Cairo was experiencing up to twenty-five homicides a day at the time.

'Poisoning is very common in Egypt,' he wrote in a report of his fellowship for the Rockefeller Foundation. 'It is doubtful that there is any place in the world where as much toxicology is done as in this institute.'[29]

Moritz summarized his experience in Cairo in a letter to Sidney Burwell:

> I had a very interesting time in Egypt, and saw more things of the 'believe-it-or-not' variety than I thought possible. Crime is a flourishing industry along the Nile, and they have many original ideas as to its performance. With the exception of Denmark I know of no place where all branches of medico-legal activity are so highly organized and centralized in a federal department. The medico-legal experts are well trained, and their work compares favourably with the best I have seen.[30]

Overall, from his survey of systems across Europe and Africa, Moritz discovered a wide range in quality of medico-legal practice. Some cities were quite good. Most systems were not.

'My experience to date, particularly that part of it acquired on the continent, is of value, not because of the good things that I have learned, but rather because I have learned of so many practices to be avoided,' he wrote to Wolbach. 'I feel that I have made a long journey and spent an inordinate amount of time to study organizations and methods that are fundamentally bad.'[31]

* * *

When Moritz returned from Europe in September of 1939, Lee micromanaged his introduction to her department at Harvard. She arranged almost immediately for him to deliver a series of lectures there on legal medicine. She urged a series of visits with Governor Saltonstall, Massachusetts State Police Commissioner Paul Kirk and the head of the FBI laboratory in Washington. In late September she held a dinner for Moritz at The Rocks, at which she wanted him to speak on legal medicine for thirty to forty minutes. 'I would like to have you make a little talk on legal medicine in general – what it is and why, what you have been doing in your two years abroad, what the needs in this country are, and what the prospects are at Harvard for fulfilling them,' she told him. 'There will be many doctors, some lawyers and probably some of the New Hampshire medical referees, and we have asked the local undertaker, deputy sheriff and chief of police. It will be a chance for some missionary work, but as you know it mustn't be too technical, nor, shall I say, too "gory".'[32]

Lee's friend Ludvig Hektoen invited Moritz to give a lecture to the Institute of Medicine of Chicago – his first talk outside the Boston area. The University of Chicago wanted him to speak to their students, too. Lee had one piece of business advice for Moritz: if you want to be taken seriously, make them pay. 'I am firmly convinced that you should ask for or accept an honorarium for your lecture,' she told him. 'In my opinion it is poor policy to give anything [for] free and the way you start is the way you will have to finish. Don't hold yourself or your information and experience too cheap!'[33]

Lee also suggested that Moritz consider writing an article about legal medicine for the Chicago newspapers, with the rationale that it would be a good idea to inform the public about medical examiners and their purpose.[34]

In January 1940, Moritz approached Lee with an unusual proposal. Would she accept the editorship of the *American Journal of Medical Jurisprudence*? It would be advantageous to have the journal associated with the Department of Legal Medicine and control over its editorial policy, but Moritz did not have the time to commit to the work. 'I know of no better place in the country for this task,' Moritz said, adding that Lee would have a free hand over editorial policy.[35]

The mere notion of Lee as editor of a professional journal is astounding. To be sure, she had unparalleled knowledge of the medico-legal literature, but she didn't have a university degree. Editorships were reserved for leaders of a profession. Lee's only official credential was honorary membership of the Massachusetts Medico-Legal Society and a founding membership in the New Hampshire Medico-Legal Society. A layperson, however sophisticated, at the helm of a journal would be highly unusual to say the least – particularly a woman.

Although flattered by the suggestion, Lee declined the assignment. She said she was too old to put that much work into editing a journal.

A short time later, in February 1940, the Department of Legal Medicine became operational. On 9 February Harvard honoured Lee fittingly on the opening of the department's laboratory with an afternoon tea. The guest list for the event included department heads from Harvard, deans from the schools of law and medicine, the university president and trustees, deans and department heads from Tufts and Boston universities, Attorney General Paul Dever and Governor Saltonstall.[36]

A few days later, Lee wrote Burwell a thank-you note. 'I'm still thinking of our grand party of last Friday and still wishing to say a nicer thank-you for it,' she said. 'It was a lucky day for legal medicine, for Alan Moritz and for me when you became dean of Harvard Medical.'[37]

Lee's endowment continued to cover the salaries of Moritz, assistants and support staff, but the Rockefeller Foundation now provided $5,000 for two three-year fellowships to train doctors for careers as medical examiners.[38] Two young pathologists, both of whom planned on careers in legal medicine, were selected as the department's first fellows: Dr Herbert Lund, a graduate of the University of Pennsylvania School of Medicine, and Dr Edwin Hill, who had received a degree in chemical engineering from MIT and his medical education at Tufts.[39]

One persistent problem yet to be resolved was the need for a steady supply of 'clinical material' – dead bodies. Lee's plan for a medical examiner's office near Harvard, which would have dealt with that issue, wasn't going to materialize any time soon.

'I can see one absolutely essential requirement for the development of any real department at Harvard and that is some active responsibility for medical legal work,' Moritz wrote to Burwell. 'I would as well contemplate teaching surgery without a surgical practice or obstetrics without delivering a baby as to think of developing a university department of legal medicine without an inflow of clinical material.'[40]

Despite his appointment as an instructor in legal medicine, Dr Timothy Leary was territorial about his office. He had been medical examiner in Suffolk County for thirty years before Moritz arrived on the scene and was reluctant to allow outsiders, including Lee, to usurp his authority. Lee and Burwell persuaded Governor Saltonstall to appoint Moritz as an assistant to Leary, leaving the veteran medical examiner explicitly in charge.

Moritz was also appointed medico-legal consultant to the Massachusetts State Police. Medical examiners and district attorneys were notified that he would respond to any part of the state to consult or assist with forensic autopsies at no cost to the county.

The calls did not come.

It soon became clear that Moritz and his team of investigators at Harvard were unwanted. Local police didn't appreciate outsider 'college boys' telling them what to do.

When Moritz arrived uninvited at one crime scene, he found a man busy washing blood off the walls. The local sheriff said he didn't want his men to get blood on their uniforms. At that point, cleaning up evidence made little difference, since the residence where the death had happened was packed with dozens of curious locals, contaminating the scene and leaving their fingerprints everywhere. When Moritz complained, the sheriff told him to shut up or leave.[41]

For its first two years, the department had had few deaths to investigate outside the Boston area. Then, on the afternoon of 31 July 1940, Moritz received a teletype message from the state police headquarters: 'DR ROSEN, MEDICAL EXAMINER, NEW BEDFORD. REQUESTS ASSISTANCE OF DR MORITZ IN EXAMINATION OF BODY OF UNIDENTIFIED PERSON FOUND IN DARTMOUTH.'[42]

Five Works Progress Administration workers picking blueberries on their lunch break had discovered an extensively decomposed body hidden in brush beneath a tree on a local lovers' lane. The body appeared to be that of a young woman, fully clothed, bound with rope at the ankles and wrists. There were no visible signs of trauma. Beneath the body, the workers found a small flying red horse pin, a souvenir of the Mobil Oil Company. Moritz brought the remains and a sample of the foliage that had been under the body back to Harvard. Three weeks later, after careful study of all the evidence, he was able to tell the New Bedford police the name and address of the deceased, how and when she was murdered and who did it.

Her name was Irene Perry. She was twenty-two years old and had vanished in June when she left home to get ice cream for her two-year-old son. Among her remains were five small bones: she had been four months pregnant at the time of her death.[43]

Near Perry's body, investigators discovered a knotted loop of rope that appeared to have been used to strangle her.

Harvard investigators did an experiment with fifty female volunteers of the same age and size as Perry to measure the length of rope that would be needed to strangle them. After a hundred attempts – none of the volunteers was harmed – the average was within about a centimetre (half an inch) of the length of the noose found with the body. Chemical analysis of the rope revealed that it was a type sold in bulk and used in mills, farms and industrial shops. A matching piece was found in the basement of Perry's boyfriend, twenty-five-year-old mill worker Frank Pedro.

How long had Perry been dead? Four groups of carrion insects – those that deposit eggs on decomposing flesh – were found on her body. Based on an analysis of the developmental stages of the larvae, investigators concluded that she had to have been dead for at least a month and could not have been killed after 1 July. The foliage beneath her body included branches of sheep's laurel and low blueberry plants, which had grown during the current season until covered by the body. Based on the stage of development of the young leaves, it could be deduced that the plants were killed on or after 15 June. That left a two-week window, which was consistent with the date Perry was last known to be alive: 29 June.

Pedro was charged with first-degree murder. Despite the scientific evidence linking him to the crime and probably to the great frustration of Moritz and Lee, the jury was not convinced and Pedro was acquitted of the charge in court.

* * *

A compelling reason for locating a department of legal medicine at Harvard was the potential for collaboration with the university's prestigious School of Law. A close relationship between the two departments could result in a true medico-legal programme, with medical examiners providing lectures about medical evidence to law students and lectures for medical students about legal matters.

As a practice exercise, the Department of Legal Medicine planned to conduct a series of moot-court sessions with medical and law students participating. Medical doctors were generally ill-equipped for the adversarial arena of the courtroom. The average doctor was no match for an attorney skilled in the rhetorical arts. An unprepared doctor could be led beyond observable facts into speculation or doubt or be made to look like a liar, incompetent or a quack. The moot-court sessions provided a useful way for medical students to learn how to answer questions, how to separate fact from opinion and how to testify while under verbal attack.

Lee felt strongly that the department should also begin conducting educational conferences. These meetings of professionals from across the country were important ways to learn the latest methods and procedures. Conferences and seminars were traditional ways for groups of professionals to keep up with current research and news, hear from leaders in the field and maintain relationships with colleagues. Lee pushed to schedule the first one.

On 17 May 1940, she sent Moritz the outline of a two-day medico-legal conference that could be held once or twice a year. The intended audience was doctors and medical students from Harvard, Tufts and Boston universities, the Massachusetts State Police, Boston city police, undertakers, FBI special agents and the press. Subjects to be covered during those two days included:

- **Causes of death**
  Gunshot wounds
  Incised and punctured wounds
  Burns

Electrical (lightning, power)
Chemical (acid, alkali)
Flames (inhaled, swallowed, external, moderate or
    destructive)
Scalds
Insolation

Asphyxiation

Drowning (freshwater, saltwater)
Hanging
Strangulation
Suffocation

Poison

Inhaled
Injected
Absorbed
Swallowed
Alcohol
Carbon monoxide

Diseases

Coronary disease
Other diseases

Abortion

• Conditions of body after death

Effects of

Immersion
Heat and cold
Incineration
Insects or other animals
Embalming
Burial
Agents to destroy body and evidence
Natural decomposition

Rigor mortis

Areas of lividity to determine position of body at
 death

Examination of alimentary tract to determine stage
 of digestion

• **Procedure in cases of different types**

Accident

Murder

Suicide

Dropping dead

Found dead

Hospital cases

• **Protection of evidence**

What to look for

How to gather up a body

How and where to look for means of identification

Care and disposal of effects

Not too much haste to bury or dispose of body[44]

Each topic would be presented from the viewpoint of
those in medicine, law, the insurance industry and the police.
Lee's plan also included a detailed list of potential speakers.

She proposed holding the conference in Boston in the
autumn of 1940. It would include a banquet at the Ritz-
Carlton during which the attorneys general from Maine,
New Hampshire Vermont, Rhode Island, Connecticut and
Massachusetts would speak. For the keynote address, Lee
suggested either Governor Saltonstall or Alan Gregg of the
Rockefeller Foundation. The exhibits she envisaged included
books useful for police and medical examiners, samples
of records and reports, displays of photographs, X-rays,
shooting targets, powder marks and body identification by
dental records.[45]

Despite Lee's enthusiasm and detailed plans, no such conference was held in 1940. Perhaps it was too soon for the department to undertake a major professional conference. Moritz did not support the idea at the time.

Lee did, however, manage to persuade Timothy Leary to attend the annual meeting of the National Association of Coroners in Philadelphia, a city where the debate on changing to a medical examiner system was beginning to take shape.

At their 1940 meeting, members of the Medical Society of the State of Pennsylvania had passed a resolution recommending the abolition of the coroner system and its replacement with a hierarchy of medical examiners trained in pathology. Although only advisory in nature, the recommendations of medical societies were given serious consideration by lawmakers. Discussion at the next coroners' association meeting was expected to be lively.[46]

Dr J W Battershall, the medical examiner in Bristol County in southern Massachusetts and past president of the Massachusetts Medico-Legal Society, received a provocative invitation from P J Zisch, executive secretary of the coroners' group. 'I cannot impress upon you too forcibly the advantages that you will secure by coming to Philadelphia to attend our convention,' Zisch wrote. 'I say this in all sincerity.'[47]

Unable to go to the meeting, Battershall sent the letter to Lee, who was expecting visitors to The Rocks and could not attend herself. Neither Moritz nor Alan Gregg was available either. Still, Lee thought somebody from Boston should accept the invitation.

'It seems to me that possibly the future of the medical examiner system may be at stake and that certainly the medical examiners should be well represented at this meeting,' she wrote to Burwell. 'I think it's important that the right people be urged to go and speak for the medical examiner system.'[48]

Lee pulled out all the stops to persuade Leary to go to Philadelphia. She resorted to flattery and offered to pay his travel expenses. 'Of all men connected with legal medicine, none stands higher than you in the respect and admiration of those who know, and no one could be a better representative, not only of the profession, but also of the Massachusetts Medico-Legal Society,' she wrote to him.[49]

Reluctantly, Leary agreed. 'In my opinion efforts to convert that particular group of persons to a belief in the medical examiner would be a waste of energy,' he replied. 'However, since I understand that they are going to discuss the medical examiner system, and since you feel that we should be represented at the meeting I shall be happy to attend... Though not on the programme, and not a member, I hope that I shall be permitted to represent vocally the birthplace of the system.'[50]

The meeting was uneventful. Leary was correct in predicting that no minds would be changed. The 1940 debate was only one infinitesimally small incremental step in Philadelphia's progress towards the medical examiner system: the city established a medical examiner's office in 1951.

* * *

In its first year of operation, the Department of Legal Medicine had assembled a teaching faculty that included Moritz, Leary, Brickley and Dr Joseph T Walker, director of the Massachusetts State Police laboratory. Two doctors were in fellowship training and five others taught on a part-time basis or were involved in research, including an attorney who was a fourth-year medical student.[51] The department conducted a course on legal medicine for third-year medical students of Harvard, Tufts and Boston universities that had an average lecture attendance of 200 to 250 students.

i Frances Glessner Lee (right) as a child with her brother John (left), mother (centre) and sister Martha (on her mother's lap) in 1906.

ii Frances Glessner Lee as a teenager.

iii Label designed by Frances Glessner Lee for the George Magrath Library of Legal Medicine.

iv Group shot of the seminar in homicide investigation at Harvard Medical School, November 1952. Frances Glessner Lee sits at the far right.

v The Glessner residence at 1800 S. Prairie Avenue, Chicago, designed by H H Richardson.

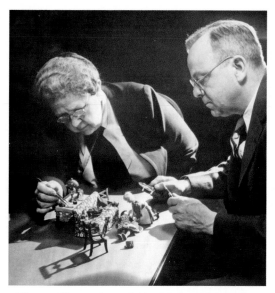

vi Frances Glessner Lee and Alan Moritz with items from the Nutshell Studies of Unexplained Death, late 1940s.

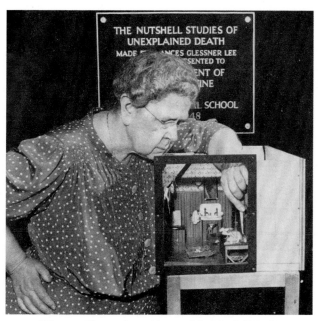

vii Frances Glessner Lee with one of the Nutshell Studies of Unexplained Death, 1949.

viii Three-Room Dwelling (for more details see page 245).
Blood stain patterns are an important clue in this home where a family
has been found shot dead. The victims include a baby killed in her crib.

ix Three-Room Dwelling (for more details see page 245).
To enhance the ambiguity of the dioramas, Lee intentionally
obscured the faces of most of the victims.

x Log Cabin (for more details see page 246).
Finding the tiny bullet lodged in this diorama is key to understanding why the man in the log cabin is dead. Lee based the cabin that this diorama is set in on the playhouse Isaac Scott built for her at The Rocks.

xi Blue Bedroom (for more details see page 247).
A shabby room is the grim locale for one man's violent death.
In the background, the factory where the victim worked.

xii Dark Bathroom (for more details see page 247).
Water-stained planks beneath the sink and worn linoleum in this orderly,
but modest, bathroom are signs of a residence past its prime.

xiii Burned Cabin (for more details see page 248).
After spending a small fortune to build it, Lee took a blowtorch
to this diorama in homage to the Florence Small case of 1916.

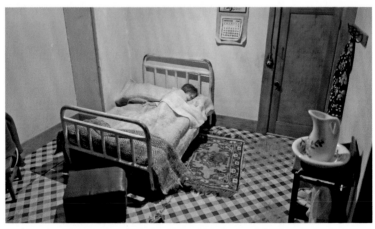

xiv Unpapered Bedroom (for more details see page 248).
This is the only interactive diorama. Pulling a cord at the front of the cabinet
in which the diorama is contained, works a hidden mechanism that lifts the
pillow next to the victim to reveal a vital piece of evidence.

xv Pink Bathroom (for more details see page 249).
The figures in Lee's dioramas were custom-made and dressed in
hand-made clothing. Lee carefully finished figures to represent
injuries and signs of decomposition.

xvi Attic (for more details see page 250).
Bundles of documents, many scrawled with indecipherable writing
and carefully folded, litter the scene where this woman died.

xvii Woodman's Shack (for more details see page 251).
This cluttered space, strewn with rubbish and broken furniture,
was home to three people. One of them is now dead. Empty liquor
bottles may illuminate the sad state of affairs.

xviii Barn (for more details see page 252).
The first of the Nutshells built by Lee and also the largest.
The barn was made using wood from an old shed at The Rocks.

xix Saloon and Jail (for more details see page 253).
Lee's dioramas include many hidden details, such as a poster
for a boxing match on the interior wall of this bar.

xx Striped Bedroom (for more details see page 253).
Empty beer bottles and a tub of dry ice are the dismal artefacts
of an ice cream factory worker's death.

xxi Living Room (for more details see page 254).
A pile of stubbed-out cigarettes and a body on the stairs
disturb this comfortably middle-class residence.

xxii Living Room, detail (for more details see page 254).
A dish of scale-model matches made from slivers of wood
and miniature books with actual printed pages.

xxiii Two-Storey Porch (for more details see page 255).
In this diorama the laundry hangs on wooden pegs that Lee hand-carved from matchsticks. Inside each apartment, the kitchens are furnished but not visible.

xxiv Kitchen (for more details see page 256).
Bread fresh from the oven, potatoes being peeled in the sink…
The dioramas are filled with clues and extraneous details.

xxv Garage (for more details see page 257).
Shortages of steel and rubber meant toy cars were scarce during
World War II, when most of the dioramas were made. Lee could
only find one automobile in the correct scale for her models.

xxvi Parsonage Parlour (for more details see page 258).
Her purse and butcher-shop purchase nearby on a chair,
the body of a brutalized teenage girl disturbs the room of
a residence closed for the season.

xxvii Red Bedroom (for more details see page 259).
Alcohol is a recurring presence in Lee's Nutshell dioramas.
This victim's room appears in disarray.

During the year, faculty members were involved in the investigation of seventy-two deaths in Massachusetts and performed fifty-six autopsies. In sixteen cases, Moritz and his colleagues examined autopsy material that had been sent in to the department from other jurisdictions.

Of those fifty-six autopsies, new evidence disclosed during the examinations resulted in a complete change in the criminal status of thirteen cases. Nine that were suspected homicides were determined to be accidental, suicide or natural causes. In the other four, homicides would have gone undetected were it not for the postmortem examination.

'It is interesting to speculate as to the number of cases of homicide that go unrecognized each year because of incomplete investigation of cases of obscure death,' Moritz wrote in the department's first annual report.

Along with investigating deaths in Massachusetts, Moritz consulted in the investigation of murder cases in Maine, Rhode Island and New York. He also maintained an active public-speaking schedule, presenting talks on legal medicine to lay audiences, medical societies and lawyers in Connecticut, Illinois, Missouri, Nebraska, New Hampshire, New York, Ohio, Pennsylvania and Rhode Island.

Drawing from the knowledge gained during his fellowship in Europe, Moritz also wrote a book, *The Pathology of Trauma*. He dedicated it to Frances Glessner Lee.

CHAPTER 8

Captain Lee

1940–1944

Lee had a dream: one modern, centralized medical examiner's office located in Boston for the investigation of all unexpected or suspicious deaths in the state of Massachusetts. A facility with a morgue and laboratories equipped for toxicology, microscopic pathology, X-rays and photography.[1]

There would be one chief medical examiner for the state, several assistant medical examiners at the headquarters and a sufficient number of deputy medical examiners to attend scenes anywhere they occurred. The staff would be civil service employees, removed from influences of politics and corruption. Through its affiliation with Harvard's Department of Legal Medicine, the office would become the training ground to produce a stream of medical examiners, growing until there were enough qualified professionals for the entire country.

Boston's expertise in legal medicine would be available for investigations throughout New England and across the United States. The agency would serve as a veritable national institute of legal medicine, consulting with local police, coroners and medical examiners from coast to coast, a forensic medicine counterpart of the FBI.

Dr Roger Lee asked Frances Lee to sketch out her plan: he

knew people who could get the ear of Governor Saltonstall.[2] Her scheme for Massachusetts ran to four typed pages, including a bibliography and a list of more than two dozen people from which an advisory board could be drawn.

As her personal physician, Dr Lee advised Lee to start taking it easier. Now aged sixty-two, she had an enlarged heart, hyperglycaemia, hypothyroidism, glaucoma, hearing loss, severe arthritis of both knees and an untreated diaphragmatic hernia.[3] 'I emphatically believe that you ought not to work as hard as you are working; that you should try to do all the work you have to do in two hours; that you ought to be out of doors sitting for two hours and take a drive every afternoon,' Dr Lee said.[4]

Despite the doctor's warnings, Lee hardly cut back on work. By 1941, she had sold her Chicago residence and was living full time at The Rocks, much preferring the fresh air and rural way of life. But she still maintained an active schedule, travelling throughout New England and the East Coast and frequently visiting her home town. A modern, centralized medical examiner's office at Harvard was never far from her mind.

* * *

Cocoanut Grove was a popular nightclub in Boston's Bay Village neighbourhood. The club had music and dancing, floor shows, food and free-flowing post-Prohibition alcohol. Once a speakeasy and mob hangout, it was now the place where film stars, athletes and assorted celebrity seekers went to be seen.[5]

A former complex of warehouses and a garage, Cocoanut Grove was a confusing maze of corridors, dining rooms and bars. The newest room, the intimate Melody Lounge, was approached by walking along a corridor and down a flight of stairs. It was decorated with a proliferation of artificial palm trees with paper fronds. Like the rest of the club, the lounge's decor evoked a tropical resort, with rattan and bamboo accents and silky fabric draped on the walls and ceiling.

On Saturday night, 28 November 1942, Cocoanut Grove was packed when fire erupted in the Melody Lounge. The flames spread rapidly along the decorative material and may have been fuelled by a flammable gas used as a refrigerant at the time. Escape from the inferno was hampered by an inadequate number of exits. The club had only one main entrance: a revolving door that was soon blocked by a crush of bodies trying to escape. Four hundred and ninety-two people died – thirty-two more than the building's legally authorized capacity. It was the second-deadliest single-building fire in US history, after the 1903 Iroquois Theatre fire in Chicago.

Moritz was involved in the recovery, identification and postmortem examination of victims. Officials approached the recovery in a systematic way, establishing an on-site command post for the coordination and control of resources. Bodies were tagged at the scene before being moved to the morgue.

In the wake of the tragedy, Moritz and Lee discussed methods of using teeth to identify the dead after mass-fatality incidents. 'Among the victims there were approximately 200 that were so badly burned that it was impossible to establish identification by their external physical characteristics,' Moritz wrote to Lee. A large proportion of the deceased had dental repairs that were recognizable by their dentists, but it was impossible to find dentists to identify every victim. 'It seems that there should be some simple way by which a dentist could leave a code number of some kind on or in a repair so that it could be readily traced.'[6]

* * *

Although often happy to give her money away, Lee was also financially shrewd enough to take full advantage of her gifts when it came to taxes. In 1942, she was reminded by her accountant that she had been paying for the storage of her mother's Steinway piano for several years. He asked whether she wanted to continue paying that bill. The piano was a Model D Parlour Concert Grand, the second-largest made by Steinway. The custom-made case of carved and inlaid mahogany had been designed especially for Lee's mother by the distinguished artist Francis H Bacon. Theodore Thomas, the founding conductor of the Chicago Symphony Orchestra, had visited the Steinway factory to inspect and approve the instrument before its delivery.[7] The piano had particular significance to Lee: her parents had purchased it in New York in 1887 on the same trip as her miserable tonsil surgery.

Lee decided to give the piano to Harvard. 'I do not play the piano and my small cottage home is too restricted in both size and quality to house an instrument as handsome or as large,' she wrote to Roger Lee. 'It would make me a great pleasure if I could present it to Harvard University for the president's home.'[8] Harvard president James Bryant Conant and his wife Grace were pleased to accept.

'You might be interested to know that the piano is safely in Mrs Conant's hands but that I was unable to get "Department of Legal Medicine" inlaid on it anywhere,' Lee wrote to Moritz afterwards. 'Perhaps I can do better with the next donation.'[9]

Lee deducted the value of the piano from her personal taxes as a charitable gift and eliminated the cost of storing it. Shortly afterwards, with the US now involved in World War II, the Conants were displaced from Harvard's president's house, which was given over to the navy. The Conants lived temporarily in a much smaller home next door. They had no room for the piano and paid to keep it in storage for the duration of the war.

* * *

A teaching institution needs teaching materials. Books are a good start, and Lee had created a library that was second to none. Other sorts of media are also valuable for instruction: photographs, illustrations, films, models. There weren't a lot of instructional materials available in the area of legal medicine or, as it was increasingly being referred to, forensic medicine, so Lee took it upon herself to have such materials created.

She was determined that her department would have the latest and best in instructional media. She helped it acquire photographs and lantern slides that were useful for lectures. Letters between herself and Moritz indicate plans to produce an autopsy film for educational purposes. An artist was hired to cast the head of a volunteer to create three models depicting various injury deaths, intended for study. One of the plaster heads illustrated a victim with a gunshot through the temples; the second the victim of a hanging, a distinct ligature mark around the neck and the whites of his eyes with the pinpoint blood spots known as petechiae that are characteristic of asphyxial deaths. The neck of the third head was severed deeply enough to show underlying structures in sufficient detail for a trained eye to discern that the victim had been cut from the left to the right.

As an additional contribution to the teaching materials, a young doctor on his fellowship, Russell Fisher, worked on a 'fauna of decomposition' exhibit with preserved examples showing the life cycle of insects commonly found in proximity to dead bodies. In the case of Irene Perry, recognizing the stage of development of these insects could help estimate how long she had been dead.

While on his fellowship at the University of Edinburgh, Moritz had told Lee about a collection of photographs of bullet wounds there that were useful for study. This gave Lee an idea. She offered to shoot hogs at The Rocks with a variety of bullet calibres, then have the skins preserved to demonstrate the different wounds each bullet produced.

Ultimately, however, shooting pigs at The Rocks wasn't necessary. Lee hired an artist to craft rectangular plaster plates, hand-painted to simulate wounds from a variety of ammunition fired from a range of distances. The finely detailed models showed the abrasion and stippling of an entrance wound and the jagged shape common in exit wounds. Forty-four gunshot-wound models were fabricated at a cost of $60 per plate. The collection would have cost Lee more than $2,600, or about £21,500 in present-day terms – a substantial amount for an instructional visual aid.

Although she had grown to respect Moritz's abilities and intelligence, Lee sometimes wondered if they shared a vision of the purpose and goals of the Department of Legal Medicine. A pathologist at heart, Moritz was involved in research of burn injury and publishing his results: work typical of a medical academic that Lee considered important but a lower priority. She was more concerned with training, educating and pushing the field of forensic medicine forward.

During a visit with Moritz in Boston in November 1942, Lee asked him a series of questions about the department and wrote down his immediate answers. Her intention was apparently to assess the doctor's grasp of the field of legal medicine and the department he led in order to ensure that their vision and goals were congruent. Lee returned to The Rocks and wrote down her own answers, which she sent to Moritz to review and give a more studied response.[10]

'I hope you can take time to give me somewhat expanded answers,' she wrote. 'I don't mean to be a pest but I'm trying to gather together some material which may be of use later.'[11]

Question 1: What is the overall picture – the final attainment aimed at?

Moritz's answer: 'A medico-legal Institute covering the county and serving the state as a whole in an authoritative relationship.'

Lee's answer: 'To make available scientific (medical, legal or other) skill and knowledge for the solution of otherwise unexplained deaths, accidents or those crimes concerned with personal injury and death, in order to determine the cause of death where it is obscure, to recognize preventable hazards of public health and to life, and to clear the innocent and expose the guilty.'

Question 2: By what steps is this to be reached?

Moritz's answer: 'Educate as many of the public as possible that our services are useful, and watching for political opportunities.'

Lee's answer: 'By simplifying and improving the medical examiner system where it already exists; by providing a medical examiner system in place of the prevalent coroner system; by improving the quality of medical and other scientific services available to the state by: increasing knowledge and training, promoting a higher conception of the ethics of the service, actively participating in an effort to pass new laws and amend existing laws governing the service, disseminating information and knowledge concerning scientific services already or potentially available to the state [and] promoting and partaking in scientific research.'

And so on. In all, Moritz's original responses to Lee's questions fitted on one sheet of paper. Lee's answers ran to more than three single-spaced typed pages. It was clear that Lee, a woman without a university degree, had a fuller and more comprehensive concept of the mission of the Department of Legal Medicine than the country's top forensic pathologist. The limited role she was allowed to take in the development and direction of the department she was nearly single-handedly responsible for founding must have been a source of unending frustration to her. No doubt Moritz was discomfited by the presumptuousness of a layperson, no matter how gracious and generous, who demanded that he take a test.

As a regular presence at Harvard Medical School, Lee had her own office in the Department of Legal Medicine and a key to the lift in Building E-1. In light of her ongoing involvement in departmental matters, Moritz thought it proper for the university to give her an official position. Burwell wrote to Jerome D Greene, secretary to the Harvard Corporation, recommending that Lee be appointed consultant to the Department of Legal Medicine. 'One of the things which Dr Moritz and I desire to have Mrs Lee possess is a type of authentication which will permit her to get into touch with certain organizations and individuals in the country as an individual with a visible attachment to the university and the Department of Legal Medicine,' Burwell said.[12]

The recommendation was highly unusual, since Lee had no academic credentials. 'It will be recalled that Mrs Lee is a generous supporter of the Department of Legal Medicine, both materially and through her own activities,' Burwell said to Greene in another letter.[13]

On 18 March 1943, Lee was appointed consultant to the Department of Legal Medicine. Harvard Medical School wouldn't admit female students for two more years.

Moritz told Lee that the position of consultant was as official as any faculty appointment at Harvard Medical School. 'This title would, of course, entitle its holder to use university stationery and to speak as a representative of the university,' he told her.[14]

Lee thanked Burwell for the appointment. 'I shall do my best to have something worthy of being consulted about,' she told him.[15]

Under ordinary circumstances, an appointment such as Lee's would have been announced in the *Harvard Gazette*, the university's newspaper. But word came directly from the office of the secretary of the Harvard Corporation: 'Not to be printed.'[16] Lee was not identified in the medical school catalogue as consultant to the department, but rather as honorary curator of the George Burgess Magrath Library of Legal Medicine.[17] Whether she was slighted because she was a layperson with no academic credentials or a woman among the all-male medical school faculty or for some other reason was not explained.

* * *

One of Lee's many long-standing interests was forensic odontology – the science of using the teeth and dental records for body identification. The horrors of the Iroquois Theatre and Cocoanut Grove fires were never far from her memory. The unknown haunted her. Every time she heard of an unidentified body, she felt a tug at her heart.

The teeth are the hardest, most durable material in the human body. They can tolerate decomposition or submersion in water, withstand temperatures over 1,000°C (up to 2,000°F) and survive explosions and extremes of physical forces. To a skilled eye, a single tooth can provide identifying information: a person's age, dietary habits, sex and other characteristics. Through patterns of wear, missing or broken teeth and dental repairs, teeth are as unique as fingerprints.

Lee wanted to take dental identification to a different level with a national database of dental records, much like the FBI's fingerprint filing system. An unknown body, she reasoned, found anywhere in the country, could be identified through this dental-record clearing house. But for a centralized database to work, for dental records to be classified and filed systematically, there must first be a standardized record, which did not exist at the time. Lee took it upon herself to design one. In February 1942, she sent Moritz a list she called a 'plan for unification of dental records', suggesting that they examine how the principal dental schools and colleges, and the FBI, kept this information. As ever, she went into great detail – even considering the type of index card that might be used – and she clearly wanted to be closely involved if the project went ahead.[18] At the same time, she proposed a study to research ways of using teeth to estimate time of death, determine manner of death and assist in body identification. The study would include research into:

- Natural decomposition in various stages
- Immersion in various stages
- Incineration
- Injuries due to acids or alkalis
- Trauma[19]

With a trained and knowledgeable dentist on staff, the Department of Legal Medicine could significantly advance the field of forensic odontology. Once again, Lee's proposal went unheeded, for reasons that are not documented.

* * *

By 1944, despite Lee's best efforts to educate the public, coroners had been replaced with medical examiners in only a few northeastern states.[20] Nearly ninety per cent of the US population was still under the jurisdiction of coroners. Of the 300,000 deaths every year that were the result of violent or unknown circumstances, only 10,000 occurred within a jurisdiction with access to a competent medical examiner. The number of murders that went undetected every year was probably in the thousands, and how many people were charged with crimes they did not commit is anybody's guess. In Massachusetts, the value of Moritz's forensic investigations spoke for itself. During his first two years on the job, his work cleared at least six individuals from homicide convictions and identified perpetrators in nine other cases where the police would have made no further investigations.[21]

A few states had improved their laws somewhat. In Ohio, for example, the law regarding the circumstances under which autopsies were required had been updated to be more in line with a medical examiner system, but the state still had elected coroners signing death certificates.[22]

Even where medical examiners practised, flawed statutes limited their effectiveness. Some states didn't allow medical examiners to perform autopsies without the approval of the attorney general. Many restricted the involvement of medical examiners to cases known to be the result of a criminal or negligent act. The problem was that it wasn't always obvious when criminal or negligent acts had occurred, and deaths that appeared ambiguous weren't investigated further.[23]

To Lee's disappointment, in the sixteen years since the National Research Council report had been published in 1928, only one state, Maryland, had rid itself of coroners and adopted a centralized, statewide medical examiner system. Coroners in Maryland had been notoriously corrupt and ineffective. In cities such as Baltimore, they were politically connected doctors who were appointed to their offices and granted a lucrative side business. Since coroners came and went as centres of political power shifted, there was no incentive for them to maintain or improve their competence. They kept the job, done well or not, so long as they were loyal to the right people.[24]

In Baltimore and Annapolis, the cause and manner listed on death certificates were usually made up without an investigation or even an examination of the body. Coroners found various creative ways to get payoffs from undertakers and grieving families. One tactic was reportedly to 'slow-walk' the death certificate or withhold it from vital records that were kept under governmental authority. Since the death certificate was required in order to file probate and for various other purposes, a family member or funeral director had to chase down the coroner and pay ten dollars for a document that should have cost fifty cents from the local vital records office.

Maryland's state medical society, the Medical and Chirurgical Faculty of the State of Maryland, or MedChi ('chirurgical' is derived from the Latin for 'surgical'), didn't mince words. In testimony before state lawmakers, the organization's leaders called the existing system racketeering. In 1938, MedChi took the opportunity to introduce legislation abolishing county coroners and replacing them with a novel statewide medical examiner system. The law established a chief medical examiner for the state of Maryland, based in Baltimore, who had autonomy to investigate unnatural deaths without the need for permission from prosecutors or the police.

To insulate the chief medical examiner from public pressure and political influence, the office was put under the authority of the independent Post Mortem Examiner's Commission. This was a model of governance that had not been tried anywhere else. The members of the commission included the chair of pathology at Baltimore's two medical schools, the Maryland health secretary, the state attorney general and the Baltimore city health commissioner.

Today in Maryland, the chief medical examiner cannot be threatened or intimidated or have the agency's budget cut in retaliation for not cooperating with political officials.

He or she can only be removed from the job by majority consent of the five members of the Post Mortem Examiner's Commission. The state's centralized Office of the Chief Medical Examiner, insulated from political and public influences, is perhaps the fullest embodiment of Lee's vision of legal medicine in the country.

In hopes of replicating the success of Maryland's system, Lee had personally been in touch with public officials, medical associations, legal organizations and civic groups actively engaged in the abolition or improvement of the coroner system in eleven other states. Like Magrath, she was a tireless advocate of the medical examiner system. She had her driver take her to speak at clubs and ladies' societies throughout New England to spread the gospel of scientific death investigation. Her correspondence lists her as giving talks to the Kiwanis Club of Concord, the Laconia Women's Club, the Women's Club of Meredith, the Dover Women's Club, the Sandwich Women's Club and the Science Club at Plymouth Teachers' College in New Hampshire.[25] She undoubtedly spoke dozens of times on the subject of medical examiners to a wide variety of audiences in hopes of getting others to see the importance of her cause.

In 1943, Virginia's governor appointed a panel to study the abolition of the coroner system and draft a law introducing medical examiners. Lee travelled to Richmond to meet with Dr William T Sanger, president of the Medical College of Virginia, and Colonel Charles W Woodson, superintendent of the Virginia State Police. It isn't clear whether she was able to schedule a meeting with Governor Colgate Darden, despite several attempts to speak with him directly,[26] but she did prepare five pages of comments about Virginia's proposed new system. She suggested that the medical examiner's office be authorized under an independent commission, as it was in Maryland, insulating the medical examiner from public and political pressure.[27]

Another place where Lee believed she could make a difference was the District of Columbia – the federal district that encompasses the city of Washington. In her view, it spoke poorly that the nation's capital, home to several very fine medical schools, did not have a modern medical examiner system.

World War II had transformed Washington into a bustling city. Ramping up for war had required an influx of personnel. From 1940 to 1943, the population ballooned from 690,000 to more than 900,000 with no end of growth in sight. Housing was in such short supply that temporary dormitories were erected on the National Mall. Just across the Potomac River, the War Department dedicated its new five-sided headquarters, known as the Pentagon – the largest building in the world at the time. The District of Columbia would never be the same.[28]

Advancing Lee's cause in the populous city wouldn't be easy. Abolishing coroners in DC required an act of Congress. Prior to the introduction of 'home rule' in 1973, Congress controlled the district's budget and had ultimate authority over Washington.

Lee began her effort by lobbying elected officials from New Hampshire: senators Styles Bridges and Charles W Tobey and representatives Foster Stearns and Chester Morrow. She enlisted the help of Fulton Lewis Jr, a prominent radio personality for the Mutual Broadcasting System, who was based in Washington. Building public support was critical if she was going to get a medical examiner law passed. 'Believing yours to be the most influential voice heard over the radio, I appeal to you to take up this matter,' Lee wrote to Lewis.[29]

At long last, a bill to establish a medical examiner office in the District of Columbia was introduced in Congress in 1945. Lee went into action to press elected officials:

I cannot too strongly urge your support of this bill – it would be of inestimable value to the District of Columbia. Certainly the most scientific skill should be made immediately accessible in Washington, of all places, in determining the cause of unexplained deaths without first going through the clumsy laborious and expensive routine of the coroner's office.[30]

The bill never made it to a vote.

Despite the setback, Lee was undaunted in her reform efforts. She never expressed discouragement or a sense of defeat. What she could not accept was inactivity or resignation when faced with institutional inertia. The important thing was to push ahead, one incremental step at a time. As she searched for ways to advance her agenda in whatever state she was invested in at the time, she also kept her eye on what was happening across the country.

Her home state of Illinois, for example, had not advanced towards a medical examiner system in the decade she had been following the issue. Lee realized that if the goal of establishing such a system was unrealistic, then the existing system must be reformed from within by improving the knowledge and expertise of coroners and coroner physicians. What better way to do that than to become one of them?

Although no longer a full-time resident, in December 1941, the sixty-four-year-old Lee was appointed as a consulting deputy coroner for Cook County, which includes the city of Chicago. She was paid one dollar as a symbolic gesture to give her professional legitimacy.[31]

She singled out Oscar Schultz of the Institute of Medicine of Chicago – to whom Magrath had introduced her back in 1932 because of his involvement in the report comparing medical examiner and coroner systems – for criticism for seeming to have given up trying to reform Illinois. Schultz 'is of the type who is licked before he starts', Lee confided to Moritz. 'I think, although this is not for publication, that he spends a good deal of time and energy in explaining why he didn't do a thing, when a small amount of that same time and energy might have accomplished that thing.'[32]

Others across the country were aware of Lee's views and activism. When the coroner issue arose in Oklahoma, Dr W Floyd Keller, a pathologist and prominent member of the Oklahoma City Clinical Society, contacted her for advice. Existing Oklahoma law required a justice of the peace, who lacked medical or scientific training, to attend deaths as a coroner. Abolishing the coroner system would require changing that law.[33] Lee urged Keller to stay the course, no matter what:

> I earnestly hope that your law passes in January, but if it doesn't, don't let that stop you... Our knowledge of the experience in other states suggests that the effort to bring this change about must be steadily maintained to the last minute – even, if possible, increased. It is my belief that in a matter of this kind it is necessary to have every potentially affected group actively enlisted on your side... In some other states where this change from coroner to medical examiner has been attempted the medical men who worked so hard for it became discouraged when their efforts failed on the first try. They felt, and not without justice, that they could not continue to devote any more of their busy days to the cause. Disappointed, therefore, they quit, thinking to resume their activities later at a more suitable or convenient time. But what actually happens is that they fail by this lapse of time to capitalize on what has already been built up. The enthusiasm of the supporters is lost by even a temporary pause in the presentation of the need, the benefit and the advantage of the proposed change. The foundation disintegrates, and by the time the right moment seems

to come around again, it means starting from scratch, doing all the work all over again.[34]

The reform effort in Oklahoma failed. However, in Oklahoma City, an agreement was reached between city and county officials and the Oklahoma University Hospital. They created a county-wide homicide squad, or what *The Daily Oklahoman* called a 'murder-clue team', to attend all questionable and violent deaths. The practice of coroner inquests was discontinued. A justice of the peace still served as coroner, but he would be accompanied on every case by an Oklahoma University Hospital doctor to examine the deceased and the scene before anything was disturbed.[35]

* * *

Reforming laws was a work in progress. The medical aspects were being addressed by Harvard and subsequently by other medical schools. The other structural part of legal medicine's three-legged stool was the police.

Lee began to develop an affinity for police officers in the late 1930s. She was particularly interested in working with state police organizations, which covered an entire jurisdiction, rather than the limited territories of city or county police. State troopers tended to have more formal education, they were better disciplined and regularly underwent training; Lee also felt that the quality, ability and organization of state police officers were superior to those of local law enforcement.

A police radio receiver was installed in Lee's cottage at The Rocks. She spent countless evening hours listening to police despatch chatter. Through an atmospheric fluke, she was able to pick up broadcasts from the Virginia State Police, which she listened to so regularly that she became able to discern personalities and goings-on at different police barracks. The disembodied voices of the police radio were almost like family.

'I've fallen completely under the spell of the Virginia State Police, beginning with the Superintendent, his lovely wife and his two sweet little girls,' Lee wrote to Colonel Woodson in Virginia, 'and going down through HQ and Divisions 1 to 5 inclusive, and must confess that although Division 5 still qualifies as "pet", HQ and Division 1 are close runners-up!'[36]

Her relationship with police helped her formulate plans to improve their crime-scene skills. She began with Colonel Ralph Caswell of the New Hampshire State Police, whom she knew through her brother George, who had been active in New Hampshire politics. Caswell was a no-nonsense cop. A native of Stafford, New Hampshire, he was appointed head of law enforcement for the state's Department to Enforce Prohibition in 1922. When Prohibition ended, he became an investigator in the state attorney general's office. In that role, he created the state's fingerprint database; he was then among the first detectives of the New Hampshire State Police when the agency was formed in 1937. When he was appointed superintendent of the state police in that same year, he placed an unusually high priority on training for his officers.[37]

Caswell also served as a member of the State Liquor Commission, which oversaw the retail sale of alcohol in New Hampshire. Once, having found several cases of liquor on his porch, a gift from liquor dealers intended to win him over, he called a press conference. He announced that he had broken every bottle and warned that any dealer who attempted to bribe him in the future would be banned from state liquor stores.[38] Lee began holding conferences to bring together police supervisory personnel and members of Harvard's Department of Legal Medicine. These one- or two-day conferences were held in the Magrath Library, the New Hampshire State Police headquarters in Concord or, on many occasions, at The Rocks. They included sessions on weapons and ammunition, death by violence and poisoning, preserving evidence at crime scenes and related topics. Moritz often presented a session describing the autopsy process.

The training received in Lee's conferences made police officers better prepared and more effective at crime scenes. In recognition of her contribution to the New Hampshire State Police, Caswell named her the organization's director of education. He commissioned her as a captain in the New Hampshire State Police in 1943 – the first woman in the United States to hold such a rank. She was sixty-six years old. As the original certificate states, Lee's commission granted her 'general police power to enforce all criminal laws of the state, and to serve criminal processes and make arrests under proper warrants in all counties'.

Some have characterized Lee's role with the New Hampshire State Police as merely honorary, but nothing could be further from the truth. 'This was *not* an honorary post,' Caswell later said. 'She was actually a full-fledged captain with all the authority and responsibility of the post.'[39]

Lee never made an arrest during her career as a police officer. But from then on, she always carried a gold badge in her purse and identified herself as Captain Lee.

As her interest in law enforcement grew, Lee envisaged the development of a new speciality within police work. Just as there were specialists in medicine – cardiologists, neurologists and so on – so there were areas of specialized expertise in law enforcement, such as fingerprinting and the examination of disputed documents. She believed that homicide should be a specialist area with dedicated personnel trained with specific expertise.

She called the position she was thinking of a 'medico-legal investigator': what would be known today as a homicide detective. While homicide squads existed in some police departments and there were officers called homicide detectives, none had the advanced training in legal medicine that Lee proposed. As her vision of the scope of the department solidified, she listed some of the purposes of the Department of Legal Medicine in regard to training specialized law enforcement officers as:

- To create the profession of medico-legal investigator and to standardize its requirements.
- To give the medico-legal investigator a proper attitude toward his calling as well as toward the public and to develop his sense of responsibility toward both.
- To give him a background of the history of his profession as well as its relation to other branches of the government.
- To train him in the basic skills and abilities peculiar to his work.
- To acquaint him with the general types of forms and reports he will be required to fill out.
- To develop in him a sense of the need for full and generous cooperation with other government departments with which he works.
- To stimulate in him a desire for further knowledge.
- To teach him that legal medicine should be taken out of politics.
- To teach him that he is a seeker for truth – that his duty is to present that truth and fearlessly adhere to it.
- To instil in him the desire and ability to improve his profession, not alone in its workings, but in its repute in the minds of the lay as well as the professional public.
- To develop in him a sense of loyalty to and pride in his profession and an appreciation of its scientific value and of its essential dignity.[40]

But the momentum that had been building within the Department of Legal Medicine was brought to a halt by a disconcerting letter to Lee from Dr Sidney Burwell, dean of the medical school, in April 1944.

'An alarming possibility occurs,' Burwell wrote. 'Dr Moritz has been offered an extremely attractive opportunity to take a position in another medical school. It is so attractive that he is bound to consider it seriously and I am sure that he is now doing it.'[41]

Suddenly, everything that Lee had worked so hard to build at Harvard seemed at risk of crumbling.

CHAPTER 9

In a Nutshell

1944–1945

'Five years ago the department consisted of a newly appointed professor and some empty rooms on the third floor of Building E-1,' Moritz wrote in a report to Sidney Burwell, on 15 May 1944. 'No one, including the professor, had any definite idea of what was to be done or how to do it.'[1] Now, after five years of operation, Moritz said, it was time to step back to assess the experiment and discuss whether the Department of Legal Medicine had the promise of ultimate success.

In many respects, the department appeared productive. Moritz was performing autopsies and consulting on deaths throughout Massachusetts. Members of the department were involved in research and publishing papers. Lectures were being delivered to medical students from Harvard, Tufts and Boston universities. But the collaboration that had been expected with Harvard's School of Law never materialized. Four doctors had been trained in the fellowship programme, with two of them subsequently taking up positions at other universities to develop legal medicine programmes of their own. As the United States was drawn into World War II, qualified candidates for the fellowship training became unavailable. One of the fellows was called up by the army, leaving only one remaining at Harvard doing research.

'It is expected that at the conclusion of the war there will be more applications for fellowships in legal medicine than can be accepted,' Moritz continued. The department desperately needed more staff to handle the increase of activity expected when men were released from military service.

The heavy workload was taking a toll on Moritz. As the department's only full-time member of staff, he found himself pulled in multiple directions. Attending medical meetings to represent legal medicine and Harvard was a professional obligation. He was asked to give testimony about legal medicine before state lawmakers in various other states. He consulted with universities developing legal medicine programmes, including the University of Washington and the University of California at Los Angeles. At the same time, he needed to be in the autopsy room, instructing students and fellows in postmortem examination. Many of his cases, of course, were criminal matters that ended up in court, meaning additional hours of preparation and testimony. Finally, he was also involved with Lee and the conferences in legal medicine she was conducting for medical examiners, coroners and coroner physicians, prosecutors, police officers and insurance company executives.

The bottom line: Harvard Medical School needed to increase its full-time staff to at least three, with another pathologist and a toxicologist. The salaries required seemed like a huge expenditure, but the return to the community in the form of autopsy services throughout Massachusetts could be substantial. Tufts and Boston universities would also benefit, as Harvard, by agreement, provided lectures in legal medicine for all the medical schools in Boston.

'It is possible that the university did not fully realize the extent to which it was committing itself in undertaking the development of a department of legal medicine,' Moritz wrote in his report. 'It would be better to abandon the project entirely than to persist in an attempt so handicapped as to be foredoomed to failure.'

If Moritz's report was a gambit to get increased funding and attention for the department, it worked. The Rockefeller Foundation granted an additional $75,000 over a ten-year period. Lee, who had been donating $1,000 a year for three years to pay for expenses, increased her annual gift to $3,000 for five years.[2] Moritz decided to stay.

Lee was pleased with his decision. Yet she couldn't help but notice the cracks in the veneer of their relationship as Moritz continued to lead the department as he saw fit, sometimes in direct contradiction of her wishes and proposals.

Despite the lukewarm response from the rest of the university, particularly the law school, to the Department of Legal Medicine, Lee was convinced that Harvard could do for law enforcement what its prestigious School of Business had done for the corporate world. Harvard Masters of Business Administration – MBAs – practically ran the country, and the distinction conferred by that degree went far beyond the value of a sheet of paper.[3]

Degree programmes for police had been developed at several universities, including those of California and Chicago. At the time, however, no curriculum offered to police officers included material on legal medicine – there was nowhere in the United States where you could train as a homicide detective. Lee and Moritz spent a great deal of time discussing how to address this. Neither of them was certain what police wanted or needed to know, nor if police departments would be interested in enrolling in educational programmes at Harvard.

Colonel Caswell, the New Hampshire State Police superintendent, sent Lee on a mission to survey police departments in New England. Driven by one of Caswell's officers in a police car, Captain Lee visited state police and medical examiners in New Hampshire, Massachusetts and Maine, and was shown professional courtesy along the way.

She questioned senior police officers about training in legal medicine, assessing their familiarity with the subject area and soliciting ideas for topics that should be covered in a course. She produced a detailed, nine-page report of her survey. One insight she gained was that, within police departments, different people needed to understand different things. Officers who investigated unexplained deaths should know the practical aspects of legal medicine. But before you could reach these officers, the 'top men' in each department needed to be educated about what legal medicine was and how it could help their investigations. 'In a word, to sell legal medicine to the state police heads in order that they may be enlightened enough to detail their troopers to take the next course', was what Lee recommended in her report.[4]

It was clear that the subject had to be taught from the top down. Lee suggested a nontechnical one- or two-day course for police chiefs and top investigative officers that explained what could be found out with legal medicine, what material and information was needed, what would be taught to the junior officers and how it would help police departments.

For police officers, Moritz and Lee considered developing a one-year course at Harvard to provide in-depth training in forensic investigation. Moritz circulated a letter to police departments in New England to gauge interest in the proposal and to recruit the first class of twelve students. The proposal withered on the vine when too few candidates were found with the basic prerequisite of two years of university, including physics and chemistry coursework.

As an alternative, Lee suggested an intensive course – a one-week seminar held in the Magrath Library. The course shouldn't be overly technical, just what state troopers absolutely needed to know. 'The men dealt with are those of average education without technical medical knowledge,' she said. 'They are to be taught the practical how-to-do aspects of crime detection from the medical point of view, in words of one syllable, to make them efficient in bringing in the material for examination... While it would be a feather in a trooper's cap to take a course at Harvard, he shouldn't be frightened off by fear of it being over his head.'

* * *

As Lee well knew, no aspect of any investigation was more important than the crime scene. There was only one opportunity to process a scene the right way. An error or oversight there could alter the whole trajectory of an investigation. Police had to be taught to use their powers of observation before stumbling through a scene and disturbing the facts. They needed to know how to recognize evidence that might be significant in order for it to be preserved and documented. *How does one teach how to observe?* Lee pondered.

'The matter of providing students with first-hand experience in at-the-scene observation became of paramount importance and was under frequent discussion' between Moritz and herself, Lee said. Using an actual crime scene would be ideal but not practical.[5]

'The problem of teaching a group of students was insurmountable, as they could not, in a body, be taken to the scene of an unexplained death to study at their leisure,' Lee said. 'Why not? Because time was important, conditions changed, crowds of "interested bystanders" get in the way, but chiefly because until a case has cleared the courts it should not be a matter for free public discussion. And once it has cleared the courts, the clinical material has undergone such changes as to be valueless for teaching purposes, and the scene and its surroundings have been practically wrecked.'

Students could be shown photographs or movies from crime scenes, but that process would be leading them by the nose, pointing out evidence to them. That was very different from the process of finding evidence at an actual scene, with no photographic framing to direct the attention.

'It has been found that visual teaching is the most valuable, but lantern slides and motion pictures, although important, do not give the third dimension, nor the opportunity for prolonged study that is requisite,' Lee said.[6]

Out of the blue – as she had done when talking to Magrath at Phillips House all those years ago – she thought of the Chicago Symphony Orchestra diorama she had created for her mother and the boxes of doll's-house furnishings and bisque pieces in the attic of The Rocks. 'Why not let me make a model that will contain the settings for a scene and the body in its place?' she said to Moritz. 'Could you not teach from that?'[7]

Moritz's reaction is not noted, but presumably he was interested. Lee began work straight away. She contacted Ralph Mosher, who did carpentry and various other odd jobs at The Rocks, most recently building a wine cellar. 'I have some special work to be done which I can only describe as the making of a particular type of wooden box, to be approximately 18 x 18 inches [46 x 46cm] square,' she wrote to him. 'There will be detail work which I can explain later.'[8]

Mosher wrote back asking for clarification. 'If you will send me the details I will be glad to do it for you,' he said. 'If you give me a little idea of what tools I would need, it would help. I may have to come by train and would not want to bring unnecessary tools.'[9]

'The work I want done is building some model miniature rooms, so what you will need in the way of tools will be your smallest and finest ones,' Lee replied.[10]

She envisaged creating a series of dioramas presenting crime scenarios that were deliberately ambiguous, forcing the student to observe and ponder. It was important that they look as realistic as possible, lest police officers think they were being asked to play with doll's houses. She decided early on to work in a familiar scale: 1:12, the same proportions she had used for the Chicago Symphony Orchestra and Flonzaley Quartet models. The dioramas would be designed for an imaginary investigator about 15cm (6in) tall.

The first diorama Lee made was based on a case Magrath had investigated, of a man who had hanged himself under curious circumstances. The dead man had been an unpleasant, manipulative fellow who repeatedly coerced his wife by threatening suicide until he got his way.

'In the original, the old man went to the cellar carrying a rope in his hand – he placed the rope over some overhead piping and attached one end of it thereto, the other end containing a noose,' Lee told Moritz. 'After that he stood on a convenient box, bucket or crate with the noose around his neck and waited to be coaxed down.'[11] One day, his stand broke, unexpectedly resulting in his strangulation.

In order to conceal the real deceased's identity in the diorama, Lee decided to have the death take place in a typical New England barn rather than a cellar. To build this, she had Mosher salvage aged wood from an old barn building that had been on The Rocks property when the Glessners acquired it. Mosher used a saw to carefully remove the naturally bleached and worn surface of the lumber, creating sheets of wood 2mm ($\frac{1}{12}$in) thick. The sheets were cut into 1.25cm ($\frac{1}{2}$in) strips, then glued together to make scale-model 5 x 15cm (2 x 6in) planks with aged wood on both sides.

Mosher's barn is 69cm (27in) tall from the base to the weather vane and about 60cm (2ft) square. Lee filled the interior with straw and an assortment of farm implements, including a scythe made from an oyster knife. Through the back window is a large, hand-painted photograph – a view of the Franconia Mountains from Bethlehem Junction, Lee's local railway station. Over the barn door hangs a horseshoe with the open side down – the unlucky way. A 2.5cm (1in) tall hornets' nest, camouflaged so well that it is easily overlooked, is tucked beneath the eaves.

Inside the barn, the lifeless body of Eben Wallace (the name Lee invented for the tiny deceased) dangles from the hoist, a flimsy wooden crate crushed beneath his feet. (For more details about this diorama see Appendix page 252.)

Lee began work on the dioramas while World War II was still raging. Many materials were rationed or scarce, including steel and other metals, some kinds of wood and even the equipment necessary to make the dioramas. Before Mosher could make miniature pieces, he needed to produce miniature tools: small-scale chisels and planes to work the wood. Lee tried to purchase a $13.95 jeweller's lathe from Sears Roebuck in Vermont, but was informed that electrical motors were rationed and she needed to apply for permission from the War Production Board.[12] She duly filled out a form PD-1A, an Application for Preference Rating. In the space for the purpose for which a priority was requested, she wrote 'Dioramas (miniature models) for scientific study and instruction'.[13] It took two months, but she got her lathe. She was not so fortunate, however, in securing a priority number for a saw and motor that Mosher also needed.[14]

Obtaining materials and spare parts for more usual purposes could be difficult, too. Even when it came to asking International Harvester for materials, being the daughter of a beloved co-founder proved to be of no benefit. When Lee needed a replacement exhaust pipe for the International Harvester A-6 truck at The Rocks, the company told her they could not send a replacement until the old one was returned. This did not sit well with Lee, as that would require the truck to be out of commission for several days while waiting for the replacement part.[15]

'We are in the midst of haying and it would greatly inconvenience us to be without the use of this truck for three or four days,' she wrote to the company in which she still held a substantial portion of stock.[16] It was no use; nothing could trump government war rationing.

Sheet metal, nails and screws, hinges, wire – all varieties of metal items were scarce. If a screw was available, it was often not the right size or colour. Even a half-used spool of wire was precious for the project. In the winter of 1944, a friend in Cambridge sent Lee a length of wire. 'The package containing the wire which you sent me has been received, and I am extremely grateful to you for your thoughtful and generous gift,' she wrote. 'It will be far more value in my work on the NUTSHELL models [the Nutshell Studies of Unexplained Death, as she called her dioramas] for the Department of Legal Medicine at the Harvard Medical School than you can have any conception of, for it is much needed, and as you know, is pricelessly rare.'[17]

Six-centimetre (¼in) brass hinges, necessary to hang miniature doors with hardware in the correct proportions, were unavailable anywhere. Lee searched hardware stores and suppliers far and wide to no avail. The closest she could find were twice that size and had to be individually ground down to the proper scale.[18] Since nails at the small scale she needed were not commercially available, Mosher had to make his own.

One of the scenarios Lee wanted to model was a car wreck, with a female driver dead behind the wheel. Unbeknown to the viewer, the woman had been beaten to death by her husband and the crash staged to cover up his crime. The students' challenge would be to discern whether the driver had been killed by the collision or was already dead when it occurred.

Because of steel and rubber rationing, Lee could not find a realistic vehicle of the correct scale for her models.

Production of toy cars and trucks was suspended during the war, and some companies went out of business. With some determination, she was able to find one vehicle – a 1:12 scale red roadster – but thought better of trying to simulate a realistic crash with her precious toy. Instead, she used it in the diorama called Garage, in which a dead man was found in the car in his garage, apparently gassed.

At another point, she needed some clear acrylic-based plastic known as Lucite for windows; it had to be 3mm (⅛in) thick and enough to yield thirteen pieces of various small sizes. She told her supplier in Boston that she would buy a piece of 3mm Lucite of any size that she could cut the pieces from. 'Lucite is on priority and cannot be purchased,' the supplier told her. All the company had was a 36cm (14in) panel of 6mm (¼in) Lucite that had been rejected by the navy because it scratched too easily.[19]

'I shall be very glad to have the panel of Lucite as I can use it to very good advantage,' Lee wrote along with an order for brad nails. 'Thank you for obtaining the precious articles for me.'[20]

For some of the models, she was forced to use glass taken from a picture frame for windows. But, once the war was over, she was able to acquire thin sheets of acrylic to use as windowpanes.

Lee spared no effort or expense to give her dioramas authenticity. For whiskey bottles to ornament the models, she acquired labels of Town Tavern and Crab Orchard brand liquor from the National Distillers Products Corporation, from which she made miniature replicas.[21] She hired an artist to paint backdrops and another to create a miniature oil painting of her cottage at The Rocks, 2.5cm (1in) tall and twice as wide, to hang over a living-room fireplace.

For a kitchen scene, she purchased a small bauble in the form of a working hand-mixer. Made of gold, it was meant to hang from a charm bracelet, but she painted it grey to look like steel. This one piece of jewellery, just a prop, probably cost more than a day's wages for the typical worker at the time.

Lee wanted her models to look realistic: lived-in and shabbily cluttered. The deaths she chose to depict were those of people of modest means: prostitutes, a prisoner, the poor and the marginalized. Finding furniture and other furnishings for such humble settings proved difficult. Lee wrote to a miniature furniture-maker in Dunstable, Massachusetts, seeking shabby, worn furniture, but discovered that while 'I have never seen more exquisite work nor more faithful replicas than yours', his work was too good for her purposes.[22]

'I am not representing the finest pieces nor period pieces, but am trying to show the typical furnishings in lower-middle-class homes, or in poverty-stricken shacks or tenements,' she said, 'mostly the furniture of that nondescript type which one cannot imagine as even having been procurable at any place but a secondhand store.'

Mosher made many of the furniture pieces by hand: scale-sized wardrobes, bedside tables, chairs. To make sure the results were as realistic as possible, Lee asked a forestry professor at Yale for a list of varieties of wood with a grain fine enough to be plausible at 1:12 scale.

Realistic human figures for the death scenes did not exist commercially either. All the figures available in the doll's-house supply catalogues were posed in a fixed position with the feet on a base to make them stand upright. This was not at all suitable for Lee's purposes, so she made her own. The heads, left over from the miniatures she had made decades previously, were finished with wigs or painted plaster to simulate hair. Torsos and limbs were filled with sawdust, cotton, sand or lead shot as necessary to give the body the proper heft and appearance. Stiff wire was employed to hold a body in position and represent rigor mortis. Lee carefully painted the porcelain skin of the figures to show lividity, carbon monoxide poisoning, decomposition and signs of violence.

Dressing the dolls was another exacting affair. 'The most difficult matter is the texture of the material used – that of men's suits being perhaps the hardest to simulate,' Lee said. 'The materials must meet many requirements. They must be thin and pliable, but not transparent; they must be capable of taking a crease; they must not ravel easily, and for draping purposes, they must be such that they can be wet without damage; and of course the colour and pattern must be correct, but while all these can sometimes be found in one piece of goods, it may still be unusable as the texture is out of proportion.'[23]

Lee revelled in the most minute details. 'Most of the furniture and small objects work – doors and dressers open, stove lids lift, corks come out of bottles, grindstone is a real one and turns, halter and belt buckles work, some books open and have printed pages inside, the knitting is real,' she wrote.[24] The figures, although fully clothed, had underwear on beneath. Anything less would be indecent.

Lee carefully applied red nail polish to simulate blood spatter on walls, puddles of blood, and bloody footprints on the floor. The walls around light switches were smudged with fingerprints. With cloth wrapped around her fingertip, Lee spent hours rubbing a worn spot on a piece of linoleum flooring to make it look authentically aged. She included things that would never be seen by observers – a stamp-sized poster for a boxing match inside a saloon that is only visible to a 15cm (6in) tall patron walking inside, and graffiti scrawled on a jail-cell wall.

'I found myself constantly tempted to add more clues and details and am afraid I may get too "gadgety" in the process,' Lee said to Moritz. 'I hope you will watch me and stop me when I go too far.'[25]

Within a matter of months, Lee and Mosher had made a barn, a bedroom, a kitchen, a living room and at least three other dioramas. In honour of Isaac Scott, Mosher built a log cabin based on Lee's childhood playhouse. Another model was inspired by the garage at her parents' Prairie Avenue home. Many more dioramas were planned. 'I have in prospect, or completed, two hangings; two shootings; two assaults with blunt weapon; one natural cause; one drowning; one found dead; one arson (I do not know yet how that gentleman was killed – am open to suggestions); and one poison,' she told Moritz. 'I need more traffic accidents – hit-and-run, collision and non-collision with some good evidence (shreds of clothing, etc., but not too commonplace or obvious); also another shooting or two, a stabbing, more poisonings, carbon monoxide, and a couple of puzzling Found Deads.'[26]

The most elaborate diorama Lee built consisted of two nearly identical side-by-side rooms. On the left, the scene showed the moment after a man had been shot to death. He was sprawled on the living-room floor. The room to the right, finished exactly the same as the other, showed conditions after a trooper had helpfully moved the victim to the couch. The trooper was standing, taking notes, while the wife swept up the debris of china broken when her husband collapsed. In the officer's hand was a pencil made from a toothpick, with a tiny lead nib. The notebook had tiny indecipherable notes. Around his neck, on a very fine platinum chain, was a whistle that actually worked. Although at first glance the two scenes appeared nearly identical, there were more than thirty differences between them that the student observing them was expected to detect. Unfortunately this diorama was irreparably damaged in the 1960s.

One of Lee's early models was a rural two-room cabin. Its resident was clearly not a wealthy man – the tarpaper roof had been patched – but it had the basic necessities: a comfortable chair in a warm spot near the wood stove, a wide, iron-framed bed and a simple kitchen, well stocked with food and with a kerosene stove. After spending countless painstaking hours and thousands of dollars to make an exquisitely detailed diorama, Lee took a blowtorch to her work. Inspired by the Frederick Small murder of his wife Florence, and the arson, she carefully burned most of one corner of the cabin until the bed began to fall through the floorboards. In the foreground, on top of a chest of drawers, was a soot-smudged alarm clock.

It is difficult to assign an accurate monetary value to the dioramas. Lee did not keep itemized accounting on each model, and some materials were used in more than one. By some estimates, the cost of material and labour in producing each diorama ranged from $3,000 to $6,000, represented by an expenditure of £32,000–£64,000 today.

* * *

The first week-long seminar in homicide investigation for police officers took place in 1945. Two sessions were to be held each year, in April and October, around the conference table in the Magrath Library. Lee hailed the seminar as a new chapter in scientific police work.

'Believing firmly that the efficient policeman is an informed policeman, [I have] made every effort to provide the police students with the most modern and progressive scientific training possible to procure for them,' she said. 'The old days are gone – the days when "brogue and brawn" were the requisites to make a city foot patrolman, and today the policeman is an educated, well-trained gentleman,' she said.[27]

Lee orchestrated the homicide seminar like a social engagement. Attendance was by invitation only. During her travels visiting various police departments, she kept notes on potential students. She looked for police officers who were bright, had attended university and were early enough in their careers to benefit from the specialized training. If an officer was within a few years of retirement, she ruled him ineligible, believing that he wouldn't make full use of the training in his remaining time on the force. She also personally interviewed the student candidates' supervisors and chief to make sure they were committed to taking full advantage of the training. She did not want to waste a place in the classroom if the graduate would later be assigned to a desk or the evidence room.

She insisted that all law-enforcement agencies pay the full price for the seminar and that it be paid by the department, not the officer. This was to get agencies invested in the programme, both literally and figuratively.

During the week of the seminar, officers heard lectures about blunt-force and stabbing injuries, asphyxiation, poisoning, fires, drowning and a variety of causes of death. They observed an autopsy performed by Moritz and, of course, they interacted with the Nutshell Studies of Unexplained Death.

At the end of the first day, each officer was assigned two Nutshell dioramas to study. They were given about ninety minutes to observe each one. Later in the week, they stood before the class and gave a verbal report. After some discussion, the point intended to be illustrated by each model was disclosed to them.[28]

The models were installed behind black cabinets in a darkened gallery. Most of the illumination was from the miniature light bulbs within them. Lee sat in the room while the students worked, making herself available to answer general questions but never giving away hints.

Students were told that the dioramas weren't meant to be solved like a real criminal case. The models didn't contain complete information – there were no autopsy findings, witnesses couldn't be asked questions and, in most cases, the full faces of the dead were not shown.

'It must be understood, these models are not "whodunits" – they cannot be solved merely by looking at them,' Lee said. 'They are intended to be an exercise in observing, interpreting, evaluating and reporting.'[29]

Most importantly, the Nutshells were intended to teach the viewer to resist jumping to conclusions, making a snap judgement and only noticing evidence fitting a favoured hypothesis. 'One of the essentials in the study of these Nutshells is that the student should approach them with an open mind,' Lee said. 'Far too often the investigator "has a hunch" and looks for – *and finds* – only the evidence to support it, disregarding any other evidence that may be present. This attitude would be calamitous in investigating an actual case.'

Lee encouraged students to think of the Nutshells as a moment frozen in time – 'as if a motion picture were stopped at such a point'. Some unknown sequence of events had occurred, and the diorama represented the moment the officer arrived on the scene.

'The students should be warned that they must whittle their perceptions down to as fine a point as possible in order not to overlook pertinent details,' Lee said. 'It should be explained to them that much of the detail in the models has nothing to do with the actual problem, but is present as scenery – stage setting – in order to show the kind of people who occupied the premises or their state of mind.'[30]

She recommended that students observe each diorama slowly and methodically, beginning at one spot to their left and looking around the room in a clockwise direction, from the periphery to the middle. She urged them to look at everything with an open mind and allow the truth suggested by the evidence to let itself be known.

* * *

The seeds of legal medicine planted in the police officers' homicide seminar would need tending if the field were to grow and flourish. Knowledge and skills introduced during the seminar had to be kept updated. Lee wanted her graduates to keep the momentum going, to maintain the professional relationships they had formed during the week, to network and exchange information and work together on major cases as necessary. To that end, at the same time as she began the seminars, she formed a non-profit organization called Harvard Associates in Police Science (HAPS). Graduates of the seminar were given membership of HAPS, which held advanced homicide seminars and promoted professional development. According to its articles of incorporation, the purposes of HAPS were:

- To organize and unite persons who have completed a seminar on legal medicine for police officers at Harvard Medical School.
- To encourage the enlargement and improvement of medical science in crime detection.
- To encourage research work in scientific crime detection.
- To promote the highest standards among law enforcement officials having charge of criminal investigations.
- To meet in convention and disseminate precise data to members with respect to crime prevention and detection, and to put forth full power in any movement that has as its aim crime reduction.
- To provide the police with the latest developments in laboratory and other scientific aids in crime detection, and
- To bring about closer cooperation between police and medical science.[31]

Lee treated the officers attending the homicide seminars very well, making sure that they were as comfortable as possible.

She purchased cigarettes for the men and in a shrewd piece of marketing had packs of matches with 'Legal Medicine' printed on them. It was her hope that the officers would take the matches and prompt conversations about legal medicine back home.

On the second night of each seminar, Lee hosted a dinner at Boston's Ritz-Carlton. She spent lavishly on these meals, fussing over the smallest details. She personally drew up the seating chart, placing officers from the most distant cities next to each other to facilitate friendships and conversation. Insisting on the finest in food, drink and service, she spent an amount comparable to £20,000 today for a dinner with forty guests. The floral centrepieces alone cost close to £5,000 in present-day currency. Lee insisted that her guests dine on gold-leaf place settings, so the hotel spent the equivalent of £52,000 to purchase a set of china that was reserved exclusively for the homicide seminars.

'These were wonderful affairs,' recalled Charles L Banino, general manager of the Ritz-Carlton. 'She treated her guests as if they were royalty. They could have anything they wanted and as much as they wanted – as long as they behaved like gentlemen.'[32]

A typical menu included such extravagant items as boola-boola soup, paillettes, celery hearts, radishes, olives, broiled filet mignon with sauce bordelaise, petits pois à l'eau, Anna potatoes, endive and watercress salad, omelette suédoise flambée, coffee, mints and cigars. For many of the officers attending the seminar, it was the finest meal they had had in their lives. Lee was 'probably the fussiest patron we ever had,' Banino said. 'And we loved her.'

The opulent meal was part of Lee's overall desire to impress upon the students that they had been privileged to receive specialized training from some of the best minds in the country. They now belonged to an elite corps and were expected to conduct themselves accordingly. They had been given a gift in the education they were receiving and had a duty to apply their newly gained knowledge in their work.

Upon completing the seminar, each student was given a diploma from Harvard Associates in Police Science. It was important to Lee that they have a diploma that said Harvard on it, to let them know they had accomplished something significant. Each student was also given a HAPS lapel pin and a photo of the entire class as a keepsake.

At the conclusion of the seminar, Lee rose to address the group:

> There is no place for guesswork in any sort of police work whatever, especially not in homicide investigation. The investigator seeks out the truth: the whole naked incontrovertible truth, let it finish where it may. He is not protecting or avenging anyone, but is seeking, through patient, painstaking, accurate hard work, what happened, never making a guess and then searching for evidence to support it. Patience, an infinite capacity for taking pains, absolute accuracy, thoroughness: there is no substitute for these. If you cannot approach a case with these convictions, you should resign at once. There is no place for you either in police work. Say to yourself over and over, 'There is absolutely no place for guessing in police work' and perhaps you will learn it.[33]

* * *

Lee planned on donating the Nutshells to the Department of Legal Medicine at Harvard. 'I am making arrangements to determine, through my tax advisor, how the models may take their place in the Department of Legal Medicine most advantageously for all concerned,' she wrote to Burwell. 'When this has been decided I will write you a formal offer along the lines that you and I have discussed.'[34]

Months later, Lee made her formal offer. 'I dislike to attach conditions to a gift but for the sake of clarity I will say that I understand these models will be adequately installed and protected,' she wrote. 'I prefer that they shall not be on public exhibition but that they will be kept for the use and, I hope, benefit of those who are taking our seminars.'[35]

Harvard thanked Lee for the promised donation with a tea party on 23 January 1946. The guest list included Harvard president James Conant and his wife, Dr and Mrs Roger Lee, Dean Sidney Burwell and his wife, Alan and Velma Moritz, Alan Gregg of the Rockefeller Foundation and Lee's children, John Glessner Lee and Martha Batchelder.

Despite the outward show of generosity, Lee was growing unhappy with Harvard and the Department of Legal Medicine. Moritz had accepted a position as chief pathologist at Peter Bent Brigham Hospital alongside his regular duties, taking more time and attention away from departmental matters. Lee had the sense that she was tolerated only because of the promise of her estate. In all fairness, she was exploiting Harvard to her advantage as well, using the university's prestige to advance the field of legal medicine. But she didn't feel that she was being taken seriously for her contributions.

'Mrs Lee expressed the opinion that she was not as hospitably received in the Department of Legal Medicine as she would like to be and was eager to be,' Burwell wrote in a memorandum, 'and that she was too much of an honoured guest and not enough of a participant.'[36]

CHAPTER 10

Murder at Harvard

1946–1949

In the spring of 1946, state lawmakers in Virginia passed Senate Bill 64, which abolished the coroner system and established the office of chief medical examiner to investigate unexplained deaths. To shield the medical examiner from public pressure and political influence, he was under the authority of a five-member independent commission – much like the arrangement Lee had widely recommended. Lee wasted no time in ensuring that Virginia's system got off on the right foot by advocating the hiring of a former Harvard legal-medicine fellow as the first chief medical examiner. Two candidates were at the top of her list: Dr Herbert Lund and Dr Herbert Breyfogle. They were both young, brilliant and well qualified for the job.

A third candidate, Dr Russell Fisher, who had helped Lee with her teaching materials a few years earlier, had received his medical education at the Medical College of Virginia (MCV). MCV president Dr William Sanger asked Moritz to take Fisher into Harvard's fellowship programme with the thought that he might return to Virginia as medical examiner one day. Lee felt that, while Fisher was intelligent and capable, he would not be ready for such a pivotal role for a few more years because he had not yet finished his pathology training.[1] She shared her views with Sanger and

Colonel Charles Woodson, superintendent of the Virginia State Police, both members of the commission overseeing the medical examiner's office. In a unanimous decision, the commission appointed Breyfogle as Virginia's first chief medical examiner.

The law that established the office of chief medical examiner also authorized the creation of a Department of Legal Medicine at the Medical College of Virginia. Breyfogle was appointed an assistant professor, and the new department commenced operations in 1948.[2]

*　*　*

It didn't take long for newspaper reporters to hear about the scientific homicide seminars for police officers at Harvard and the unusual crime-scene models used for instruction. The odd combination of murder and doll's houses was ideal for feature stories. The *Boston Globe, Providence Sunday Journal* and many other newspapers ran stories about the Harvard Department of Legal Medicine and the heroic exploits of a new generation of scientific medical examiners.

These stories tended to cast Lee as a peripheral figure if she was mentioned at all – a wealthy matron who made morbid doll's houses – and understated her role as a leader in the field and as a driving force behind the department. Lee was willing to accept this self-effacement if it made a useful hook for a story and helped spread the word about legal medicine. Moritz apologized to her about her being kept anonymous and not given credit for her pioneering work.

'As [far as my] "complete anonymity" is concerned, it doesn't exist,' she wrote in reply. 'I have had all kinds of write-ups from the beginning. Let's put all our efforts into bringing the subject of legal medicine before the public and making it both understood and valued as well as popular.

It really doesn't matter to any but a few who is backing it, and those few know, so let's call it a day.'[3]

The biggest coup to date happened in the spring of 1946, when Lee was approached for a story in *Life* magazine. *Life* was the country's pre-eminent pictorial news weekly, with a circulation of about 13 million readers. A large-format magazine known for its superior photography, it was anxious to feature the Nutshell Studies of Unexplained Death.

A *Life* photographer spent several days at Harvard shooting the dioramas. The magazine wanted to present them to its readers as if they were students in the seminar, with each brief preliminary report assigned to the corresponding diorama. There was just one problem: the magazine also wanted the answers behind each scene.

'*Life* is still very much interested in getting a story, but feels the "solutions" are indispensable,' magazine staffer Jeff Wylie told Lee. 'I explained that you had said we would be free to draw our own conclusions and I told the editors that I thought you would confirm correct deductions that we might make. The editors now, in the cantankerous way that editors have, want to know why – if you will confirm our guesses – you can't agree to give us the full solutions. In other words, *Life* doesn't want to play a guessing game.'[4]

Participating in the story was an opportunity to bring legal medicine to a huge national audience. But if everybody knew the solutions, the value of the Nutshells for teaching would drop to zero. Lee compromised. She allowed *Life* to print witness statements, but not the complete report used during the homicide seminar. She let the magazine reveal some clues but withheld the solutions.

The Nutshells made their national debut in the 3 June 1946 issue of *Life*. An un-bylined feature ran on three pages in the front of the magazine, in a prime spot as the first photo feature after the 'letters to the editor' section. Lee was mentioned as the founder of the Department of Legal Medicine but not shown in a photo. There were photos of four of the Nutshells: Living Room, Dark Bathroom, Two Rooms and Striped Bedroom. The only photograph of people was four men looking at the Barn.[5]

* * *

Police officers who had attended the Harvard seminar were pleased to report to Lee how they applied the training to investigations. After one seminar, Lieutenant R F Borkenstein of the Indiana State Police Laboratory told her about a recent case involving a man who had been found after being immersed in water for about three months, his body so badly decomposed that the local police and coroner had abandoned the possibility of identifying him through fingerprints.

Having learned about skin slippage and de-gloving – in which the epidermis separates from the underlying layer of the skin – at the homicide seminar, Borkenstein thought to look inside the gloves the deceased had been wearing when he was found. These had been discarded along with the dead man's clothing, but had not yet been destroyed. Inside the gloves was skin with legible fingerprints, leading to the identification of the body.

'The coroner, an undertaker, was not familiar with the fact that the skin from the hands separates under these conditions,' Borkenstein told Lee. 'The cause of death will probably never be known as no autopsy was done. I am lighting a torch to carry against this condition, and hope that something will come of it in the future.'[6]

Knowledge imparted at the homicide seminars was also disseminated when students returned home. A Delaware trooper presented a training session based on his experiences at Harvard, including the observation of an autopsy. One of his trainees, using this secondhand information, later interrupted a coroner's physician who was about to begin a postmortem examination by opening the deceased's skull.[7] 'That's wrong,' the trooper told the doctor. 'The abdomen should be opened before the skull. That's how they do it at Harvard.' Sawing the skull can damage veins in the membrane surrounding the brain, obscuring signs of intracranial bleeding. Opening the abdomen first allows blood vessels of the head and neck to drain into the torso, so any blood subsequently found on the surface of the brain won't have been caused by the saw.

The coroner's physician did not take kindly to the unsolicited advice and walked away. A supervisor called the trooper into his office to explain himself. 'I thought you had us take a course because you wanted us to learn something and then put that to use,' he said. 'There is a right way and a wrong way, and that was the wrong way.'[8]

In the homicide seminar held during the first week of April 1947, Moritz presented a session on how he and the Boston medical examiner's staff had recovered and identified the 493 victims of the Cocoanut Grove fire and the chemical analysis for fumes that may have been responsible for many of the deaths.[9] J H Arnette, a chemist with the Texas State Police laboratory, was present at Moritz's presentation. One week after his return to Texas City, a cargo ship in the city's port loaded with 2,000 tons of fertilizer exploded. Arnette, having just attended the seminar, knew exactly how to begin the process of recovering and identifying the casualties. He set up a command centre at the scene to centralize the recovery of remains, and obtained tags to identify victims before they were removed from the scene.[10]

At least 581 people were killed, including all but one of the twenty-eight-member Texas City Volunteer Fire Department. More than sixty victims were never identified, and the remains of scores of people were never found. It was the worst industrial accident in American history and, without the influence of Lee's seminar, the aftermath would have been overwhelming for the local law enforcement.[11]

* * *

Eighteen men went through fellowship study at Harvard's Department of Legal Medicine during its first decade of existence. Of those eighteen, half were still working as medical examiners by 1947 – in Massachusetts, Virginia and Vermont. The remainder had returned to general pathology or were working in other fields.[12]

By this time, medical examiners had replaced coroners in ten states.[13] Some progress had been made towards Lee's goal, but three out of four Americans still lived under the jurisdiction of coroners.

The Department of Legal Medicine, through the efforts of Moritz and Lee, had been actively involved in efforts to reform laws in a total of fourteen states.[14] With the assistance of Moritz and his Harvard group, legal-medicine programmes had begun at the universities of Washington, Cincinnati and Colorado, the Medical College of Virginia and the University of California at Los Angeles.[15]

Still, the Department of Legal Medicine at Harvard was far from its goal of serving as a resource for investigations throughout Massachusetts, much less as an institute of forensic medicine with a national scope. Statistically, considering the 50,000 deaths every year in Massachusetts at the time, there should have been about 10,000 cases meriting an investigation by a competent medical examiner. About half of those cases, or around 5,000 a year, would require a forensic autopsy. But in 1947 members of the Department of Legal Medicine were involved in only 1,400 investigations. They performed 385 autopsies, including 121 for Suffolk County medical examiners and 204 for investigations conducted by the state's Department of Public

Safety. This volume of autopsies was barely enough for medical examiners to maintain proficiency in the procedure.

Lee told Alan Gregg that she had doubts about Moritz's commitment to legal medicine and hinted at reducing her financial support for the department. 'She thinks [Moritz's] heart is still in pathology and always will be,' Gregg noted in his diary. 'Mrs Lee intimates rather directly that the next major financial contribution from her is more likely to be in her will than anywhere else. It is her hope that Harvard will "do as much for the police as it has for the businessman", and, quite understandably, she feels that the recent state of affairs is somewhat remote from that objective.'[16]

While the Department of Legal Medicine was performing short of expectations, Lee's homicide seminars had been consistently successful. Two groups of around thirty students were trained every year. By 1949, the seminars had been attended by officers from nineteen states and two Canadian provinces, special agents of the FBI and the US Army Military Police.[17]

Lee ran the homicide seminar entirely by herself, with no financial or administrative help from Harvard. Cara Conklin, her personal secretary, handled all correspondence. Lee arranged for the speakers, most of them affiliated with the Department of Legal Medicine, and paid the travel expenses of those from out of town. She spent a week in Boston before each seminar to oversee arrangements for the classroom and the banquet. She treated everybody to the elegant dinner at the Ritz-Carlton, provided cigarettes and matches, paid for the diplomas and lapel pins, and personally covered all expenses related to the seminars. Meanwhile, the proceeds, in the form of registration fees, went to the Department of Legal Medicine, which Lee was also still supporting financially.

Despite their success, not everybody at Harvard was supportive of the seminars. There were some who thought cops were out of place on an Ivy League campus. Dr George Minot, co-recipient of the 1934 Nobel Prize in Physiology or Medicine for his pioneering work on pernicious anaemia, dashed off his thoughts in a letter to Burwell. 'Why should Harvard Medical School have anything to do with courses for training policemen or their associates?' he complained. 'It seems that the Medical School is to become involved in giving courses or instruction to individuals who haven't the slightest idea of ever getting any degree. There is, of course, no question that well-trained individuals in so-called police laboratories are well worthwhile, but I am simply asking myself why should Harvard have anything to do with this anyhow.'[18]

Lee believed that police work was not beneath the Ivy League and used her influence to ensure that the homicide seminars remained at Harvard. She also began inviting female police officers. The first women to attend, in April 1949, were also among the first female troopers of the Connecticut State Police: Evelyn J Briggs and Kathryn B Haggerty. After that point, every seminar included at least two female students.

Lee went out of her way to make sure that the women felt welcome. While female police officers weren't unheard of at the time, they were sufficiently rare for male students to think the women were secretaries or had blundered into the wrong room. 'We were informed by some of the male members of the group that our entrance on the first day had been somewhat disconcerting to them,' said state trooper Lucy E Boland, who in October 1949 was among the second group of women to attend the seminar. 'They were startled when Captain Lee introduced us as state policewomen.'[19]

Boland described an incident during a laboratory exercise in which students observed the effect of poisons on mice. After assuring Lee that she had no fear of mice, Boland was startled by a sudden movement out of her peripheral vision and jumped back, bumping into Lee. 'I was embarrassed because of the fact that I had bumped into her, but ashamed of my retreat after having boasted that I was not afraid,' Boland said. 'Captain Lee immediately put me at my ease, however, when she told me that she has no fear of mice, but that frogs petrify her, since she never knows where they are going.'

Interacting with female police officers was good for the male students. During breaks, men flocked around the women to talk about how they were faring in police work. 'Few of the states represented at Harvard had ever had any contact with policewomen and were amazed to find that Connecticut is so healthily supplied,' Boland said. 'Many of them said that they have been fighting for years to have women added to their departments, without success, but felt that, after talking to us, they could go back to their superintendents, commissioners, etc., with added ammunition for the fight.'[20]

* * *

Meanwhile, a larger goal, introducing legal medicine to the general public, remained elusive. Lee had another ambitious idea: a dramatic theatrical film about the department. Through a friend in the New York publishing world, she got the ear of Samuel Marx, a story editor in charge of the screenwriting department of Metro-Goldwyn-Mayer Pictures (MGM). 'We feel that an interesting motion picture of a semi-documentary nature can be made dealing with your work in the field of crime,' Marx told Lee.[21]

Lee sent personalized Christmas letters and spoiled her boys in Virginia and New Hampshire with gifts of smoked turkeys, boxes of fresh citrus fruit and copies of Dr LeMoyne Snyder's book *Homicide Investigation: Practical Information for Coroners, Police Officers, and*

Other Investigators. Snyder, who had received his medical education at Harvard, was medico-legal director for the Michigan State Police. He was involved in the formation of the Department of Police Administration at Michigan State University – now the School of Criminal Justice – and the Michigan Crime Laboratory.[22]

Published in 1944, *Homicide Investigation* was the standard textbook for police academies and university criminal-justice programmes for more than three decades. When the first edition was published, Lee wrote to the author to praise his text. Snyder replied with flattery: 'Your remarks made me feel very good indeed, particularly as you are recognized throughout the country as a real authority on the subject.'[23]

In 1948, Snyder passed along to Lee an inquiry from a friend, Erle Stanley Gardner, author of the Perry Mason novels. The bestselling author in America at the time, Gardner regularly contributed to major magazines throughout the country. A practising attorney as well as a writer, he had recently begun a project to reinvestigate cases of people who claimed to have been railroaded by the authorities and convicted of murders they did not commit. Gardner enlisted the help of police, investigators, forensic scientists and other experts in what he called the 'Court of Last Resort', and ended up writing a feature article on it for *Argosy*, a pulp magazine trying to clean up its image by shifting from fiction to true-crime articles.

Some time later, Gardner read an article in the *Los Angeles Times* about the homicide seminar for police officers at Harvard and became interested in wangling a seat for himself in the classroom. The seminar was something new and different and might result in some ideas for his writing. Snyder, a member of Gardner's expert panel for the Court of Last Resort, introduced the author to Captain Lee.

Lee was uncertain at first. 'I thought it over for a long time, for I have strenuously avoided inviting outsiders,' she told members of the HAPS board. 'But, I thought he might do some good.'[24]

Gardner was invited to attend the seminar in October 1948. Learning the modern methods of scientific death investigation was an eye-opener for him. 'He was the most interested, and the most deeply affected person by the group of men he met,' Lee said.[25]

Lee challenged the author about his Perry Mason books. 'Your stories are formulaic,' she complained to Gardner. 'The police are portrayed as uneducated fools who are bettered by a defence lawyer who acquits his client based on mistakes that never should have happened. Why don't you write stories that depict the police accurately?'

'If I told the truth,' Gardner said, 'the book would end after a page and a half.[26]

'I just can't believe this is the kind of people that make up the State Police,' he told Lee.

'They are,' she said, 'and the sooner you get through writing about Perry Mason and the police going around in circles about him, the better.'[27]

Gardner's impression of Lee was memorable. 'Because she had an orderly mind and a logical mind,' he said, 'she was able to comprehend police work in a way that enabled her to make a shrewd and accurate appraisal of individual cases as well as overall planning of what was being done and an accurate estimate of what should be done.'[28]

Sold on the importance of legal medicine, Gardner telephoned Harry Steeger, publisher of *Argosy* and another member of the Court of Last Resort expert panel. Steeger travelled to Harvard from New York City for the last day of the homicide seminar. Afterwards, he and Gardner discussed a book, perhaps a series, featuring a state trooper or medical examiner who used the latest scientific tools to solve murders.

During the week of the seminar, Gardner happened to be finishing a Perry Mason novel called *The Case of the Dubious Bridegroom*. During breaks in the sessions, he dictated the novel by telephone to his secretary in California. When the book was finished he dedicated it to Lee, autographed the first copy off the printing press and sent it to her. He also sent autographed copies to each officer attending the homicide seminar.[29] Lee wrote to Gardner's editor at William Morrow with an unusual request for one uncut sheet from the printer, called a signature, with the first thirty-two pages of the book. 'I want to have it photographically reduced to my scale and use it in a tiny book for one of my Nutshell models,' she explained. 'I hope this is not asking too much. And I also hope for permission to reproduce that much of the book – of course not for sale! And please don't tell Mr Gardner.'[30] Sadly there is no record of whether or not the publisher complied.

An enthusiastic convert to legal medicine, Gardner now promised Lee 'a book in which a state police organization is shown to an advantage'.[31] But he had one favour to ask of her: her assistance in getting authentic background experience. He wanted to spend time with state police to glean realistic details, to follow the progress of actual murder cases. Names and other details would be fictionalized for the purposes of his stories, to avoid violating privacy or risking a lawsuit. 'One of the things that I do want is to see some organization of state police working on a difficult murder case – watch the way the whole thing is handled, and pick up on my background from seeing the machinery in operation,' he told her.

Lee believed that Gardner could be useful for the advancement of legal medicine and cultivated her relationship with him. With his name on it, a book that was authentic and favourable to police would be tremendously valuable in bringing legal medicine to the general public. 'A lively correspondence with Erle Stanley Gardner has developed,' she told Moritz. 'I fancy we can swing him to write just about anything we want.'[32]

Contacting her state police friends in Massachusetts, New Hampshire, Connecticut, Pennsylvania, Maryland and Virginia, Lee arranged a road trip for Gardner. She told Charles Woodson in Virginia that Gardner admitted that he had been 'taking the wrong attitude towards the police, tending to belittle them in favour of some amateur detective hero, and he intends writing a book using a trooper as the star performer. I believe he can do the police much good if he will write from their angle, provided he gets the background complete and accurate, and this is most important.'[33]

Gardner attended a second homicide seminar, held during the last week of April 1949. This time, he was accompanied by Harry Steeger and other members of the Court of Last Resort panel: LeMoyne Snyder, private detective Raymond Schindler and lie-detector expert Leonard Keeler.[34] Immediately after the seminar, Lee and Gardner spent two weeks travelling from state to state, from Boston to Richmond, driven by Lee's chauffeur. Gardner brought along cameras and dictation equipment, working while on the road.

In Baltimore, the two met with members of the Maryland Post Mortem Examiners Commission at the Elkridge Country Club. Dr Howard Maldeis, who had been chief medical examiner since the system was created a decade earlier, had unexpectedly fallen ill and died in January. Maryland was in need of a replacement.[35]

Maryland's medical examiner was under the authority of an independent commission, with laws that ensured their independence and autonomy. There were two well-regarded medical schools in Baltimore – Johns Hopkins University and the University of Maryland – and the city was positioned to take a leading role as a nucleus of legal medicine.

Lee told the commission members that Russell Fisher – whose promise she had recognized some years earlier – was

Moritz's brightest prospect. Fisher had by now completed his pathology training and a three-year research fellowship. Young and ambitious, he had missed his opportunity to return to Richmond as chief medical examiner for Virginia. Lee recommended him highly for the position in Maryland.[36] Gardner vouched for Fisher as well, assuring the commission members that the pathologist was smart and had the strength of character to resist attempts at political influences.

In September 1949, Fisher was appointed chief medical examiner for the State of Maryland.[37] Within a year, he began a fellowship training programme. The ultimate vision for the Maryland Office of the Chief Medical Examiner was an Institute of Legal Medicine, just like the one at Harvard.[38]

* * *

MGM was interested in producing a different kind of motion picture, a film done in a documentary style, telling a fictionalized true story. The appetites of American film audiences had changed since World War II. They wanted movies that were more realistic, less idealized reflections of everyday life. Crime stories and mysteries were perennially popular, but legal medicine presented an untapped approach.

'Our belief is that a very effective story can be developed from this material,' read an MGM report. 'The most interesting thing about it is that the detective in the case is not the usual Dick Tracy type, but a doctor – a medical examiner – for a refreshing change. As a matter of fact, the medical examiner is involved in real police cases, yet for some reason or other he has never, or rarely at least, been used in pictures.'[39]

MGM entered into an agreement with Moritz to develop a motion picture tentatively entitled *Murder at Harvard*. The writing assignment was given to Leonard Spigelgass, who had most recently co-written the screenplay for *I*

Was a Male War Bride, starring Cary Grant. The studio agreed to pay $10,000 to Harvard University in return for the cooperation and assistance of the Department of Legal Medicine. Moritz would be given final word on the script to ensure technical accuracy.

University officials were unsure about the propriety of lending the Harvard name to an endeavour in popular entertainment. Sidney Burwell pressed the case to the Harvard Corporation. Legal medicine had been hampered by archaic laws and a lack of financial support, he argued. This wouldn't change until the general public was aware of the need for improvement. 'I am of the opinion that a good motion picture might do more good on behalf of public enlightenment as to the need for improvement in the practice of legal medicine than thousands of pages written for medical journals and thousands of speeches made before medical societies and bar associations.'[40] In the end, the Harvard Corporation allowed MGM to use the university's name.

Spigelgass drafted a ten-page synopsis for *Murder at Harvard* that opened with the various experts involved in the investigation of suspicious and violent deaths sitting around a conference table in the Magrath Library. 'Mrs Lee has in the meantime joined the group,' Spigelgass wrote. 'The conference is adjourned and we cut to Mrs Lee's most recent contribution to the teaching collection of Nutshell Studies of Unexplained Deaths. Until now Mrs Lee's presence at the conference has been unexplained. She is obviously an anomalous figure in the cast. Until now the story has not had a principal character nor has it had cohesive action. It has been a documentary account of a joint enterprise between university and state law-enforcement agency depicting the nature and magnitude of the problem presented by obscure deaths and the surprises that come when [expertise] is applied to its solution.'[41]

As Spiegelgass imagined it, the camera would close in on the Burned Cabin diorama and fade into a flashback of George Magrath's investigation of the Florence Small murder and arson. From there, the film would tell the story from the founding of the Department of Legal Medicine to the present day. Lee told Spiegelgass that she did not desire personal publicity, but wanted popular attention focused on the field of legal medicine. She recommended that he base his story on the Irene Perry murder.

Spiegelgass wrote Lee out of the story. Because she wanted to focus public attention on the field of legal medicine rather than on herself, her role in the development of forensic science was marginalized. Her contributions as a reformer, educator and activist were largely lost to history.

Shortly after Lee reviewed the film script, *Scientific Monthly*, a publication of the American Association for the Advancement of Science, contacted Moritz about writing an article about scientific crime-detection techniques. Moritz suggested that the magazine ask Lee to write the article, which they did.[42] Like the suggestion that she – a woman who essentially didn't even have a high-school diploma, much less a professional credential – edit the *American Journal of Medical Jurisprudence*, this was an astonishing request.

Lee certainly thought so. 'I would like to accept your offer,' she replied to their inquiry, 'but...I am totally unqualified to write such an article as you suggest.'[43]

She also didn't have the time to do it. Aside from a full schedule of meetings and talks to community groups, she was busy editing a collection of papers based on presentations to the homicide seminar for Charles C Thomas, publisher of Snyder's *Homicide Investigation*.

* * *

When, at the end of January 1949, Howard Karsner retired as director of the Pathology Institute at Western Reserve University – and his former deputy Harry Goldblatt had taken a job elsewhere – Moritz jumped at the chance to take the position he had long coveted. Lee was not surprised that he chose to leave Harvard. He had had to be coaxed and prodded along the way into legal medicine, making no secret of his preference for clinical pathology and research. Legal medicine was still in its adolescence, not yet accepted as a legitimate field of medical practice. It was a sordid and tawdry business, doctors playing cops and robbers, and had never been warmly welcomed in the refined environment of the Harvard campus.

'Members of the faculty of the Harvard Medical School looked down upon Legal Medicine,' Lee said. 'They felt that when Dr Moritz, a pathologist of note, had been willing to take a position as head of the Department of Legal Medicine, that it was a step down or several steps down.'[44]

Moritz felt that he had done what he had been asked to do – develop an academic medical department – and it was time to turn his attention to his own interests. He explained his motivation in a letter to Lee:

I am not unmindful of my obligations to you, to Harvard University and to the Rockefeller Foundation. I am not unmindful of the many persons in this department who may be disturbed to a greater or lesser degree by my leaving. However, I have devoted twelve years, which is approximately one-third of the productive period of my life, to legal medicine and I am now faced with the crucial decision of what I want to do during my last fifteen years. I have decided to turn to something that will probably be less important from the standpoint of social welfare but will undoubtedly give me more pleasure in the doing.[45]

By then, the relationship between Moritz and Lee had cooled. It was still cordial, but Moritz bristled at Lee's meddling in department affairs and continual demands for her seminars. For her part, Lee felt that Moritz was always more interested in his own career than in legal medicine. She had also come to learn that he could be duplicitous, taking credit for her work while saying things behind her back to undercut support for her ideas.

On the heels of Moritz's departure, medical school dean Sidney Burwell announced his retirement. Like sand shifting beneath Lee's feet, everything was suddenly uncertain – the book she was working on, the MGM movie, the homicide seminars, even the Department of Legal Medicine itself.

CHAPTER 11

The Decline and Falls

1949–1961

Moritz's departure in February 1949 threw the Department of Legal Medicine into turmoil. After a decade of his leadership, with Lee in the background, everything that had been built to date was threatened unless a strong successor could be found to carry its mission forward. Without a department head of Moritz's stature, there was concern that other personnel might leave for more secure and rewarding situations.

'We will be sunk if any or all of them should leave us at this time for self-protective reasons,' Lee told Roger Lee. 'If you will think with me of the seriousness of our predicament: if we lose the only people who are trained for the special work they are doing, it would set us back tremendously as there is no outside field from which to recruit other workers.'[1]

Moritz nominated Dr Richard Ford to replace him. Ford had graduated from Harvard Medical School and done a surgical internship at Boston City Hospital before spending three and a half years in the Pacific during World War II. He had served in combat with a portable surgical hospital and, for the last eighteen months of the war, had commanded an air-force hospital. He was commissioned as a major before returning home in 1945.[2] After his fellowship training in the Department of Legal Medicine, he was appointed to succeed Timothy Leary as medical examiner for the Southern District of Suffolk County. A first-rate forensic pathologist, he was dedicated to his work as medical examiner. Within pathology, his main interest was trauma – the types of injury he had treated during the war.

The war seemed to have affected Ford deeply. He had a dark side with a tendency to outbursts of a fiery temper. Visitors to his office were often disturbed by grisly crime-scene and autopsy photos on display. Despite his personality issues, however, Ford's abilities as a forensic pathologist and medical examiner were unquestioned. Lee was certainly willing to give him the benefit of the doubt: 'The more I see of Doctor Ford, the more highly I think of him,' she told Roger Lee.[3]

* * *

In the spring of 1949, MGM producer Frank Taylor sent Moritz a script for *Murder at Harvard* that the pathologist considered acceptable. Since he was no longer with Harvard, however, whether the film could still go forward depended on several factors, including the consent of Ford as the acting head of the Department of Legal Medicine. Ford agreed to cooperate.

Moritz wrote to Burwell encouraging Harvard to allow MGM to make the film for the sake of legal medicine. 'During the past ten years I have travelled from one end of the country to the other in an attempt to arouse public interest in the need for improvement in the practice of legal medicine,' Moritz said. 'It seems to me that a proper kind of motion picture prepared and distributed by an organization such as Metro-Goldwyn-Mayer Corporation might well accomplish more in a few months than could be accomplished in many years by any other means.'[4]

Harvard had one objection to the movie: the title. The university did not want a picture distributed under a title that was 'lurid or otherwise offensive'.[5] *Murder at Harvard* became *Mystery Street.*

As Lee had suggested, the story of *Mystery Street* is based loosely on the case of Irene Perry, with some of the details changed. In the film, Barnstable County police officer Pete Morales, played by Ricardo Montalban, is investigating the discovery of a skeletonized body on the Cape Cod seashore. With little more than a box of bones for evidence, he seeks assistance from the Department of Legal Medicine at Harvard. Dr Arthur McAdoo, the Moritz/Ford department head portrayed by actor Bruce Bennett, employs the latest ripped-from-the-headlines scientific methods to help solve the case, including identification, ballistics and forensic photography that had been pivotal evidence in the Ruxton murder case years earlier in Scotland. Using forensic anthropology, McAdoo determines the deceased's age, sex, occupation and cause of death: a bullet wound. Morales thinks he has the guilty man, but McAdoo's dispassionate adherence to following the scientific facts wherever they lead shames the cop into investigating further, and ultimately results in the apprehension of the real murderer. In a nutshell, science clears the innocent and convicts the guilty.

Mystery Street was the first major theatrical motion picture filmed on location in Boston. Filming took place during October and November 1949, with Harvard Square, Beacon Hill and the Harvard Medical School campus all featured.[6] Scenes depicting the Department of Legal Medicine include shots of the bullet-wound models and mannequin heads acquired by Lee, but the Nutshell Studies of Unexplained Death do not appear.

According to the agreement with MGM, $10,000 was to be paid to Harvard for the Department of Legal Medicine as soon as shooting began in October. By December,

Harvard had not yet received the money.[7] Ever shrewd in the ways of business, Lee demanded that MGM uphold its end of the agreement. She insisted that Ford step up and take responsibility as head of the department and collect the money from the studio. Ford, in turn, sought direction from Dr George P Berry, successor to Burwell as dean of the medical school, since the deal had been made before Ford had arrived at Harvard and he had not been party to it.

'Mrs Lee has asked me repeatedly whether the money was yet forthcoming,' Ford said to Berry. 'She has stated emphatically that the original arrangements for this motion picture concerned her alone… I gather from several conversations with Mrs Lee that she has a very proprietary interest in this whole matter.'[8]

Failure to collect the money owed to Harvard, he continued, could jeopardize gifts from Lee in the future. 'I am…absolutely certain that if [payment] does not come to the department not only will it jeopardize the quarter of a million dollars eventually promised but it will also cut off the generous gifts which have been received continually into our special fund for the last ten years,' Ford said.

Harvard got the money.

Mystery Street opened to positive reviews. A *New York Times* critic said, 'There is more science than mystery in this cops-versus-killer number, but it is an adventure which, despite a low budget, is not low in taste or its attention to technical detail, backgrounds and plausibility. It is strong on authenticity.'[9] Spigelgass was nominated for the Academy Award for his story.

Today, *Mystery Street* is an obscure film-noir murder mystery. To fans of forensic science, it is known as the first modern procedural crime drama. The forerunner of *Quincy M.E.*, *CSI: Crime Scene Investigation* and programmes of that ilk, *Mystery Street* established a formula that has become one of the most popular genres in film, books, network and cable shows, podcasts and reality-based programming. Interest in forensic science is so pervasive among the general public that it has produced a so-called *CSI* effect – people now have unreasonably high expectations of scientific evidence.

* * *

It soon became apparent that Ford did not have the temperament to head the Department of Legal Medicine. He had little appetite for research, teaching or the administrative duties that came with the position. Lee confronted him bluntly with what she saw as a serious problem. 'I must confess that it is a mystery to me why the Department of Legal Medicine should be dying on its feet,' she wrote in a letter to him, 'but it certainly is moribund at present, and I shudder to think of the enormous task of re-establishing its former, none-too-perfect, activities... Have you any suggestions as to how the department can be restored to life?'[10] Ford had no suggestions to offer.

Lee shared her dismay at the state of her beloved department with Alan Gregg of the Rockefeller Foundation. 'I must confess that I am greatly disappointed in Dr Ford, as it seemed to me that he was a well-trained and skilful man who was really enthusiastic about legal medicine (and I am still of that opinion) but for some reason that I cannot fathom he seems unable to recognize a big opportunity when it lies right in his hand,' she wrote. 'I am loath to discuss this situation with him, as I have already tasted his quick and fiery temper and feel that I have already had all the unpleasantness that I should accept from the personnel of the department.'[11]

Lee hadn't always agreed with Moritz, but at least he got things done. Ford seemed content to sit and wait for something to happen. Under his leadership, the Department of Legal Medicine was doing little research or anything else of note.

Lee had also received negative feedback from the Harvard establishment about the homicide seminars in particular. Allowing state police on the medical school campus was pushing the envelope, but Harvard drew the line at city cops. The university would not allow Boston police officers to attend the seminars, even though these were entirely organized and underwritten by Lee.[12]

'In my opinion, the department is rapidly dying on its feet,' Lee told Gregg, 'and that after another year of such a continued slump, I should have no further interest in giving it either my financial or moral support.' Gregg advised her to cut back her involvement with Harvard, both personally and financially.[13]

Lee made some decisions. She would continue to use Harvard for her homicide seminars but withdraw any other support for the department. There would be no more gifts during her lifetime. And the Nutshell Studies of Unexplained Death would not be given outright to Harvard Medical School. A letter to her banker regarding her taxes for the year 1950 made her intentions clear. She asked about the legitimacy of deducting the wages paid to her cabinetmaker, Alton Mosher (Ralph Mosher's son, who took over the business when his father died), wanting to know if this was 'a proper deduction since the models are no longer becoming the property of Harvard'.[14]

* * *

True to his word, Erle Stanley Gardner returned to forensic science in his 1950 book *The Case of the Musical Cow*. The novel, dedicated to Moritz, is based on a case in which the pathologist had been involved during his fellowship training in Scotland. Rather than featuring Perry Mason – to the chagrin of many who bought the book – the protagonist is a state trooper who uses the police crime lab to clear an innocent suspect and convict the guilty. Gardner paid tribute to Magrath as well, dedicating his 1955 Perry Mason book *The Case of the Glamorous Ghost* to him.

Lee and the Department of Legal Medicine were singled out for praise in Gardner's 1952 book, *The Court of Last Resort*, which devotes a chapter to the Harvard homicide seminar. 'Captain Frances G Lee is a fabulous character, a woman of around seventy who has donated a fortune to establish a school of legal medicine at Harvard University,' he wrote.[15]

After the photo feature in *Life*, Lee and her Nutshell Studies of Unexplained Death were featured in numerous newspaper stories and in national magazines: *The Saturday Evening Post, Coronet, Yankee, Popular Mechanics* and many others. The angle of a wealthy elderly woman who made doll's houses of death was irresistible. But Lee felt that writers like Gardner and Harry Steeger were using her to draw in readers. She continued to want the focus on legal medicine rather than on herself – at least during her lifetime.

'I have had to restrain their eagerness at times as they seemed to want to use me as the dramatic figure in their publicity and I feel that the subject itself is dramatic enough and that it is in better taste to omit the personal slant,' Lee told her advisory board. 'But once I am safely dead, there is nothing I can do about this – if it will further the development of the work, let them use me if it will be right in your eyes, but otherwise leave me out of it.'[16]

Despite her aversion to publicity, Lee was bombarded with letters from people who had heard about the millionairess and her interest in police science. People wrote to her with pleas for help, requests for money and offers for commercial endorsements. Some told sad stories of injustice and baffling mysteries. She begged off pleas for help from convicted murderers, the desperate loved ones of missing persons, the institutionalized and the mentally ill who sent her pages of scrawled handwriting. 'In desperation, I am writing you this letter that you will be able to help, or advise me, as to what I can possibly do to be released from this place, as I am not insane,' wrote a resident of the Mayview State Hospital who claimed to have been deliberately inoculated with syphilis.[17]

Lee was offered investigative and forensic artist services and approached with an assortment of endeavours. The Automotive Safety Association tried to pique her interest in traffic safety.[18] An entrepreneur from Long Beach wanted her help in launching a national database of shoplifters and petty thieves for use by retail businesses.[19]

John Crocker Jr, a young clergyman at Trinity Church in Boston's Copley Square, wrote to Lee on behalf of Charles E Warren, who was serving a life sentence at Charlestown Prison. 'He has read of your interests and work in penology in Earl [sic] Stanley Gardner's book *Court of Last Resort*,' Crocker wrote. 'He himself is in the process of writing a book about himself and the Charlestown Prison. I have not read any part of the book, but he has been in the prison longer than anyone now there. He wants very much to interest people of real stature in his case.'[20]

Lee's reply was civil but direct. 'While I am entirely sympathetic with your activity on behalf of Mr Charles E Warren I am sorry that I am not in a position to give him any assistance,' she wrote. 'I am interested solely in medico-legal subjects and know nothing concerning the subject of criminology, and I cannot add the smallest iota of additional burden to that which I already carry. I admire and like Mr Erle Stanley Gardner but his overenthusiastic friendship has given his readers a false impression of what I do.'[21]

An exception was made for a distraught mother whose teenage son had died through autoerotic asphyxiation. This dangerous practice involves the use of strangulation or suffocation to heighten sexual arousal during masturbation or intercourse. Partially suspended or strangled by a rope or belt, a person went to the threshold of unconsciousness. Death could be an unintended consequence.

The mother, a Mrs Wright of Anaheim, California, asked Lee about the shocking and disturbing circumstances under which her son had been found, unclothed and with a cord wrapped around his body. The death was ruled a suicide. Mrs Wright wondered whether it could have been murder. Did such things happen?

Lee took the questions to her experts at Harvard, then reported her findings to Mrs Wright, explaining the death, mother to mother, compassionately and yet with an unflinching clinical frankness that laid out the facts for the grieving woman in order to dispel her lingering doubts.

'This appears to be an accidental death, in no way out of keeping with adolescent sexual experimenting,' Lee told Mrs Wright. 'Cases of this type are not common, but occur with sufficient frequency to be well recognized.'[22]

She answered Mrs Wright's questions in the format used in law enforcement, and concluded:

Q.1. Will the rings in the trachea fracture by hanging, especially when all of the weight is not on the noose around the neck?

A.1. Not ordinarily, but it could happen. Removal of the neck organs could produce these fractures under certain circumstances.

Q.2. Should the eyes have been completely closed if the subject were conscious when hanged?

A.2. This is inconclusive. It might be either way.

Q.3. Isn't it possible that the subject was unconscious when hanged?

A.3. Possible, but unlikely. There is no proof and appears to be no evidence that would suggest this possibility.

Q.4. Have you ever known of a male tying himself around the scrotum?

A.4. No, but I have known of other acts as unaccountable
      or even more so. Great ingenuity is often exercised in
      sexual experimentation.

* * *

In 1950, at the age of seventy-three, Lee faced her greatest
challenge to date: a diagnosis of cancer. She was admitted
to Phillips House, where she had spent so much time with
George Magrath years earlier. With the spectre of her own
mortality looming, Lee took steps to ensure that the flame
of legal medicine would not be extinguished by her death.
She established a trust and formed the Frances Glessner Lee
Foundation to continue sponsorship of the homicide seminars
for police officers and Harvard Associates in Police Science.

In order to make sure that her directions were followed
to the exact degree, she also formed an advisory board
consisting of five people she considered most trustworthy and
fully informed of her vision of legal medicine: her daughter,
Martha Batchelder; former US Army Judge Advocate Ralph
G Boyd of Boston; Charles Woodson, superintendent of the
Virginia State Police; Francis I McGarraghy, former air-
force criminal investigator and FBI special agent; and her
banker, Allan B Hussander.

'Each member of the advisory board has been chosen
by me, primarily because I had some implicit confidence in
his ability and good judgement,' Lee told them, 'but also
because I believed in his understanding of and sympathy
with my aims.'[23]

In 1951, Lee wrote a letter to her advisory board that
she labelled 'Top Secret.'

It seems to me well that you should know something
of my problems in starting the Department of Legal
Medicine at the Harvard Medical School. First, I am,

and always have been, a lone worker and have never found it satisfactory to work at something that has been gone over and over by others until the original meaning and spirit have all been worn out of it. Therefore, when an opportunity came to me to start something completely new in the medical line, I was delighted to take it on. As a girl, I was deeply interested in medicine and nursing, and would have enjoyed taking a training in either one. This was not possible, so legal medicine, including medicine and just ordinary common sense, together with some smattering of detective work, made an immediate appeal to me. However, I found that no one including alas! my own self, knew exactly what legal medicine was supposed to mean, and at the time – around 1930 – that I first took an active part in its development, there was very little printed material available to help me. So it was necessary to proceed by mainly strength and awkwardness, but fortunately with the skill, knowledge and training of Doctor Magrath to guide me (he, in turn, had really started from scratch), I have been able to accomplish a good deal. Considering that in 1930 the world in general, the medical world in particular, and specifically I myself had very little idea of 'what it was all about', I feel that great strides have been taken in the twenty years since the beginning of the Department at Harvard.

First, I think it was timed right; next, I think that Dr Sidney Burwell, who became dean at about that time, realized that legal medicine was the first entirely new department in a medical school in many years, and so decided to ride to personal success on it; and third, I think that Dr Moritz, the first active head of the department, was eager for personal publicity and thought he might get it through legal medicine.

For me, it has been a long, discouraging struggle against petty jealousies, crass stupidities and an obstinate unwillingness to learn that has required all the enthusiasm, patience, courage and tact that I could muster. Being by nature and training a somewhat shy and timid person, this has been a lonely and rather terrifying life that I have lived. Chief amongst the difficulties I have had to meet have been the facts that I never went to school, that I had no letters after my name, and that I was placed in the category of 'rich woman who didn't have enough to do'. Also, being a woman has made it difficult at times to make the men believe in the project I was furthering, although sometimes, I must own, being a woman had its advantages… But the discouragements have been plentiful and severe, but still I feel that I have surmounted most of them and have succeeded in my purposes, perhaps more than I deserved but not more than the magnitude my subject merited…

My whole object has been to improve the administration of justice, to standardize the methods, to sharpen the existing tools, and to make it easier for the law enforcement officers to do 'a good job' and to give the public 'a square deal'.

Harvard has not been very broad-minded or very generous in its attitude towards the Department of Legal Medicine, but the Rockefeller Foundation has been much more sympathetic. Dr Moritz was willing to 'play ball' as long as there was something in it for him, but never without a fight; and Dr Ford is much the same, although Dr Moritz was active and Dr Ford is inert. Had there been true collaboration from the beginning, legal medicine could have been much farther advanced than it is today, but perhaps that would have been growing too fast.

But at any rate, here we are. Please don't let things slump down and disappear. You five will have to learn to go ahead, no matter how many times you are knocked down. But you men already know this far better than I have ever learned it, and then there are five of you to compare the bruises.[24]

What followed in the same letter were more than five single-spaced sheets of paper with detailed instructions about conducting the homicide seminars, the selection and vetting of students, a timetable for organizing the seminars, how to line up speakers for lectures and the seating arrangements and menus for the group dinner. No aspect was overlooked. According to Lee's directions, the dinners 'must be carried out with conspicuous elegance, generosity and friendliness'.

Then she returned to the subject of continuing her work:

I suspect that since you are mostly men, you may not run into some of the difficulties that I have from the very outset [...] It has been my intention in whatever I have done, to bring about an upgrading of the police in the United States and to thereby place them in a position where they are deserving of the respect and honour which is rightfully theirs, and I charge you with continuing my efforts along these lines to the end that there may be an improvement in the administration of justice in this country. If, singlehanded, I have been able to accomplish as much as I have, you – five of you – with your wider experience and stable masculine judgement, should be able to accomplish wonders... I am herewith handing you a lighted torch to bear, with complete confidence that you will not let the flame go out, and so accept my heartfelt thanks and appreciation for the help you have already given me by showing your interest and belief in my work and for the comfort I have in knowing that it will be carried on – farther and more widely than I have been able to do – when I have to leave it.

As for Harvard, Lee was unsparing with her views:

For the past twenty years I have given all of my time and energy and thought, indeed all of my waking hours, to the effort to establish securely legal medicine in the United States, not merely to establish a department of legal medicine at the Harvard Medical School, although that has been a basic part of the overall picture. Harvard has the reputation of being old-fogeyish and ungrateful and stupid and I have indeed found this reputation to be deserved. I therefore have no special wish to further Harvard, but I do feel that there is already there a department together with its library and other equipment, much of which is unique and cannot be duplicated. Moreover, Harvard has a clear-cut and well-recognized reputation as the first department of legal medicine in this country. Therefore I recommend to the board and to the foundation that they favour Harvard whenever possible, but I have placed certain restrictions upon Harvard... I warn you each and every one that Harvard is clever and sly and will need to be watched constantly or she will take advantage of you and apply any funds you may grant her to her own purposes. This has been so marked a tendency in my lifetime that I have preferred to spend the money myself to procure what I wanted and then to give the result to Harvard. I suggest that whenever possible, you do the same.

Lee concluded her letter with some final words of advice for her board:

Don't forget, it is legal medicine to be built up, not Harvard Medical School. Also keep an eye upon tax problems.

* * *

Despite the increasing disabilities of advancing age, including heart disease and repeated fractures, Lee maintained a busy schedule for the remaining eleven years of her life. Active in professional associations, she attended the second meeting of the American Society for Forensic Science. She was the first female member of the International Association of Chiefs of Police, frequently attending their meetings, as well as those of the Massachusetts and New Hampshire Medico-Legal Societies, the New England Policewomen's Association and many others.

Along with Alton Mosher, she resumed work on several more Nutshell Studies of Unexplained Death. Alton created a scale model of the Swedish porch of Lee's residence – an enclosed stone patio with a fireplace. Every miniature stone used in the model matched the shape of those in the actual porch, reproducing it in the most minute and authentic detail. Lee also worked on a multiple-room diorama and a large model of an apartment building.

The Rocks continued to be a gathering place for law-enforcement officials. Lee's son John described the activity at his mother's house during a weekend visit:

> We had not been visiting more than a few hours when who should arrive but Captain Schwarz of the Connecticut State Police, and wife. Needless to say, the conversation fell heavily on police work and legal medicine affairs for the remainder of the weekend. Interesting, but I couldn't contribute much, as my own crimes are not for public discussion. The latest of these was covering the 220 miles to Littleton in five-and-a-half hours flat, including breakfast. This averages 40 mph including breakfast, which means I spent a lot of time at 65 or more, which is too fast for Vermont's twisty roads. So when the Captain, who had travelled the same route, started to compare notes on elapsed time, I was understandably vague.[25]

* * *

In December 1951, Lee visited the FBI again and attempted to schedule a meeting with J Edgar Hoover to discuss the need for a national dental record database. Hoover told Lee that his official duties, regrettably, made it impossible for him to meet her, and referred her to one of his staff.[26] According to a director's office memo circulated to FBI associate director Clyde Tolson, 'When informed of Mr Hoover's absence, Mrs Lee declined to talk with anyone else and stated that she wanted to arrange an appointment with Mr Hoover to discuss a matter that she had written about.'[27]

This time, Lee did not get her audience with Hoover.

* * *

In the mid-1950s, Harvard officials began considering gently guiding Lee to the door. She turned seventy-six – the age of mandatory retirement at the university – in March 1954. The Harvard Corporation noted this fact within weeks of her birthday. In April, David W Bailey, the corporation secretary, contacted George Berry, the medical school dean, about whether Lee's honorary curatorship of the Magrath Library should be terminated.

By then, Lee's involvement with Harvard was limited. She was at the medical school for little more than the twice-yearly homicide seminars, and her titles with the university were largely ceremonial. Aside from occasional requests for lecturers at the seminars, the burden she posed was minimal. Berry questioned whether it was prudent to bite, however gently, a hand that fed the university.

'No salary from Harvard is involved,' Berry said. 'Mrs Lee has made generous contributions to our work. Unless changes in the times have posed financial problems for her since she told us about the plans she had for the disposition of her estate, I believe that the Department of Legal Medicine will find that she has left substantial sums in her will. In the light of these circumstances, I hope that the corporation will agree that an exception is justified.'[28]

Nine days after, Bailey informed Berry that Lee would be allowed to keep her honorary title. 'I have talked again with President Pusey about the matter, and he agrees that under the circumstances it will be a happy thought to leave Mrs Lee's present appointment undisturbed, despite the fact that she has almost totted up the psalmist's four score years.'[29]

Berry shared the good news with Ford, saying, 'You will agree with me, I am sure, that persuading them to continue to let her hold this honorary post was in our best interests!'[30]

The following year, the issue of Lee's 'retirement' was put to rest for good. 'So you may have a written record in your files,' Berry wrote to Bailey, 'I write to tell you that we do wish to continue Mrs Lee on the university's roster as Honorary Curator of the George Burgess Magrath Library of Legal Medicine even though she has passed the compulsory retirement age. It is reasonable to assume, furthermore, that we shall continue Mrs Lee in the honorary post indefinitely.'[31]

* * *

That same year – 1955 – Colonel Woodson, superintendent of the Virginia State Police, received an enticing invitation from Lee through her foundation: the opportunity to spend two weeks in England and one in Germany for the purpose of studying the police systems in those countries.

As a prominent member of the law-enforcement community and an officer in the International Association of Chiefs of Police, Woodson thought it prudent – even though he had known Lee for years and was a member of her advisory board – to check with the FBI to see whether the agency knew of any affiliation she may have with subversive organizations or individuals. It was the height of the Cold War, and a link to communism could ruin a career.[32]

The FBI special agent in charge of the Boston field office filed a report to J Edgar Hoover about meeting Lee at a reception she held at The Rocks for the annual conference of the National Association of Attorneys General. 'This reception reportedly cost Captain Lee approximately $3,500 and she imported caterers from New York City to handle all arrangements,' the report said. 'The bureau has previously been advised with regard to the background of Captain Lee. She is approximately seventy-five years of age, practically an invalid, and has been deeply interested in criminology and legal medicine for many years.'[33]

The all-clear was given by teletype from the Boston field office to the FBI headquarters, then relayed to Woodson: 'NO DEROGATORY INFO CONTAINED IN BOSFILES PERTAINING TO HER.'[34]

* * *

In the late 1950s, the tranquillity of The Rocks was disturbed by workmen from the New Hampshire Highway Department. A new expressway was being surveyed that would transect the Glessner estate, separating about a third of the land from the rest of the property.

Approaching eighty years old, practically deaf and blind, Lee was as willing as ever to muster up a battle. 'I've been fighting the Highway Dept. to take their darned road elsewhere, but to no use,' she wrote in a letter to her son John.[35]

According to Lee, the highway crew said to her, 'As soon as it is determined exactly how much of your land we will take you will be offered a fair price for it.'

'Oh no, it won't be a fair price,' she responded. 'You will offer me the lowest figure you think you can get away with. If you don't do that you will show that you are not a good businessman.'

The workmen and Lee bore each other no ill will. 'If I must lose my farm, you will find me a good loser,' she told them. 'I will not make unnecessary difficulties but will cooperate with you to the best of my ability.' They agreed to do the same.

Lee invited the workmen to lunch and served them cocktails before the meal. 'I had them come up to lunch two weeks ago and gave them a swell meal,' she wrote to John. 'We had some drinks all around before lunch and I drank to them individually and by name and added, "Down with the Highway Department!"'

The workmen drilled core samples to assess the underlying geology of the area. 'I was praying for quicksand but they got solid granite,' Lee said. They gave her two pieces of granite core taken from her property: heavy cylinders of grey rock about 60cm (2ft) long. She had them polished and made into table lamps.

The road surveyed by the workmen became Interstate 93, which now runs from Boston through Concord, Massachusetts, and the White Mountains to Waterford, Vermont. Lee remained living in her cottage at The Rocks until difficulty with walking limited her mobility. In 1957, she purchased a home-sized trailer – mobile home – and had it placed behind the cottage. Made of gleaming aluminium and finished in white and lavender enamel, it looked like a space-age module in the rustic setting of The Rocks. Lee was delighted with her new scaled-down accommodation. Inside the trailer, she could move about without a wheelchair or walker. Everything was new and it worked. The place was well illuminated, had plenty of hot water for one person and more electrical outlets than Lee knew what to do with.

Alton Mosher set a table and comfortable chair in front of a large window with a view of Mount Washington, and Lee planned to begin writing her own books there.

In the summer of 1958, Lee broke a rib while leaning over an armchair to pick up a letter that had dropped to the floor but, despite her increasing frailty, her spirit and energy never flagged. Whatever the obstacle, she put it behind her at day's end with a shaker of cold, delicious martinis. 'The cocktail hour has come to be important time with me – not for the liquor, but for the pause, the relaxation, the daintiness and prettiness of the service,' she said in a letter to her family. 'In the day-to-day living, it is unwise to let it become entirely utilitarian – some of the graces and formal gracious living must be included or one would go completely to seed.'[36]

In another letter, Lee reflected on her life. 'As I sit quietly here, an old woman, I think back over my life and realize what a wonderfully rich life it has been,' she said. 'Recently I read somewhere that when we are young, we cannot understand the problems of the old for we haven't experienced them yet ourselves, and when we are old we have largely forgotten the problems of the young. But I haven't forgotten, and I believe I am nearer a sympathetic understanding of the problems of those younger than they think possible. Anyway, it's a good world and I am grateful I have been given a chance to play a part in it.'[37]

* * *

In February 1961, Parker Glass, assistant to Ford in the Department of Legal Medicine, wrote to Lee with heartbreaking news. An accumulation of snow and ice on the roof of Building E-1 had allowed water to leak onto the Nutshell Studies of Unexplained Death. Several dioramas had suffered water damage.

'The most serious damage is to the large model in the centre of the room, the water from the roof coming directly into that model,' Glass wrote. 'When discovered, the model (I suppose because of the excessive dampness) had been growing mould on many of the leather and cloth components. It is truly a sorry sight to see.'[38]

Lee inspected the Nutshells, made such repairs as were possible and had them back in their cabinets in time for the autumn 1961 seminar – the last she attended, as her cancer had returned.

CHAPTER 12

Postmortem

1962–present

Frances Glessner Lee died at her home at The Rocks on 27 January 1962, a month short of her eighty-fourth birthday. The immediate cause of her death was intestinal obstruction related to liver cancer that had metastasized from breast cancer. She had ascites – an accumulation of fluid in the abdominal cavity – due to the liver failure, as well as decompensating heart failure that produced a generalized swelling of her body.

The mass held for Lee at the packed Littleton church was attended by, among others, most of the employees of The Rocks, most of the staff from the Department of Legal Medicine, six New Hampshire state police officers in uniform, and eight or ten police officers from other states.[1] She was buried in the Maple Street Cemetery in Bethlehem, New Hampshire.

News of her death brought accolades from throughout the United States and overseas. 'Mrs Lee was unquestionably one of the world's most astute criminologists,' said Parker Glass, who had been secretary for the Department of Legal Medicine since the days of Magrath. 'She was acquainted with and respected by top criminologists all over the world.'[2]

Cyril Cuthbert, founder of the forensic science laboratory at Scotland Yard, said Lee was 'the only person in the world going out of her way to teach legal medicine to police'.[3]

The obituary written by Erle Stanley Gardner appeared on the front page of the *Boston Sunday Globe*. He gave the piece to the newspaper at no charge as a labour of love. Part of it read:

> She was...my personal friend because I appreciated her grim, relentless pursuit of an objective, her uncompromising insistence on the best and her loyalty to the causes she espoused and to her friends generally.
>
> Capt Lee had a strong individuality, a unique, unforgettable character, was a fiercely competent fighter and a practical idealist.
>
> She was a wonderful woman.[4]

During her lifetime, Lee had numerous honours and awards bestowed on her: an honorary doctorate of laws from New England College in 1956; two years later an honorary law degree from Pennsylvania's Drexel University.[5] She was an honorary captain in the state polices of Maine, Vermont, Massachusetts, Virginia and Connecticut, and in the Chicago Police Department, as well as an honorary major in the Kentucky State Police and an honorary captain in the US Navy.[6] In recognition of her extraordinary contributions to the advancement of legal medicine and forensic pathology, the Institute of Medicine of Chicago created a category for her: Citizen Fellow of the Institute of Medicine.

One recognition she was never granted was the one that would have held the most profound meaning for her: an honorary degree from Harvard.

* * *

Without Lee's support, the Department of Legal Medicine at Harvard Medical School went into a death spiral.

By 1963, Harvard estimated that consulting on nearly 400 postmortem cases a year cost the university about $50,000 annually – over £330,000 in today's terms, an amount considered to be an unacceptable burden. A committee reporting to Harvard president Nathan M Pusey and medical school dean George P Berry recommended that the Department of Legal Medicine be made into a division in the Department of Pathology.[7]

After repeated clashes with his colleagues, Ford was relieved of his academic duties, and his appointment to the Department of Legal Medicine ended in June 1965. He continued to serve as Suffolk County medical examiner. Harvard ceased operations of the Department of Legal Medicine on 30 June 1967.[8] The Magrath Library of Legal Medicine was subsumed into the collection of the medical school library, now called the Countway Library of Medicine.

Lee's legacy at Harvard is commemorated with the appointment of the Frances Glessner Lee Professor of Legal Medicine. As of this writing, this position is held by a paediatric anaesthesiologist who is the director of the Center for Bioethics. Harvard does not have a forensic pathologist on the medical school staff.

* * *

As head of pathology at Case Western Reserve University, Alan R Moritz was involved in the founding of the Law and Medicine Center, which aimed to become one of the country's premier institutes of forensic medicine education.[9] In a 1958 *True* magazine article, he estimated that as many as 5,000 homicides went undetected every year in the United States. 'It is an amazing truth that in most localities of the United States, the official medical examination of unexplained deaths is so casual and inexpert that clever murderers often go free,' he said.[10]

Moritz was involved as an expert witness in the inquiry into the murder of Marilyn Reese Sheppard in Bay Village, Ohio, which occurred on 4 July 1954. An investigation by Cuyahoga County coroner Dr Samuel Gerber, a well-regarded medical doctor, pointed to the victim's husband, neurosurgeon Dr Samuel Sheppard. Sam Sheppard was found with nonlethal injuries and claimed that a 'bushy-haired man' was responsible for killing Marilyn and attacking him.

The investigation was conducted poorly from the onset, beginning with the failure to secure the crime scene. The Sheppard house had been open to bystanders, including an American football player, Cleveland Browns quarterback Otto Graham, who was a friend of the family. Local newspapers turned on Sheppard. Coverage of the case was so intense that the US Supreme Court ruled that the excessive publicity denied him a fair trial.[11]

Sheppard was acquitted of murder in a 1966 retrial. By then an alcoholic unable to practise medicine any longer, he later performed as a professional wrestler as 'Killer' Sam Sheppard. Marilyn Sheppard's murder was the basis for the television series *The Fugitive* and the subsequent film.

Moritz lived until 1986, when he died of natural causes at the age of eighty-eight.

* * *

On 3 August 1970, Dr Richard Ford died of a self-inflicted gunshot to the head.[12]

* * *

Lee left an estate worth almost $1 million at the time of her death – close to £17 million in today's terms. The bulk of this was divided between her two surviving children, John G Lee and Martha Batchelder, with a portion set aside for the

Frances Glessner Lee Fund for the Study of Legal Medicine. Harvard was not mentioned in Lee's will: the university was left nothing.

In 1978, John G Lee and Martha Batchelder donated The Rocks to the Society for the Protection of New Hampshire Forests to continue the conservation and restoration efforts begun by their grandfather, John Jacob Glessner, a century earlier.[13] As a provision of their gift, The Rocks must always have a crop in its fields. For more than three decades that crop has been Christmas trees. The Rocks is open to the public and hosts activities throughout the year, ranging from a network of well-maintained trails to school trips for children to learn about making maple syrup.

In August 2018, the New Hampshire Division of Historical Resources unveiled a historical highway marker on Route 302 at The Rocks, honouring Lee as the mother of forensic science and the creator of the Nutshell Studies of Unexplained Death.[14]

The Glessners' Prairie Avenue home changed ownership several times over the years. The heirs of the family property deeded the house to the Armour Institute, now the Illinois Institute of Technology, which leased it to the Lithographic Technical Foundation. In 1965 it was put on the market for $70,000 and, with no takers, H H Richardson's landmark residence was slated for demolition. It was saved from the wrecking ball when a handful of local architects and preservationists joined to form the Chicago School of Architecture Foundation, which bought the house for $35,000 in December 1966. Programming and exhibitions began within a year, and a regular tour programme started in 1971.[15]

In 1994, the foundation spun off the Glessner House Museum as a separate non-profit corporation. The museum is open to the public for tours and special events in the Historic Prairie Avenue District on Chicago's South Side.

While the original floorplan remains intact, the residence has undergone extensive work to restore original appearances and furnishings. Members of the Glessner family have returned many pieces of furniture and decorative objects to bring the house back to its appearance in its heyday. Three generations of Glessners are responsible for 1800 S Prairie Avenue surviving to this day.

In March 2019, the Glessner House Museum unveiled the restoration of Lee's childhood bedroom, including her bed designed by Isaac Scott.

* * *

Lee presided over every homicide seminar without fail until shortly before her death. In her later years, communicating with her involved yelling into a hearing aid the size of a packet of cigarettes, which she held aloft. The seminars continued to be held at Harvard under the supervision of Martha Batchelder until 1967, when Harvard put an end to them.

Russell Fisher, chief medical examiner for the State of Maryland, who had trained with Moritz and was one of Lee's favourites, approached Harvard about continuing the homicide seminars in Baltimore. With the consent of Lee's heirs, the president and fellows of Harvard College voted to lend the Nutshell Studies of Unexplained Death permanently to the Maryland Medical-Legal Foundation for the purposes of training police officers in the renamed Frances Glessner Lee Seminar in Homicide Investigation.

When the first seminar was held in Baltimore from 6 to 10 May 1968, Fisher assigned the Nutshell cases to participants. The reviewer of the cases, the keeper of Lee's confidential solutions to the dioramas, was Parker Glass, who, aside from Lee, had spent more time with the dioramas than anyone else. Having looked at the Nutshell Studies for more than twenty years, he couldn't help but notice that a few things were out of place – possibly the result of jostling during the move from Boston.

'There are two minor items that might be changed,' he wrote in a letter to Fisher's secretary, Dorothy Hartel. 'In the scene showing the gal dead in a closet with her throat cut, the little knife is missing. Should be beside her hand on the floor. In the living room scene showing the wife dead on the stairway, there is a vase on the floor beside the divan. It should not be there. One of the boys [attending the seminar] insisted that this was indication of some kind of struggle in the room. If I am invited for the next seminar, I perhaps could look over the models in their new home for any misleading changes.'[16]

* * *

Today, the Frances Glessner Lee Seminars in Homicide Investigation are held at the Forensic Medical Center for the State of Maryland in Baltimore. They are conducted in accordance with the traditions set by Lee, although admission is more open than her strict invitation-only rules. Students still receive a diploma that says 'Harvard Associates in Police Science' and a HAPS lapel pin. Every seminar has a group photo.

On the second night, seminar participants go out for dinner at one of the best steakhouses in Baltimore. Food is not served on gold-leaf plates, but it's still a pretty good meal.

In 2017, after the seminars had been conducted in Baltimore for half a century, a law firm representing the president and fellows of Harvard College sent a letter to Harvard Associates in Police Science, saying that their clients were 'troubled by the implication that Harvard Medical School and your organization are affiliated'.[17]

At their request, lest students mistakenly believe they are receiving a degree from Harvard, the HAPS website and the diplomas given at the conclusion of the seminar now include the disclaimer 'Not affiliated with Harvard University'.

The Nutshell Studies of Unexplained Death are still used as Lee intended, for training police officers to observe and report their findings. One of them – Two Rooms – was irreparably damaged or destroyed in the 1960s, leaving eighteen in existence that are still used for teaching. What exactly happened to Two Rooms is unknown.

Although more than seventy years old, the Nutshell Studies serve a purpose that cannot be duplicated by any other medium. Not even state-of-the-art virtual reality approaches the experience of viewing a three-dimensional setting.

Despite their continued usefulness, by 2017 the Nutshells were suffering the ravages of time. Some materials were cracking and warping. Exposure to years of heat and ultraviolet light had caused damage to surfaces. Several of the dioramas contained sheets of asbestos that in some cases was crumbling, possibly posing a danger to those who maintained the models. An ageing electrical system created an unknown risk of fire.

So, for the first time since Lee had assembled them, the Nutshells underwent extensive conservation by experts from the Smithsonian Institution's American Art Museum in Washington, DC. Under the direction of object conservator Ariel O'Connor, they were painstakingly cleaned, repaired and strengthened to slow or stop the effects of age. Smithsonian lighting director Scott Rosenfeld replaced the incandescent bulbs with custom-made computer-controlled light-emitting diodes encased in small glass bulbs designed to mimic vintage lighting. The electrical system now uses less energy, produces less heat and damaging wavelengths, and poses less risk of fire. By the time the team of conservators, artists, model-makers and lighting experts had finished working on them, the Nutshell dioramas had been preserved for generations.

For three months in 2017 and 2018, the Nutshell Studies of Unexplained Death had their first – and probably only – public exhibition, at the Smithsonian's Renwick Gallery, located across the street from the White House. More than 100,000 people attended the exhibition entitled *Murder is Her Hobby*. At the time, it was the second-most attended exhibition in the history of the museum. When it was over, the dioramas were carefully packed in custom-made boxes and returned to their cabinets in the Forensic Medical Center in Baltimore, where they continue to be used in the homicide seminars. The Nutshell Studies are not open to the general public.

* * *

Today, the United States is served by a patchwork of 2,342 separate death-investigation systems – some statewide, some county-wide, some regional. No federal laws or national standards regulate how unexplained deaths should be investigated.[18] There is little consistency from place to place in terms of who conducts a death investigation, that person's qualifications, the conditions under which a forensic investigation is indicated or how it is conducted. How a death is investigated depends on where a person dies. Since Boston introduced medical examiners in 1877, the growth of medical examiner systems throughout the United States has been painfully slow. Of the 3,137 US counties, more than two thirds are still served by coroners. About half of the total American population is still under the jurisdiction of coroners.

Every year, approximately a million sudden and violent deaths in the United States are referred for forensic investigation. At least half of them are never subject to a thorough inquiry by a qualified forensic pathologist. There is no way to estimate how many murders slip beneath the radar every year in the United States.

At the time of writing, medical examiner systems are present in the District of Columbia and twenty-two states: Alaska, Arizona, Connecticut, Delaware, Florida, Iowa, Maine, Maryland, Massachusetts, Michigan, New Hampshire, New Jersey, New Mexico, North Carolina, Oklahoma, Oregon, Rhode Island, Tennessee, Utah, Vermont, Virginia and West Virginia. The most recent state to convert from coroners to medical examiners was Alaska in 1996.

Fewer than a third of the twenty-eight states with coroners require them to have training in forensic science.

Eleven states are exclusively on the coroner system (Colorado, Idaho, Kansas, Louisiana, Nebraska, Nevada, North Dakota, Ohio, Pennsylvania, South Dakota and Wyoming), while seventeen have both coroners and medical examiners. For example, Los Angeles, Ventura, San Francisco and San Diego have medical examiners, while the remainder of California is served by coroners.

Despite the efforts of Lee, Oscar Schultz and many others dating back to the 1940s and earlier, Cook County – which includes the City of Chicago – had no medical examiner until 1976. As the only medical examiner office in Illinois, the agency covers half of the state's population. The rest of Illinois comes under the jurisdiction of 101 coroners – some elected, some appointed – of various backgrounds. By law, they are required to take a one-week course of basic coroner training upon assuming office.[19]

Only one jurisdiction – Charleston, South Carolina – has ever reverted from medical examiners to a coroner system. In 1972, the city implemented a dual system in which a medical examiner shared responsibility with a coroner. As one might expect, the approach was plagued with conflict.

Public confidence in death investigation was so low that political efforts were undertaken to pull all funding from the medical examiner's office. Since 2001, Charleston has been served by elected coroners.[20]

The reasons for inertia against the adoption of medical examiner systems are the same as they were in Lee's time: political opposition, resistance to giving up control at a local level, the fairly high initial investment required to set up a well-equipped medical examiner office. One of the most serious obstacles to the wider acceptance of the system is a severe shortage of manpower – there simply aren't enough forensic pathologists to serve the entire United States.[21]

According to the National Association of Medical Examiners, there are 400 to 500 forensic pathologists working as medical examiners in the United States. The country needs two to three times as many to cover the population sufficiently, but medical schools are not producing forensic pathologists in great numbers.[22]

Since Lee established the first training programme at Harvard's Department of Legal Medicine, the number of forensic pathology fellowship courses in the United States has grown to thirty-nine. At present, seventy-eight forensic pathology fellowship positions have been approved by the Accreditation Council for Graduate Medical Education. Only fifty-four of these are actually funded, and about twenty per cent are vacant in any given year for lack of a suitable fellowship candidate.

In recent years, an average of thirty-eight board-certified forensic pathologists have entered the workforce annually. This number is not enough to replace pathologists who are reaching retirement age, much less to expand medical examiner systems throughout the country.

Attracting doctors to careers in forensic pathology is difficult. Aside from the salary differences between the public and private sectors, the work is frequently unpleasant and often conducted in facilities that are ageing and underfunded. Whether these trends can be reversed remains to be seen.

* * *

Although the medical examiner system has been slow to spread throughout much of the world, Lee's influence extends far beyond America. Dozens of police officers from the UK have attended the Frances Glessner Lee Seminar in Homicide Investigation and the Harvard Associates in Police Science advanced homicide seminar. Methods and practices learned at the seminars are used daily by investigators around the world.

Lee's most profound influence may be in having spawned the huge interest in forensic science in popular culture. Her lasting legacy is having raised in the public consciousness the expectations for a competent, diligent, professional crime scene investigation.

In recent years, public awareness of Lee and her work has grown in the UK and beyond. One of her dioramas, a Nutshell previously thought to be lost, was discovered in a loft and displayed as part of an exhibit – *Forensics: The Anatomy of Crime* – at the Wellcome Collection in London in 2015. This singularly rare exhibition of a Nutshell outside the United States was widely covered by newspapers and other publications in the UK. Lee and the Nutshell Studies continue to capture imaginations – they were the subject of a radio programme by poet laureate Simon Armitage on BBC Radio 4 titled *In a Nutshell* and featured on Billy Connolly's television series *Tracks Across America*.

* * *

Despite Lee's abiding belief in the superiority of the medical examiner system, it would be inaccurate to claim that the system doesn't have problems. A search of news stories from recent years will reveal scandals and crises in Boston, Connecticut, Los Angeles, Chicago, Delaware and many other medical examiner offices.

A study by the US Department of Justice found that investigators examine the crime scene in only about sixty two per cent of cases referred for medico-legal investigation. The prudent approach to questionable deaths is to have a trained investigator at every scene, every time.[23] Fewer than half of the forensic investigations involve an autopsy and, despite what viewers of procedural crime dramas are led to believe, death scenes are processed for criminal evidence in only about five per cent of investigations.

According to Dr Randy Hanzlick, past president of the National Association of Medical Examiners, about a third of medical examiner offices in the United States lack a toxicology laboratory. The same proportion lack a histology laboratory and in-house X-ray services. The absence of these essential tools can lead to cutting corners, needless delays and tragic unforeseen circumstances.[24]

In 2013, an eleven-year-old boy died while staying at a Best Western motel in Boone, North Carolina. He was found to have died from carbon monoxide poisoning. Exhaust from a swimming-pool pump had been drawn into the victim's room by the ventilation system.[25] Two other people had died in the same motel room two months earlier. After the first deaths, the medical examiner had sent blood samples to a state laboratory to be tested for carbon monoxide poisoning. The tests took more than six weeks and results were received a week before the child died. A forensic medical centre with an in-house toxicology laboratory should have carbon monoxide results in a week or less. Had a warning about a potential leak into a motel room been raised in a timely manner, a death might have been avoided.

In many instances, the problems affecting forensic medical centres are a lack of resources, a lack of funding, a lack of training and adherence to standards of practice, and a lack of support.

* * *

The science of 'forensic science' is always evolving. DNA 'fingerprinting' is a good example. Since DNA evidence emerged into the public consciousness in the 1990s, more than 360 people previously convicted of crimes have been exonerated by DNA evidence, according to the non-profit legal organization known as the Innocence Project. The number of innocent people who were executed or died in prison will never be known.[26]

The trouble with DNA evidence is that the results can be misinterpreted. Several prominent news stories highlight the problem of such evidence being misused to implicate an innocent person. A recent study by the National Institute of Standards and Technology revealed that seventy-four out of 108 crime laboratories tested by the agency falsely implicated an innocent person in a hypothetical crime.[27] DNA fingerprinting is one of the areas now being given fresh scrutiny for scientific reliability, along with bite marks, arson evidence and conditions such as shaken-baby syndrome.

The pursuit of truth must be relentless, as Captain Lee reminds us. Scientific facts must be followed wherever they lead, to clear the innocent and convict the guilty.

A Note from the Author

On a winter morning in 2012, I was among a dozen or so editors touring the state of Maryland's state-of-the-art forensic medical centre in Baltimore. We all worked for Patch, an organization of hyper-local news sites owned at the time by AOL-Huffington Post. Through covering the news at my site, I had become acquainted with an individual active in my community, Mike Eagle, who worked as the director of IT for the Office of the Chief Medical Examiner (OCME). I asked Mike to give us a tour of the state's new facility, which he was kind enough to do.

We met with the chief medical examiner, Dr David Fowler, for an informal, off-the-record chat in a fourth-floor conference room. In the next room, behind a door labelled 'Room 417 Pathology Exhibit', was the famous collection of eighteen incredibly detailed dioramas known as the Nutshell Studies of Unexplained Death.

I knew all about the Nutshell Studies and their creator, Frances Glessner Lee. At least I thought I did. I had first written about them in 1992 for *American Medical News*, the weekly newspaper of the American Medical Association. At the time, *American Medical News* paid very well for feature stories with a medical interest angle, such as doctors with unusual hobbies. I wrote articles about a medical motorcycling club, a rather genial biker gang of doctors and allied health professionals, and a surgeon who studied ancient Egyptian medical texts.

Of the thousands of stories I wrote over the years, however, the Nutshell Studies is the one that stuck with me. I had come to know the previous chief medical examiner, Dr John Smialek, and a handful of others at the OCME by return visits to see the Nutshell Studies. Friends and family, knowing about my connection, periodically asked me to arrange a visit to see the dioramas. Every time I looked at the models, I noticed new things. The Nutshells never ceased to amaze me.

After meeting with Dr Fowler on that winter morning, Mike led our group around the dazzling 11m² (120,000sq. ft) forensic medical centre. We saw the brightly lit two-storey autopsy rooms, each a huge, gleaming, voluminous space; the biosafety suite with smaller autopsy rooms under negative pressure; the radiology room, with a CT and a low-dose full-body X-ray machine; and the histology and toxicology laboratories. It was all very impressive. The OCME of Maryland, regarded as one of the best in the United States, had a stellar facility to match its reputation.

While showing us Scarpetta House, the studio apartment-like forensic investigator training facility on the OCME's fourth floor gifted by novelist Patricia Cornwell, Mike mentioned that the agency had an opening for a new position – an executive assistant to the chief medical examiner who would serve as public information officer for the OCME. They were looking for somebody with media experience, ideally with a medical background, who had a basic grasp of the law and was comfortable dealing with police, lawyers and the public. The OCME had never had a public information officer before, so this was something new.

My background seemed to fit the criteria. I had been an Emergency Medical Technician/paramedic and even completed most of nursing school before sidling into journalism. I had worked in and around hospitals for years. Police and lawyers don't rattle me. Would I like to work in the same building as the Nutshell Studies? Yes, please.

I got the job. The leap from journalism to forensic medicine isn't as far as it might seem. Both fields are dedicated to establishing facts: who, what, when, where, why and how. Both require critical thinking and a sceptical attitude. Medical examiners, in a sense, write the last chapter of a person's life.

It didn't take long for a variety of diorama-related tasks to be added to the miscellany of my duties. Jerry Dziecichowicz, the keeper of the secret Nutshell Studies solutions, asked me to change the light bulbs in the dioramas as they burned out and showed me where the keys to the cabinets were kept. There is no manual or instructions for the dioramas, so I learned a lot about them. When filmmakers and photographers requested access, they were directed to me because I was the only person willing to take the time to accommodate them. I met members of Frances Glessner Lee's family when they came to visit and was honoured to share a fancy dinner with two of her grandchildren – John Maxim Lee and Percy Lee Langstaff – during the Francis Glessner Lee Seminar in Homicide Investigation. My understanding of Frances Glessner Lee deepened by engaging with people like William Tyre, executive director and curator of the Glessner House Museum in Chicago.

Although there was no formal title, I became the de facto curator of the Nutshell Studies. I collected images, artwork and documents related to the models. When the dioramas, fragile seventy-year-old artefacts at risk of irreparable damage, underwent conservation by experts from the Smithsonian American Art Museum in preparation for their first and only public exhibition, I was present to observe at every step. The examination of the dioramas by conservator Ariel O'Connor and her team revealed an abundance of previously unknown information about the composition of the materials Lee used and how she constructed the models.

When people see the Nutshell Studies, they often ask the same questions. How did Lee get involved in forensic science? How did she choose the cases to depict in the dioramas? Why didn't she go to university? What was she like as a person? Although I'd known about Lee for twenty-five years – maybe knew more about her than anybody else on earth – I didn't know the answers to those questions.

Lee had been the inspiration for a documentary, a coffee-table picture book, at least two collections of poetry and even a plot arc on a popular forensic science television drama. But her life story had never been told. Articles about Lee and the Nutshell Studies that I read in print and online were riddled with errors and misinformation. She was depicted as a rich old woman who made morbid doll's houses. I knew she was much more than that. She was an agent of change: a reformer, educator and advocate.

The need for Lee's story to be told became increasingly obvious. Who could be trusted to tell it fairly, honestly, diligently and thoroughly? Who could be relied upon to present the facts without trying to make Lee serve an agenda? The only person I'd trust was me. So I undertook this assignment out of respect and obligation to her legacy.

Lee demanded that investigators relentlessly pursue the facts to determine the truth and follow the evidence wherever it leads. The telling of her own story deserves no less. I approached this subject as a journalist, reporting on historical events. I have endeavoured to present the facts without speculation or embellishment. I don't know if I could ever have met Lee's exacting standards of perfection, but I hope that I have done her justice.

Appendix

Catalogue of the Nutshell Studies
of Unexplained Death

The Nutshell Studies of Unexplained Death are not mysteries to be solved, but were made for police officers to practise the observation of crime scenes. Based on actual cases, with some details changed to protect the identity of the deceased and their families, Lee built exquisitely detailed dioramas that were purposefully ambiguous. The goal of the exercise is to observe, recognize evidence that may be significant and report the findings. Lee said that each diorama is a moment frozen in time, like a still frame from a motion picture. The dioramas are a set of facts: the truth in a nutshell. It is the investigators' duty to search for that truth.

Three-Room Dwelling (c.1944–1946)

Dimensions: 30.5 x 82.5 x 83.5cm (12 x 32½ x 32⅞in)

Reported to Nutshell Laboratories Monday, 1 November 1937.

Robert Judson, a foreman in a shoe factory, his wife Kate Judson and their baby, Linda Mae Judson, were discovered dead by Paul Abbott, a neighbour.

Mr Abbott was questioned and gave the following statement:

Bob Judson and he drove to their work together, alternating cars. This was Abbott's week to drive. On Monday morning, 1 November, he was late – about 7.35am – so, when blowing his horn didn't bring Judson out, Abbott went to the factory without him, believing Judson would come in his own car.

Sarah Abbott, Paul Abbott's wife, was also questioned and gave the following statement:

After Paul had left, she watched for Bob to come out. Finally, about 8.15am, seeing no signs of activity at the Judson house, she went over to their porch and tried the front door, but it was locked. She called, but got no answer. She then went to the kitchen porch, but that door was also locked. She looked in through the glass, and then, thoroughly aroused by the sight of the gun and blood, she ran home and notified the police.

The model shows the premises just before Mrs Abbott went to the house.

NB: Dawn broke at 5am. Sunrise at 6.17am. Weather clear. No lights were on at the house. Both doors were locked on the inside.

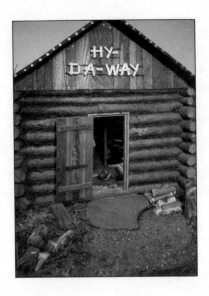

Log Cabin (*c*.1944–1945)

Dimensions: 37 x 46.25 x 60cm (14½ x 18¼ x 23⅝in)

Reported to Nutshell Laboratories Thursday, 22 October 1942.

Arthur Roberts, a local insurance salesman, was found dead by police who responded to a call from a friend of the victim, Mrs Marion Chase.

Mrs Chase was questioned and gave the following statement:

She had met Arthur Roberts at the log cabin on Wednesday, 21 October 1942, about 5.15pm. They were in the habit of meeting there. Roberts was married and was living with his wife. Mrs Chase was also married but was not living with her husband. Roberts told her at this meeting that the affair between them was ended. There was no quarrel. Mrs Chase and Mr Roberts were standing at the foot of the bunk. He turned toward the door, took a package of cigarettes from his outside pocket, selected a cigarette, but dropped it. As he stooped over to pick it up, a shot was heard – he fell flat – a gun dropped beside him. Mrs Chase says she picked up the gun, but replaced it. It did not belong to her. She then ran out of the door, jumped into her car and drove to summon the police.

The gun was identified as belonging to Arthur Roberts. Mrs Chase identified the handbag on the bunk as hers.

A single bullet had passed entirely through Mr Roberts' chest from front to back and the powder around the entrance indicated that it had been fired at a fairly close range.

The model shows the premises after Mrs Chase left, and before her return with the police officer.

Blue Bedroom (c.1944–1948)

Dimensions: 34.25 x 48.75 x 62cm (13½ x 19³/₁₆ x 24⅜in)

Reported to Nutshell Laboratories Wednesday, 3 November 1943.

Charles Logan, an employee in a box factory, was discovered dead by his wife, Carolyn Logan.

Mrs Logan gave the following statement:

On Tuesday night, 2 November 1943, she was alone in the house when Charles came home about midnight. He had been drinking and was in a quarrelsome mood. They had an argument, but she was finally able to persuade him to go upstairs to bed. She waited downstairs for him to go to sleep before she also went to bed. After about half an hour she heard him moving around and shortly thereafter heard a shot. She ran upstairs and found the situation as illustrated by the model.

Dark Bathroom (c.1944–1945)

Dimensions: 29 x 38.75 x 53cm (11⅜ x 15¼ x 20⅞in)

Reported to Nutshell Laboratories by Desk Sergeant Moriarity of the Central City Police as he recalled it.

Maggie Wilson was found dead by Lizzie Miller.

Miss Miller was able to supply the following information:

Miss Miller roomed in the same house as Maggie Wilson but knew her only as they met in the hall. She thought Maggie was subject to fits (seizures). A couple of male friends came to see Maggie fairly regularly. On Sunday night in early November in 1896, the men were there and there was a good deal of drinking going on. Some time after they left, Lizzie heard the water still running in the bathroom. Upon opening the door she found the scene as set forth in the model.

Burned Cabin (*c.*1944–1948)

Dimensions: 34.25 x 60 x 43.5cm (13½ x 23⅝ x 17¹/₁₆in)

Reported to Nutshell Laboratories Sunday, 15 August 1943.

Daniel Perkins was missing and presumed dead.

Phillip Perkins, Daniel Perkins' nephew, gave the following information:

On Saturday evening, 14 August, he had come to spend the night with his uncle, as he frequently did. In the middle of the night he was wakened by the smell of smoke and ran outside to find the house on fire and the fire engines arriving. He said he had been very confused and could not remember any other details.

Joseph McCarthy, driver of fire engine #6, was questioned and gave the following statement:

The call to the fire department was received at 1.30am, Sunday 15 August. Upon arrival of the fire engine the fire was quickly extinguished before the building was completely destroyed. He noticed Phillip Perkins, fully clothed, wandering around near the house.

The model represents the premises after the fire was extinguished and before any investigation had been started or any portion of the premises disturbed.

Unpapered Bedroom (*c.*1949–1952)

Dimensions: 30 x 61.25 x 48cm (11¾ x 24⅛ x 18¹⁵/₁₆in)

Reported to Nutshell Laboratories Monday, 4 June 1949.

An Unknown Woman was discovered dead in a rooming house (registered as Mrs John Smith).

Mrs Bessie Collins, the landlady of the rooming house, was questioned and gave the following statement:

She kept a rooming house, and on Saturday 2 June 1949, in the early afternoon, the deceased and a man rented this room until Monday morning, registering as Mr and Mrs John Smith. On Monday morning, 4 June, the man had left early – about 6.30am. He paid for the room up to six o'clock that evening and said not to disturb his wife, as she wanted to sleep late.

About three o'clock on Monday afternoon, Mrs Collins told Stella Walsh, the maid, to try to get into the room to make it up. Just before five o'clock, Stella told Mrs Collins there was something wrong. She had tried twice but couldn't wake the woman, so Mrs Collins and Stella entered the room, the door was not locked, and found the woman was cold – evidently dead. They left the room without disturbing anything, closed and locked the door, taking the key with them, and notified the patrolman on the beat.

The model shows the conditions in the room as the two women found them.

Pink Bathroom (*c.*1934–1948)

Dimensions: 49 x 36 x 52.75cm (19¼ x 14½ x 20¾in)

Reported to Nutshell Laboratories Tuesday, 31 March 1942.

Mrs Rose Fishman, a widow, was found dead by Samuel Weiss, the janitor.

Mr Weiss was questioned and gave the following statement:

Several tenants had complained of an odour and on 30 March he began looking for the source of the odour. Mrs Fishman didn't answer her bell when he rang it, and upon checking with other tenants he learned that she had not been seen recently. Therefore, he looked into her mailbox and saw that her mail had accumulated for several days. He entered Mrs Fishman's apartment, found it in order, but the odour was very strong. The bathroom door was closed. When he tried to open the door, he could only get it open a little way, and the odour was much stronger. He immediately went downstairs and climbed the fire escape to enter the bathroom through the window. He could not remember if he found the window open or closed.

The model, however, shows the premises as he found them.

Attic (*c.*1946–1948)

Dimensions: 55 x 43.5 x 32.75cm (21$^{11}/_{16}$ x 17$^{1}/_{8}$ x 12$^{7}/_{8}$in)

Reported to Nutshell Laboratories Tuesday, 24 December 1946.

Miss Jessie Compton was discovered dead in her house by Mr Harry Frazier, a milk delivery man who gave this statement:

On the morning of Tuesday, 24 December 1946, about six o'clock, he stopped at Miss Compton's kitchen door to deliver the milk. The weather was very cold and he was surprised to find the kitchen door open. He put his head inside and called, but received no answer so he went in to see if anything was wrong. After looking the house over, he went part way up the attic stairs and saw Miss Compton's body hanging there, so he went downstairs and telephoned the police.

Policeman John T Adams received the telephone call at 6.34 on Tuesday morning, 24 December, and went at once to Miss Compton's house. The snow on the path to the kitchen door was somewhat trampled and no distinct footprints could be recognized. There were unwashed dishes for one person on the kitchen table. The house downstairs was neat. The bed was made and undisturbed. However, he found the attic as represented in the model.

Woodman's Shack (*c.*1945–1948)

Dimensions: 48 x 36 x 40.25cm (18⅞ x 14³/₁₆ x 15¹⁵/₁₆in)
Reported to Nutshell Laboratories Thursday, 8 February 1945.

Ruby Jenks was found dead in a woodman's shack she lived in with Homer Cregg and Carl Stebbins.

On Tuesday, 6 February 1945, about 5pm, Highfield Village Chief of Police Lawrence W Farmer was notified by Dr George Barbour of Highfield Village that there was a dead woman in a lumberman's camp on the Pine Grove Road. Medical Investigator Chester W Dombey, Deputy Sheriff Thomas Gorman, photographer Adam Stanhope and Chief Farmer went over at once. They found Mr Cregg and Mr Stebbins there, both very drunk, and the body of Ruby Jenks on the bed entirely covered up, including her head and face. Chief Farmer pulled the blanket down and Stanhope took a picture. Dr Dombey made an examination of the body and ordered it be removed to Coffin & Graves Funeral Parlour. Mr Stebbins then lay down on the bed and photographer Stanhope took a picture of him, and also one of the outside of the shack. At the funeral parlour, Dr Dombey again examined the body and found no marks of violence. Adam Stanhope took another picture there. The two men were questioned that night and again the next day. Copies of Chief Farmer's and Dr Dombey's reports are available.

The model shows the premises as found by Dr Barbour upon his arrival at 4.25pm on Tuesday, 6 February. Mr Stebbins is lying on the bed – also Ruby. Mr Cregg is seated on the chair. US Weather Bureau report: weather clear, temperature –17 degrees Fahrenheit [–27°C], sunset 5.03pm EST.

Barn (*c.*1943–1945)

Dimensions: 68.5 x 59.75 x 73.75cm (27 x 23½ x 29in)

Reported to Nutshell Laboratories Saturday, 13 July 1939.

Eben Wallace, a local farmer, was found dead by his wife, Imelda.

Mrs Imelda Wallace was questioned and gave the following statement:

Mr Wallace was hard to get along with. When things didn't go the way he wanted, he would go out to the barn, threatening suicide. Mr Wallace would stand up on a bucket and put a noose around his neck, but she would always manage to persuade him not to do it. On the afternoon of 14 July, about four o'clock, they had a dispute. Mr Wallace made his usual threats, but she didn't follow him to the barn right away. When she did go to the barn, she found the premises as represented in the model.

The bucket usually stood in the corner just inside the barn door, but yesterday she had used it and had left it out by the pump. The rope was always fastened to the beam just the way it was found – it was part of the regular barn hoist.

Saloon and Jail (*c.*1944–1946)

Dimensions: 64.5 x 71.75 x 30.75cm (25⅜ x 28¼ x 12⅛in)

Reported to Nutshell Laboratories Sunday, 12 November 1944.

Frank Harris, dock labourer, was found dead in a jail cell after having been found lying on the street by City Patrolman Dennis Mulcahy.

Patrolman Mulcahy stated that on Saturday night, 11 November 1944, at half-past eleven o'clock, he was walking his beat on Dock Street. He saw a man lying sprawled out on the pavement in front of Pat's Place, a saloon. The man was breathing and smelt strongly of liquor. The patrolman called the wagon which took the man to Station 2, where he was locked up in a single cell. His union card bore the name of Frank Harris, address 271/2 Water Street. He appeared to be very drunk. There were no marks of violence on him.

On Sunday morning, 12 November, at seven o'clock, when rounds were made in Station 2, Mr Harris was found dead in his cell, as represented in the model.

Striped Bedroom (*c.*1944–1945)

Dimensions: 34 x 50 x 64.75cm (13⅜ x 19⅝ x 25½in)

Reported to Nutshell Laboratories Monday, 29 April 1940.

Richard Harvey, a foreman in an ice-cream factory, was found dead by his mother, Mrs Mary Harvey.

Mrs Harvey provided the following information:

On Saturday night, 27 April 1940, Richard came home for supper as usual and after supper went back to work. He always worked late Saturday nights to get ready for the Sunday trade. She didn't know when he came in as she had gone to bed early. Sunday morning she let him sleep while she went to church and then, as usual, proceeded to her sister for the day. When she returned home Sunday evening, Richard wasn't around, so she opened his door and found the premises as represented by the model.

Richard was married about a year ago and brought his wife home to live. She was a nice girl and they were very happy. His wife was away now visiting her parents for a few days in another state. Richard was a good boy but sometimes had a little too much to drink, especially on Saturday nights. The dishpan belonged to the kitchen. She didn't know how it came to be in Richard's room.

Living Room (*c.*1943–1945)

Dimensions: 29 x 64.5 x 62.25cm (11⅜ x 25³/₁₆ x 24½in)

Reported to Nutshell Laboratories Friday, 22 May 1941.

Mrs Ruby Davis, a housewife, was discovered dead on the stairs by her husband, Reginald Davis.

Mr Davis was questioned and gave the following statement:

He and his wife had spent the previous evening, Thursday 21 May 1941, quietly at home. His wife had gone upstairs to bed shortly before he had. This morning he awoke a little before five o'clock to find that his wife was not beside him in bed. After waiting a while, he got up to see where she was and found her dead body on the stairs. He at once called the family physician who, upon his arrival, immediately notified the police.

The model shows the premises just before the arrival of the family physician.

Two-Storey Porch (*c*.1948)

Dimensions: 104.75 x 68.5 x 59.75cm (41¼ x 27 x 23½in)

Reported to Nutshell Laboratories Monday, 5 April 1948.

Mrs Annie Morrison, a housewife, was found lying on the ground below a second-storey porch.

Harry Morrison, Annie Morrison's husband, relayed the following:

On Monday morning, 5 April 1948, at about eleven o'clock, he was in the kitchen of the top-storey apartment where he and his wife lived. Mrs Morrison had done the week's washing and was standing on the chair out on the porch hanging it out on the line to dry. Mr Morrison heard a sort of noise and went to see what it was and found conditions as represented by the model. He had a job on the late shift but was up earlier than usual that day as he hadn't worked the day before, which was Sunday.

Mrs Agnes Butler, a neighbour of the Morrisons, gave the following statement:

She lived in the apartment below the Morrisons. She bathed her baby on Monday morning, 5 April, and put him in his carriage. She had done his washing and hung it out to dry. She was cleaning up the kitchen when she heard a crash and rushed out onto the porch and saw Mrs Morrison lying on the ground below. The Morrisons quarrelled a lot and Mr Morrison didn't treat his wife very well. He drank some and Mrs Butler guessed he had lady friends besides. She heard the Morrisons quarrelling that morning.

Kitchen (*c.*1944–1945)

Dimensions: 43.25 x 64 x 63cm (17 x 25¼ x 24¾in)

Reported to Nutshell Laboratories Wednesday, 12 April 1944.

Barbara Barnes, a housewife, was found dead by police who responded to a call from the husband of the victim, Fred Barnes, who gave the following statement:

About 4pm on the afternoon of Tuesday, 11 April 1944, he had gone downtown on an errand for his wife. He returned about an hour and a half later and found the outside door to the kitchen locked. It was standing open when he left. Mr Barnes attempted knocking and calling, but got no answer. He tried the front door, but it was also locked. He then went to the kitchen window, which was closed and locked. He looked in and saw what appeared to be his wife lying on the floor. He then summoned the police.

The model shows the premises just before the police forced open the kitchen door.

Garage (c.1946–1948)

Dimensions: 72.5 x 68.5 x 68.75cm (28½ x 27 x 27^{1}/$_{16}$in)

Reported to Nutshell Laboratories Monday, 7 January 1946.

Hugh Patterson, Vice-President, Suburban Bank, was found dead in the garage by his wife, Sue Patterson.

Mrs Patterson was questioned and gave the following statement:

Hugh had gone out alone in the car after dinner on Saturday, 5 January 1946. He often did this, especially lately, and stayed out very late. Sunday morning when he hadn't come home by breakfast time, Mrs Patterson went to the garage to see if the car was there. She looked into the left-hand door and saw Hugh hanging out of the car. She then telephoned the local police station for help as she couldn't reach the doctor.

When the patrolman arrived he went around to the back, broke the glass, climbed in the window and opened both doors. He left, again through the window so as not to disturb footprints in the front. He found the garage full of gas fumes, the car's ignition turned on and the gas tank empty.

Hugh seemed troubled for some time and money hadn't been as plentiful as it once was. Some time ago, he told her that he carried heavy life insurance, with the double indemnity clause for accident, in her favour, and about that time he had deeded the house over to her. He had begun to drink a good deal lately.

The model shows the premises just after the patrolman left the garage by way of the window.

Parsonage Parlour (*c*.1946–1948)

Dimensions: 35.5 x 56 x 51.5cm (14 x 22 x 20¼in)

Reported to Nutshell Laboratories Friday, 23 August 1946.

Dorothy Dennison, a high-school student, was found dead after being reported missing by her mother, Mrs James Dennison. Mrs Dennison was questioned by Police Lieutenant Robert Peale, and gave the following statement:

On Monday morning, 19 August 1946, about eleven o'clock, Dorothy had walked downtown to buy some hamburg steak for dinner. She didn't have much money in her purse. When she failed to return in time for dinner, her mother telephoned a neighbour who stated she had seen the girl walking towards the market. Mrs Dennison also telephoned the market and the proprietor said he sold Dorothy a pound of hamburg steak some time before noon but didn't notice which way she turned upon leaving his shop. By late afternoon, Mrs Dennison, thoroughly alarmed, notified the police.

Lieutenant Peale's investigation report stated that on Monday afternoon, 19 August 1946, at 5.25pm, he received the telephone call from Mrs Dennison at Police Headquarters, and at once took charge of the matter personally. The customary inquiries began and by Wednesday, 21 August, a systematic search of all closed or unoccupied buildings in the vicinity was undertaken. It was not until Friday, 23 August, at 4.15pm, that he and Officer Patrick Sullivan entered the parsonage and found the premises as represented in the model.

Temperatures during the time period ranged from 86 to 92 degrees Fahrenheit [30–33°C] with high humidity.

Red Bedroom (*c.*1944)

Dimensions: 32 x 63 x 62.5cm (12⅝ x 24¾ x 24⅝in)

Reported to Nutshell Laboratories Thursday, 29 June 1944.

Marie Jones, a prostitute, was discovered dead by her landlady, Mrs Shirley Flanagan.

Mrs Shirley Flanagan was questioned and gave the following statement:

On the evening of Thursday, 29 June 1944, she passed the open door of Marie's room and called out 'Hello.' When she did not receive a response, she looked in and found the conditions as found in the model. Jim Green, a boyfriend and client of Marie's, had come in with Marie the afternoon before. Mrs Flanagan didn't know when he had left. As soon as she found Marie's body she telephoned the police, who later found Mr Green and brought him in for questioning.

He met Marie on the pavement on the afternoon of 28 June, and walked with her to a nearby store where he bought two bottles of whiskey. They then went to her room where they sat smoking and drinking for some time. Marie, sitting in the red chair, got very drunk. Suddenly, without any warning, she grabbed his open jackknife, which he had used to cut the string around the package containing the bottles. She ran into the closet and shut the door. When he opened the door he found her lying as represented by the model. He left the house immediately after that.

Endnotes

Abbreviations

ARM   Alan R Moritz
CHM   Center for the History of Medicine at Countway
       Library, Harvard University
CSB   C Sidney Burwell
FGL   Frances Glessner Lee
GHM   Glessner House Museum
RAC   Rockefeller Archive Center
SAC   Special Agent in Charge, the head of an FBI field office

Chapter 1: Legal Medicine

1. Lee unable to attend seminar due to heart attacks: letter from FGL to ARM, 10 August 1944, CHM.
2. *'Men are dubious of'*: Pete Martin, 'How Murderers Beat the Law', the *Saturday Evening Post*, 10 December 1949.
3. *'The models are none'*: letter from FGL to ARM, 10 August, CHM.
4. *'Resolved, that Mrs Frances G Lee'*: resolution enclosed in letter from ARM to FGL, 6 October 1944, CHM.
5. One in five deaths are sudden: about ten per cent of deaths are due to violence or unnatural causes, and about ten per cent of deaths are due to unknown or obscure causes that require inquiry. Committee on Medicolegal Problems, 'Medical Science in Crime Detection', *Journal of the American Medical Association* 200, no. 2 (10 April 1967): pp. 155–60.
6. The earliest methodical inquiries: sources for historical description of coroners include Jeffrey Jentzen, *Death Investigation in*

America: Coroners, Medical Examiners and the Pursuit of Medical Certainty (Cambridge, MA: Harvard University Press, 2009) and Russell S Fisher, 'History of Forensic Pathology and Related Laboratory Sciences', in *Medicolegal Investigation of Death*, 2nd edn, ed. Werner U Spitz and Russell S Fisher (Springfield, IL: Charles C Thomas, 1980).

7. Coroners were responsible for answering two questions: Theodore Tyndale, 'The Law of Coroners', *Boston Medical and Surgical Journal* 96 (1877): pp. 243–58.

8. Thomas Baldridge's instructions: William G Eckert, ed., *Introduction to Forensic Sciences*, 2nd edn. (New York: Elsevier, 1992), p. 12.

9. *'Upon notice or suspicion'*: Aric W Dutelle and Ronald F Becker, *Criminal Investigation*, 5th edn. (Burlington, MA: Jones & Bartlett Learning, 2013), p. 8.

10. Baldridge inquest: J Hall Pleasants, ed., *Proceedings of the County Court of Charles County, 1658–1666*, Archives of Maryland 1936, pp. xl–xli; 'An inquest taken before the Coroner, at mattapient in the county of St maries, on Wednesday the 31 Of January 1637', USGenWeb Archive, http://files.usgwarchives.net/md/stmarys/wills/briant-j.txt.

11. The deficiencies of the coroner system: Julie Johnson, 'Coroners, Corruption and the Politics of Death: Forensic Pathology in the United States', in Clark and Crawford, *Legal Medicine in History*, pp. 268–89.

12. Nonsensical causes of death: Raymond Moley, *An Outline of the Cleveland Crime Survey* (Cleveland: Cleveland Foundation, 1922).

13. Leonard Wallstein's report: Leonard Michael Wallstein, *Report on Special Examination of the Accounts and Methods of the Office of Coroner in New York City* (New York: Office of the Commissioner of Accounts, 1915).

14. *'Outrageous crooks who dispensed'*: Jentzen, *Death Investigation in America*, p. 25.

15. 'Suffolk County [...] had more coroners': James C Mohr, *Doctors and the Law: Medical Jurisprudence in Ninteenth-century America* (Johns Hopkins University Press, 1996), p. 214.

16. *'You have in the coroner'*: Tyndale, 'Law of Coroners', p. 246.

17. The scandal that precipitated the end of the coroner system: Martin, 'How Murderers Beat the Law'.

18. Chicago Police Department: 'History', Chicago Police Department website, accessed 20 April 2018, https://home.chicagopolice.org/

inside-the-cpd/history/; on Orsemus Morrison, see *A History of the City of Chicago: Its Men and Institutions* (Chicago: Inter Ocean, 1900), pp. 440–1.

19. The first death Morrison investigated: Richard L Lindberg, *Gangland Chicago: Criminality and Lawlessness in the Windy City* (Lanham, MD: Rowman & Littlefield, 2015), pp. 3–5.

20. John Jacob Glessner in Springfield: Timothy B Spears, *Chicago Dreaming: Midwesterners and the City, 1871–1919* (Chicago: University of Chicago Press, 2005), pp. 24–50.

21. Isaac Scott: Percy Maxim Lee and John Glessner Lee, *Family Reunion: An Incomplete Account of the Maxim-Lee Family History* (privately printed, 1971), p. 354; David A Hanks, *Isaac Scott: Reform Furniture in Chicago* (Chicago: Chicago School of Architecture Foundation, 1974).

Chapter 2: The Sunny Street of the Sifted Few

1. '*Aunt Helen made the move*': Frances Macbeth Glessner Journal, Glessner Family Papers, GHM (accessed through transcribed, searchable version at the Chicago History Museum); (hereinafter cited as Journal), 22 July 1878.

2. Twin Mountain House: Lee and Lee, *Family Reunion*, p. 348.

3. Henry Ward Beecher: Robert Shaplen, 'The Beecher–Tilton Affair', *The New Yorker*, 4 June 1954, https://www.newyorker.com/magazine/1954/06/12/the-beecher-tilton-case-ii.

4. '*He took a fancy*': Lee and Lee, *Family Reunion*, p. 350.

5. '*My dear, a summer*': Lee and Lee, *Family Reunion*, p. 350.

6. '*One of the finest*': Journal, 29 July 1883.

7. Buildings at The Rocks: for information about The Rocks, see *A Historical Walk Through John and Frances Glessner's Rocks Estate* (undated booklet); 'Heritage and History', The Rocks Estate, accessed 14 September 2018, http://www.therocks.mobi/about.html.

8. Neighbour Frances Macbeth invited local residents to visit: Lee and Lee, *Family Reunion*, pp. 357–8.

9. 'One day, a mountain wagon...' Journal, pp. 356–7.

10. Prairie Avenue, Chicago: William H Tyre, *Chicago's Historic Prairie Avenue* (Chicago, IL: Arcadia Books, 2008).

11. John Jacob wanted an architect of note: Lee and Lee, *Family Reunion*, pp. 327–30.

12. Henry Hobson Richardson: Finn MacLeod, 'Spotlight: Henry Hobson Richardson', *ArchDaily*, 29 September 2017, https://www.archdaily.com/552221/spotlight-henry-hobson-richardson.

13. 'I'll plan anything a man wants...' Journal, p. 327.

14. Frances's description of Richardson: Journal, 15 May 1885.

15. Description of the Glessner home: Lee and Lee, *Family Reunion*, p. 322.

16. '*Prairie Ave. is a*': Lee and Lee, *Family Reunion*, p. 338.

17. H H Richardson's death: Lee and Lee, *Family Reunion*, p. 329.

18. '*The house responds*': *Family Reunion*, p. 326.

19. The orchestra and special occasions: Lee and Lee, *Family Reunion*, p. 326.

20. '*Cannabis indicie* (Indian hemp)': Journal, 11 May 1884.

21. The Monday Morning Reading Class: Genevieve Leach, 'The Monday Morning Reading Class', *Story of a House* (blog), 4 August 2016, https://www.glessnerhouse.org/story-of-a-house/2016/8/4/the-monday-morning-reading-class; Genevieve Leach, 'The Monday Morning Reading Class, Part 2', *Story of a House* (blog), 14 August 2016, https://www.glessnerhouse.org/story-of-a-house/2016/8/14/the-monday-morning-reading-class-part-2.

22. '*The ladies' fingers were*': John Jacob Glessner, *The Story of a House* (privately printed, 1923).

23. Invitation to the Monday Morning Reading Class: Judith Cass, 'Monday Class in Reading to Hold Reunion', *Chicago Tribune*, 2 April 1936.

24. '*The nervous strain of school*': Lee and Lee, *Family Reunion*, p. 325.

25. '*Over the thresholds*': 'The House at 1800 Prairie Avenue', Lee and Lee, *Family Reunion*, p. 325.

26. '*Never shall I forget*': Lee and Lee, *Family Reunion*, p. 349, p. 351.

27. Evening entertainments: William Tyre, 'Tableaux Vivants', *Story of a House* (blog), 1 September 2014, https://www.glesserhouse.org/story-of-a-house/2014/09/tableaux-vivants.html.

28. '*We have been most*': Journal, 27 July 1884.

29. He said there was: Journal, 15 May 1887.

30. "*D is for Doctor Lincoln*": Journal, July 3, 1887.

31. Fanny began to accompany local doctors: FGL, manuscript written for *Yankee Yarns* radio show, 1946, GHM.

32. '*But cooking and surgery*': FGL, *Yankee Yarns* manuscript.

33. '*I am unmarried and*': Harvard College Class of 1894 Secretary's Report, 1909, pp. 192–3.

34. '*Yes, he's a bachelor*': C A G Jackson, 'Here He Is! The Busiest Man in the City', *Sunday Herald*, 4 March 1917.

35. Fanny rode the Ferris wheel: Journal, 25 June 1893.
36. Material about the Glessners at the 1893 World's Fair is based on various passages from the Journal during 1893.
37. Anthropometry: Oliver Cyriax, Colin Wilson and Damon Wilson, *Encyclopedia of Crime* (New York: Overlook Press, 2006), pp. 14–15.
38. For a thorough and compelling account of H H Holmes, see Erik Larson, *The Devil in the White City: Murder, Magic, and Madness at the Fair that Changed America* (New York: Vintage Books, 2003).
39. '*Before summer was out*': Harvard College Class of 1894 Secretary's Report, 1897.
40. '*On Wednesday, Frances was*': Journal, 29 March 1896.
41. Stephen Dill Lee: 'About Stephen D Lee', Stephen D Lee Institute, http://www.stephendleeinstitute.com/about-sd-lee.html.
42. Asa Candler: Lee and Lee, *Family Reunion*, p. 255.
43. Women in medicine in the late 1800s: 'A Timeline of Women at Hopkins', *Johns Hopkins Magazine*, accessed 6 April 2019, https://pages.jh.edu/jhumag/1107web/women2.html.
44. Sarah Hackett Stevenson: William Tyre, 'Mrs. Ashton Dilke visits the Glessner house', *Story of a House* (blog), 18 February 2013, https://www.glessnerhouse.org/story-of-a-house/2013/02/mrs-ashton-dilke-visits-glessner-house-html.
45. Wedding section is from Lee and Lee, *Family Reunion*, pp. 391–4.
46. 'They – the two…': *Family Reunion*, p. 394.

Chapter 3: Marriage and the Aftermath

1. The newly wedded couple: Much of this section is drawn from Lee and Lee, *Family Reunion*, p. 258.
2. Friction in the marriage: Lee and Lee, *Family Reunion*, pp. 259–63.
3. '*The Doctor said several*': Journal, 11 December 1898.
4. '*She has been quite*': Journal, 11 December 1898.
5. '*Extremely outspoken and partisan*': Lee and Lee, *Family Reunion*, p.260.
6. Gifts of stock: Journal, 27 December 1903.
7. Iroquois Theatre Fire: Bob Specter, 'The Iroquois Theatre Fire', *Chicago Tribune*, 19 December 2007, https://www.chicagotribune.com/news/nationworld/politics/chi-chicagodays-iroquoisfire-story-story.html.

8. 'It has all been': Journal, 4 January 1904.
9. George Glessner went to the theatre: Journal, 4 January 1904.
10. 'Once she undertook to': Lee and Lee, Family Reunion, p. 404.
11. Miniature orchestra: Lee and Lee, Family Reunion, p. 398.
12. 'New Year's was Frances' birthday': Journal, 5 January 1913.
13. 'Every member of the organization': Journal, 19 January 1913.
14. The Flonzaley Quartet: Lee and Lee, Family Reunion, pp. 398–401.
15. 'An unhappy time for all': Lee and Lee, Family Reunion, p. 404.
16. Candy-making: Lee and Lee, Family Reunion, p. 403.
17. Detailed notes on visitors: based on review of correspondence and records at GHM.
18. Finger Tip Theater: William Tyre, 'Chicago's Tiniest Theater', Story of a House (blog), 22 June 2015, http://glessnerhouse. blogspot.com/2015/06/chicagos-tiniest-theater.html.
19. 'The auditorium will seat': 'Hop o' My Thumb Actors Delight at Finger Tip Theater', Chicago Daily Tribune, 20 March 1918, p. 15.
20. 'If one has an imagination...': 'Chicago's Tiniest Theater', Story of a House, Glessner House Museum, 22 June 2015, http://www. glessnerhouse.org/story-of-a-house/2015/06/chicagos-tiniest-theater.html.
21. 'There seemed to be': 'Hop o' My Thumb'.
22. 'I am glad to': FGL, letter to the editor, Chicago Tribune, 30 March 1918.
23. 'I didn't do a lick': Martin, 'How Murderers Beat the Law'.
24. 'Said au revoirs to': Chicago Tribune, 15 November 1918.
25. Writing to the Monday Morning Reading Class in Chicago: Siobhan Heraty, 'Frances Glessner Lee and World War I'. Story of a House, 15 December 2014, Glessner House Museum, https://www.glessnerhouse.org/story-of-a-house/2014/12/frances-glessner-lee-and-world-war-i.html.

Chapter 4: The Crime Doctor

1. 'Dead bodies of such persons...' 'The Technique of a medico-legal investigation'. George Burgess Magrath, Transactions of the Massachusetts Medico-Legal Society, 1 February 1922.
2. ibid.
3. 'The duties of this office': Myrtelle M Canavan, 'George Burgess Magrath', Archives of Pathology 27, no. 3 (March 1939): pp. 620–3.

4. *'If the law has made you a witness'*: Erle Stanley Gardner, *The Case of the Glamorous Ghost* (New York: Morrow, 1955), dedication.

5. *'He was always cheerful'*: Letter from FGL to Erle Stanley Gardner, August 1954, GHM.

6. *'You ought to set'*: William Boos, *The Poison Trail* (Boston: Hale, Cushman, & Flint, 1939), p. 40.

7. *'More than most men'*: Letter from Frank Leon Smith to Erle Stanley Gardner, 19 February 1955, GHM.

8. *'His statements were the model of precision'*: Boos, *The Poison Trail*, p. 41.

9. Magrath in the courtroom: 'Like a Lion Resting', *The Boston Globe*, 18 December 1938, D5.

10. *'went into something'*: 'Like a Lion Resting'.

11. *'Get three drinks into'*: 'Like a Lion Resting'.

12. *'As a medical examiner'*: Letter from FGL to Erle Stanley Gardner, August 1954, GHM.

13. Avis Linnell case: 'Quick March in Poison Tragedy of Dead Singer', *Boston Sunday Globe*, 22 October 1911, p. 1; 'Murder Ends a Love Dream', *Boston Sunday Globe*, 7 January 1912, p. 8; Timothy Leary, 'The Medical Examiner System', *Journal of the American Medical Association* 89, no. 8 (20 August 1927): pp. 579–83.

14. *'It is as quick'*: 'Murder Ends a Love Dream'.

15. *'There was no primary suspicion...'*: *New York Post*, 24 November 1914. No page number, a cutting found at CHM.

16. Brimfield lawsuit: 'Sues for $10,000', *The Boston Globe*, 6 February 1913, p. 1; 'Widow Sues Medical Examiner Magrath', *The Boston Globe*, 12 January 1915, p. 1.

17. *'The condition of the body would offend a stranger'*: *The Boston Globe*, 12 January 1915, p. 1.

18. Magrath framed for larceny: 'Three Accused of Conspiracy', *The Boston Globe*, 26 January 1915, p. 1; 'Men in Morgue Under Arrest', *The Boston Globe*, 9 August 1914, p. 1.

19. The governor's decision: 'Not to Reappoint Dr George B Magrath', *The Boston Globe*, 16 July 1914, p. 1.

20. Brimfield lawsuit resolution: 'Medical Examiner Magrath Exonerated', *The Boston Globe*, 13 January 1915, p. 1; 'Reads Three Depositions', *The Boston Globe*, 15 January 1915, p. 1.

21. Larceny plot falls apart: 'Green Witness in Own Behalf', *The Boston Globe*, 28 January 1915, p. 1; 'Green Admits He Did Wrong', *The Boston Globe*, 28 January 1915, p. 1; 'Search Left

to Subordinate', *The Boston Globe*, 27 January 1915, p. 1; 'Jury Returns Sealed Verdict', *The Boston Globe*, 2 February 1915, p. 1.

22. Green, Miller and Kingston arrested: 'Like a Lion Resting'.

23. *'The coroner is not'*: editorial, *Boston Daily Globe*, 2 March 1914.

24. Reform of New York's coroner system: Milton Helpern and Bernard Knight, *Autopsy: The Memoirs of Milton Helpern, the World's Greatest Medical Detective* (New York: St Martin's Press, 1977), p. 11.

25. Death of Eugene Hochette: 'Point to a Murder Hid by Coroner's Aid', *The New York Times*, 25 November 1914, p. 1.

26. *'I should say that'*: 'Murder Hid by Coroner's Aid', *The New York Times*, 25 November 1914, p. 1.

27. 'A nearly perfect instrument...' *New-York Tribune*, 25 February 1915, p. 7.

28. Early days of the New York City medical examiner's office and laboratory: S K Niyogi, 'Historic Development of Forensic Toxicology in America up to 1978', *American Journal of Forensic Medicine and Pathology* 1, no. 3 (September 1980): pp. 249–64; Deborah Blum, *The Poisoner's Handbook* (New York: Penguin Press, 2010); Helpern and Knight, *Autopsy: The Memoirs of Milton Helpern*.

29. *'The rear end...'*: *The Boston Post*, 8 November 1916, p. 7

30. Boston molasses disaster: Stephen Puleo, *Dark Tide: The Great Boston Molasses Flood of 1919* (Boston: Beacon Press, 2003).

31. *'As though covered in'*: Puleo, *Dark Tide*, p. 109.

32. Sacco and Vanzetti case: 'Sacco and Vanzetti: The Evidence', Massachusetts Supreme Judicial Court, accessed 2 March 2019, https://www.mass.gov/info-details/sacco-vanzetti-the-evidence; Felix Frankfurter, *The Case of Sacco and Vanzetti* (New York: Little, Brown, 1927); Dorothy G Wayman, 'Sacco-Vanzetti: The Unfinished Debate', *American Heritage*, p. 11, no. 1 (December 1959).

Chapter 5: Kindred Spirits

1. Prairie Avenue in the early 1900s: This section is drawn from public signage produced by the Prairie Avenue Historic District and Tyre, *Chicago's Historic Prairie Avenue*, pp. 97–114.

2. Phillips House: Frederic A Washburn, *The Massachusetts General Hospital: Its Development, 1900–1935* (Boston: Houghton Mifflin, 1939).

3. Magrath's stories: Ruth Henderson, 'Remember GBM?' *Kennebec Journal*, 22 February 1950.

4. Florence Small murder: Lowell Ames Norris, 'Inanimate Objects Often Expose Cruel Murder Secrets', *The Boston Sunday Herald*, 21 May 1933; 'Dr Magrath Tells of Unusual Cases', *The Boston Globe*, 26 February 1932, p. 16; 'Florence Small Lost Her Head', *Criminal Conduct* (blog), accessed 5 April 2017, http://criminalconduct.blogspot.com/2011/11/small-rememberance.html.

5. *'I consider this one'*: Norris, 'Inanimate Objects'.

6. *'Showed the stove had'*: Norris, 'Inanimate Objects'.

7. *'An innocent man would'*: Norris, 'Inanimate Objects'.

8. *'I'm still trying to'*: FGL, *Yankee Yarns* manuscript.

9. The Hall-Mills murders: Julie Johnson-McGrath, 'Speaking for the Dead: Forensic Pathologists and Criminal Justice in the United States', *Science, Technology & Human Values* 20, no. 4 (Autumn 1995), pp. 438–59; Mara Bovsun, 'A 90-Year Mystery: Who Killed the Pastor and the Choir Singer?' *New York Daily News*, 16 September 2012, http://www.nydailynews.com/news/justice-story/90-year-mystery-killed-pastor-choir-singer-article-1.1160659; Sadie Stein, 'She is a Liar! Liar!' *New York Magazine*, 1 April 2012, http://nymag.com/news/features/scandals/hall-mills-2012-4/.

10. Study on coroners and medical examiners: Oscar Schultz and E M Morgan, 'The Coroner and the Medical Examiner', *Bulletin of the National Research Council*, p. 64 (July 1928).

11. *'You know, I won't'*: FGL, *Yankee Yarns* manuscript.

Chapter 6: The Medical School

1. Description of the autopsy conducted by Magrath: letter from Frank Leon Smith to Erle Stanley Gardner, 19 February 1955, GHM; 'The Routine Autopsy', Ed Uthman (website), 2 June 2001, http://web2.iadfw.net/uthman/Autop.html; 'Autopsy Tools', Ed Uthman (website), 24 February 1999, http://web2.iadfw.net/uthman/autopsy_tools.html; Nicholas Gerbis, 'What Exactly Do They Do During an Autopsy?' *Live Science*, 26 August 2010, https://www.livescience.com/32789-forensic-pathologist-perform-autopsy-csi-effect.html.

2. *'Legal medicine may be'*: FGL, *Yankee Yarns* manuscript.

3. Magrath at Harvard: letter from George Burgess Magrath to Edward H Bradford, 19 August 1918, CHM.

4. 'It is my desire': letter from FGL to A Lawrence Lowell, 30 April 1931, CHM.

5. 'Your wishes will be': letter from A Lawrence Lowell to FGL, 4 May 1931, CHM.

6. Lee asked for Lowell's complicity: letter from FGL to A Lawrence Lowell, 29 September 1931, CHM.

7. 'He really does not': letter from A Lawrence Lowell to FGL, 10 December 1931, CHM.

8. 'I am not sure': letter from Oscar Schultz to FGL, 23 June 1933, GHM.

9. 'Our fight is going': letter from Oscar Schultz to FGL, 7 February 1934, GHM.

10. Annual meeting of the AMA: letter from Oscar Schultz to FGL, 26 May 1933, GHM.

11. 'I have this morning': letter from FGL to James Bryant Conant, 24 March 1934, CHM.

12. Magrath Library opening: 'Mrs Lee and President Conant Are Speakers at Opening of Library', Harvard Crimson, 25 May 1934.

13. Magrath introduced Lee to Gregg: letter from George Burgess Magrath to Alan Gregg, 25 January 1935, RAC.

14. Lee sought Gregg's assistance: Alan Gregg diary, 14 March 1935, RAC.

15. Lee's proposal for the Department of Legal Medicine: letter from FGL to Alan Gregg, 30 March 1935, RAC.

16. 'Told her we were interested...': Alan Gregg diary, 14 March 1935, RAC.

17. 'The next time she comes...' memo from Alan Gregg to Robert A Lambert, 19 April 1943, RAC.

18. New York University Department of Legal Medicine: Milton Helpern, 'Development of Department of Legal Medicine at New York University', New York State Journal of Medicine 72, no. 7 (1 April 1972): pp. 831–3.

19. Gifts to her daughters: letter from FGL to Frances Martin and Martha Batchelder, 29 January 1934, GHM.

20. 'George seemed very pleasant': letter from Roger Lee to FGL, 1 November 1935, GHM.

21. 'Our reports about George': letter from Roger Lee to FGL, 5 June 1937, GHM.

22. Magrath's pension: memorandum, CSB, 12 February 1937, CHM.

23. *'Without bringing her into the picture'*: CSB, memorandum of a conference with Mrs Lee on 12 February 1937, CHM.

24. *'I think some action'*: memorandum, CSB, 12 February 1937, CHM.

25. Origins of the FBI: 'Timeline', Federal Bureau of Investigation, accessed 16 November 2018, https://www.fbi.gov/history/timeline.

26. FBI authority over kidnapping: 'Timeline'.

27. Hoover fired all the female agents: 'Timeline'; Winifred R Poster, 'Cybersecurity Needs Women', *Nature*, 26 March 2018, https://www.nature.com/articles/d41586-018-03327-w.

28. Lee described her plans to Hoover: H H Clegg, 'Memorandum for the Director', 16 May 1935, FBI; Mary Elizabeth Power, 'Policewoman Wins Honors in Field of Legal Medicine', *The Wilmington Journal*, 16 June 1955, p. 45.

29. *'This lady is interested'*: L C Schilder, 'Memorandum for Mr Edwards', 16 May 1936, FBI.

30. The Glessners deeded their home: Al Chase, 'Architects Vote to Turn Back Glessner Home', *Chicago Tribune*, 16 June 1937, p. 27; William Tyre, personal communication, 2018.

31. *'Was considered one of the most exclusive'*: Judith Cass, 'Monday Class in Reading to Hold Reunion', *Chicago Daily Tribune*, 2 April 1936.

32. Property returned: Chase, 'Architects'.

33. *'If Dr Magrath is to write his book…'*: letter from FGL to Sidney Burwell, 13 December 1935, GHM.

Chapter 7: The Three-Legged Stool

1. Lee's gifts to Harvard: letter from FGL to CSB, 23 May 1936, GHM.

2. Lee's ultimatum: Alan Gregg diary, 18 October 1938, RAC.

3. Burwell convened a committee: minutes of the first meeting of the Committee to Consider the Future of Legal Medicine in Harvard University, 13 April 1936, CHM.

4. *'It is my unfortunate luck'*: letter from S Burt Wolbach to Alan Gregg, 8 April 1936, RAC.

5. Searching for Magrath's successor: minutes of the second meeting of the Committee on Legal Medicine, 11 December 1936, RAC.

6. *'I was third man'*: ARM, interview by Mary Daly, 18 November 1983, Case Western Reserve University Archive.

7. *'There were several schools'*: ARM interview.
8. *'I knew little or nothing'*: ARM interview.
9. *'The more I have'*: letter from ARM to CSB, 24 May 1937, CHM.
10. *'Last summer I had'*: letter from ARM to CSB, 7 December 1937, CHM.
11. *'I have forced myself'*: letter from ARM to Burt Wolbach, 2 August 1938, CHM.
12. *'My greatest problem to date'*: draft letter from ARM to FGL, undated, CHM.
13. *'I had a letter'*: letter from FGL to ARM, 18 November 1938, CHM.
14. *'Without wishing to be arbitrary'*: letter from FGL to CSB, 16 December 1937, CHM.
15. World's Fair: letter from FGL to ARM, 15 November 1938, CHM.
16. Lee reached out to Dr Gonzales: letter from FGL to Thomas Gonzales, 4 November 1938, GHM.
17. Gonzales on planned exhibits: letter from Thomas Gonzales to FGL, 7 November 1939, GHM.
18. *'I am anxious that'*: letter from ARM to FGL, 6 December 1938, CHM.
19. *'She suggests various methods'*: CSB, 'Note on a conversation with Mrs Lee regarding the future of the Department of Legal Medicine', 9 December, 1939, CHM.
20. *'That's the way to go'*: 'Like a Lion Resting'.
21. *'Since you saw him'*: letter from FGL to ARM, 20 December 1938, CHM.
22. *'I read voraciously for weeks'*: letter from FGL to George Burgess Magrath, undated, GHM.
23. Lee's book: FGL, 'An Anatomography in Picture, Verse and Music' (unpublished manuscript, c.1929–38), GHM.
24. *'A coined word'*: letter from FGL to George Burgess Magrath, undated, GHM.
25. *'Although our work for Doctor'*: letter from Parker Glass to FGL, 17 May 1939, GHM.
26. *'It is a good time'*: letter from FGL to CSB, 20 December 1938, CHM.
27. Lee's suggestions of a statewide system: CSB, 'Memorandum of conversation with Mrs Lee', 3 October 1938, CHM.
28. Massachusetts didn't have a statewide system: 'Medical examiner and coroner systems: History and trends', *Journal of the American Medical Association*, 18 March 1998, Vol. 279, no. 11, pp. 870–4.

29. *'Poisoning is very common'*: ARM, 'Confidential Report on the Status of Forensic Medicine in Great Britain, Europe and Egypt (1938–1939)', 1940, CHM.

30. *'I had a very interesting time'*: letter from ARM to CSB, 6 April 1939, CHM.

31. *'My experience to date'*: letter from ARM to S B Wolbach, 2 August 1938, CHM.

32. *'I would like to have you make a little talk'*: letter from FGL to ARM, 18 September 1939, CHM.

33. *'I am firmly convinced'*: letter from FGL to ARM, 27 September 1939, CHM.

34. Lee's suggestion that Moritz write an article: letter from FGL to ARM, 22 April 1942, CHM.

35. *'I know of no better place'*: letter from ARM to FGL, 8 January 1940, CHM.

36. Afternoon tea for department opening: invitation to tea in honour of FGL, CHM.

37. *'I'm still thinking of'*: letter from FGL to CSB, 15 February 1940, CHM.

38. Department funding: Harvard Medical School, 'First Annual Report of the Department of Legal Medicine, January 1, 1940–December 31, 1940', CHM.

39. The department's first fellows: Harvard Medical School, 'First Annual Report'.

40. *'I can see one'*: letter from ARM to CSB, 30 July 1938, CHM.

41. Conflicts with local police: Metro-Goldwyn-Mayer, *Murder at Harvard*, 17 September 1948, CHM.

42. "Dr Rosen, medical examiner...": 31 July 1940 teletype message accompanying 9 November 1948 letter from Alan Moritz to Leonard Spigelgass, CHM.

43. Irene Perry case: 'Girl, 22, Trussed and Slain', *The Boston Globe*, 1 August 1940, p. 1; MGM, *Murder at Harvard*; 'Examination of the Body of Irene Perry, Dartmouth, Massachusetts, 7/31/1940', Division of Laboratories, Department of Legal Medicine, Harvard Medical School, CHM.

44. Conference outline: FGL, 'Basic Scheme for a Series of Medico-Legal Conferences Biennial or Annual', 17 May 1940, CHM.

45. Conference suggestions: FGL, 'Suggestions for a Medico-Legal Conference to Be Held in Boston in October 1940', 17 May 1940, CHM.

46. Medical Society recommendations: 'Physicians Rap System of Coroners', *The Philadelphia Inquirer*, 3 October 1940, p. 21.

47. '*I cannot impress upon you*': letter from P J Zisch to J W Battershall, 20 May 1940, CHM.
48. '*It seems to me*': letter from FGL to CSB, 9 August 1940, CHM.
49. '*Of all men connected*': letter from FGL to Timothy Leary, 9 August 1940, CHM.
50. '*In my opinion*': letter from Timothy Leary to FGL, 14 August 1940, CHM.
51. First-year faculty: Harvard Medical School, 'First Annual Report', 1941.

Chapter 8: Captain Lee

1. Lee's dream of a centralized medical examiner's office: based in part on untitled brief written by FGL at the suggestion of Roger Lee, 7 March 1939, CHM.
2. Roger Lee asked for plan: letter from Roger Lee to CSB, 10 March 1939, GHM.
3. Lee's medical concerns: letter from Roger Lee to FGL, 21 June 1939, GHM.
4. '*I emphatically believe*': letter from Roger Lee to FGL, 27 June 1939, GHM.
5. The Cocoanut Grove fire: Paul Benzaquin, *Holocaust! The Shocking Story of the Boston Cocoanut Grove Fire* (New York: Henry Holt, 1959); 'The Story of the Cocoanut Grove Fire', Boston Fire Historical Society, accessed 17 October 2017, https://bostonfirehistory.org/the-story-of-the-cocoanut-grove-fire/.
6. '*Among the victims*': letter from ARM to FGL, 9 January 1943, CHM.
7. The Glessners' piano: 'Music in the Mansion, Part 1: The Glessners' Piano', *Story of a House* (blog), 4 April 2011, http://www.glessnerhouse.org/story-of-a-house/2011/04/music-in-mansion-part-1-glessners-piano.html.
8. '*I do not play*': letter from FGL to Roger Lee, 12 September 1942, GHM.
9. '*You might be interested*': letter from FGL to ARM, 9 November 1942, GHM.
10. Lee's questions for Moritz: typed list of questions asked of Moritz on 20 November 1942, FGL, 5 January 1943, CHM.
11. '*I hope you can*': letter from FGL to ARM, 5 January 1943, CHM.

12. 'One of the things': letter from CSB to Jerome D Greene, 10 March 1943, CHM.

13. 'It will be recalled': letter from CSB to Jerome D Greene, 23 February 1943, CHM.

14. 'This title would...': letter from Alan Moritz to FGL, 19 February 1943, CHM.

15. 'I shall do my best': letter from FGL to CSB, 21 March 1943, CHM.

16. 'Not to be printed': Joseph S Lichty, 'Memorandum for Dr Burwell', 10 March 1943, CHM.

17. Lee not identified in medical school catalogue: letter from CSB to FGL, 20 March 1943, CHM.

18. Dental records: FGL, 'Plan for Unification of Dental Records for Dental Identification', 16 February 1942.

19. Dental study: FGL, 'Plans for a Dental Project', 16 February 1942.

20. Medical examiners in 1944: ARM, Edward R Cunniffe, J W Holloway and Harrison S Maitland, 'Report of Committee to Study the Relationship of Medicine and Law', Journal of the American Medical Association 125, no. 8 (24 June 1944): pp. 577–83.

21. 'During his first two years...': note on visit with Sidney Burwell, Alan Gregg diary, 2 February 1942, RAC.

22. Improved laws in some states: letter from FGL to Joseph Shallot, 28 July 1948, GHM.

23. Restrictions on medical examiners: Moritz et al., 'Report of Committee'.

24. Coroners in Maryland: Goldfarb, 'Death Investigation in Maryland', in National Association of Medical Examiners Past Presidents History Book, 2016 edition, National Association of Medical Examiners, pp. 224–64, https://www.thename.org/assets/docs/NAME%20e-book%202016%20final%2006-14-16.pdf.

25. Lee's speaking engagements: based on correspondence at GHM.

26. Lee in Virginia: letter from FGL to ARM, 20 March 1943, CHM.

27. Lee's suggestions in Virginia: 'Comments and Recommendations Submitted by Mrs Lee on Suggestions for a Medical Examiner System for the State of Virginia', undated, GHM.

28. Changes in Washington, DC: David Brinkley, Washington Goes to War (New York: Knopf, 1988).

29. 'Believing yours to be': letter from FGL to Fulton Lewis Jr, 29 September 1943, GHM.

30. '*I cannot too strongly*': letter from FGL to Sherman Adams, 9 February 1945, GHM.

31. Lee appointed consulting deputy coroner: letter from Cook County coroner A L Brodie to FGL, 18 December 1941, GHM.

32. She singled out Oscar Schultz: letter from FGL to ARM, 6 May 1942, CHM.

33. Oklahoma law: 'Murder-Clue Team Set Here', *The Daily Oklahoman*, 16 November 1945, p. 1.

34. '*I earnestly hope*': letter from FGL to W F Keller, 9 November 1944, GHM.

35. Oklahoma City agreement: 'Murder-Clue Team Set Here'.

36. '*I've fallen completely under the spell*': letter from FGL to Charles Woodson, 20 April 1946, GHM.

37. Colonel Ralph Caswell: 'Much Progress in Fingerprint Library for NH', *The Portsmouth Herald*, 27 February 1936, p. 3; Brian Nelson Burford, New Hampshire State archivist, personal communication, 2018.

38. Caswell on State Liquor Commission: 'Around the Town', *Nashua Telegraph*, 25 November 1961.

39. '*This was not an honorary post...*'; 'She invested a fortune in police, entertained them royally at the Ritz', Earl Banner, *The Boston Globe*, 4 February 1962, p. 46-A.

40. Lee on medico-legal investigators: FGL, 'The Department of Legal Medicine: Its Functions and Purposes', 13 July 1947, CHM.

41. '*An alarming possibility occurs*': letter from FGL to CSB, 29 April 1944, CHM.

Chapter 9: In a Nutshell

1. '*Five years ago*': ARM, 'The Status of the Department of Legal Medicine of Harvard Medical School After Five Years of Its Existence: Report to the Dean', 15 May 1944, CHM.

2. Increased gifts to the department: letter from CSB to FGL, 28 January 1944, CHM; letter from FGL to CSB, 23 June 1944, CHM.

3. Lee's thoughts on the School of Business: 'Mrs Frances G Lee – lunch', Alan Gregg diary, 16 April 1947, RAC.

4. '*In a word*': FGL, 'Suggestions for a Police Course', 19 October 1942, CHM.

5. '*The matter of providing*': FGL, handwritten note, undated, GHM.

6. *'It has been found'*: FGL, 'Dolls as a Teaching Tool', undated, GHM.
7. *'Why not let me make a model...'*: FGL, Yankee Yarns manuscript, GHM.
8. *'I have some special work'*: letter from FGL to Ralph Mosher, 9 June 1943, GHM.
9. *'If you will send'*: letter from Ralph Mosher to FGL, 11 June 1943, GHM.
10. *'The work I want'*: letter from FGL to Ralph Mosher, 8 July 1943, GHM.
11. *'In the original'*: letter from FGL to ARM, 21 August 1945, CHM.
12. Trying to purchase tools during the war: Letter from Sears Roebuck and Co. to FGL, 3 August 1943, GHM.
13. Form PD-1A: application for Preference Rating, 3 September 1943, GHM.
14. Trying to acquire a saw and motor: letter from FGL to Union Twitchell, Irving & Casson – A H Davenport Co., 21 April 1943, GHM.
15. Replacement of a truck part: letter from C E Dolham, Parts Department, International Harvester Company, to FGL, 15 July 1942, GHM.
16. *'We are in the midst'*: letter from FGL to C E Dolham, 20 July 1942, GHM.
17. *'The package containing the wire'*: letter from FGL to A J Monroe, 7 January 1944, GHM.
18. Six-centimetre brass hinges: letter from Union Twitchell to FGL, 6 January 1944, GHM.
19. *'Lucite is on priority'*: letter from Union Twitchell to FGL, 13 July 1943, GHM.
20. *'I shall be very glad'*: letter from FGL to Union Twitchell, 14 July 1943, GHM.
21. Whiskey bottles: letter from Alynn Shilling, National Distillers Products Corporation, to FGL, 19 October 1944, GHM.
22. *'I have never seen'*: letter from FGL to W B Douglas, 26 February 1946, GHM.
23. *'The most difficult matter'*: FGL, 'Dolls as a Teaching Tool'.
24. *'Most of the furniture'*: FGL, 'Nutshell Studies of Unexplained Death, Notes and Comments: Foreword', undated, CHM.
25. *'I found myself constantly'*: letter from FGL to ARM, 21 August 1945, CHM.
26. *'I have in prospect'*: letter from FGL to ARM, 5 January 1944, CHM.

27. *'Believing firmly that'*: Frances Glessner Lee, 'Legal Medicine at Harvard', *Journal of Criminal Justice and Police Science*, Vol. 42, Issue 5, Winter 1952, pp. 674–8.
28. Student reports on the Nutshells: FGL, undated manuscript about Department of Legal Medicine, CHM.
29. *'It must be understood'*: FGL, undated manuscript about Department of Legal Medicine, CHM.
30. *'The students should be warned'*: FGL, 'Nutshell Studies of Unexplained Death'.
31. The purposes of HAPS: Harvard Associates in Police Science Articles of Incorporation, 8 January 1963, GHM.
32. *'These were wonderful affairs'*: Earl Banner, 'She Invested a Fortune in Police, Entertained Them Royally at Ritz', *The Boston Globe*, 4 February 1962, A46.
33. *'There is no place'*: handwritten note on back of photograph, undated, GHM.
34. *'I am making arrangements'*: letter from FGL to CSB, 29 May 1945, CHM.
35. *'I dislike to attach conditions'*: letter from FGL to CSB, 30 July 1945, CHM.
36. *'Mrs Lee expressed the opinion'*: CSB, 'Memorandum of talk with Mrs Lee on 27 March 1945', CHM.

Chapter 10: Murder at Harvard

1. Lee felt that Fisher was capable: letter from FGL to C W Woodson, 5 August 1946, GHM; letter from FGL to C W Woodson, 20 September 1946, GHM.
2. Department of Legal Medicine at Medical College of Virginia: Mary A Giunta, *A History of the Department of Legal Medicine at Medical College of Virginia*, master's thesis, University of Richmond, 1966.
3. *'As [far as my] "complete anonymity"'*: letter from FGL to ARM, 12 July 1946.
4. *'Life is still very much interested'*: letter from Jeff Wylie to FGL, 7 March 1946.
5. *Life* magazine, 3 June 1946.
6. *'The coroner, an undertaker'*: letter from R F Borkenstein to FGL, 21 April 1948, GHM.
7. Knowledge from the seminar: Martin, 'How Murderers Beat the Law'.

8. *'I thought you had'*: Martin, 'How Murderers Beat the Law'.
9. Homicide seminar, April 1947: William Gilman, 'Murder at Harvard', *Los Angeles Times*, 25 January 1948, F4.
10. Arnette and the Texas City disaster: Martin, 'How Murderers Beat the Law'.
11. Texas City disaster casualties: Hugh W Stephens, *The Texas City Disaster, 1947* (Austin: University of Texas Press, 1997), p. 100.
12. Eighteen men in 1947: letter from Richard Ford to Alan Gregg, 19 July 1949, CHM.
13. Medical examiners replacing coroners: Martin, 'How Murderers Beat the Law'.
14. State laws influenced: 'Annual Report, July 1, 1947, to June 30, 1948', Department of Legal Medicine, CHM.
15. University programmes started: 'Annual Report'.
16. *'She thinks [Moritz's] heart'*: Alan Gregg diary, 16 April 1947, RAC.
17. Attendance by 1949: Martin, 'How Murderers Beat the Law'.
18. *'Why should Harvard Medical School'*: letter from George Minot to CSB, 24 September 1945, CHM.
19. *'We were informed by'*: Lucy Boland, 'A Few Days at Harvard Seminar', *VOX Cop*, Connecticut State Police, June 1950.
20. *'Few of the states'*: Boland, 'A Few Days'.
21. *'We feel that'*: letter from Samuel Marx to FGL, 9 February 1948, CHM.
22. Dr LeMoyne Snyder: 'Biographical Note', LeMoyne Snyder papers, Michigan State University Archives, accessed 20 December 2018, http://archives.msu.edu/findaid/ua10-3-97.html.
23. *'Your remarks made me feel'*: letter from LeMoyne Snyder to FGL, 19 July 1944, Michigan State University Archives.
24. *'I thought it over'*: minutes of Harvard Associates in Police Science meeting, undated, GHM.
25. *'He was the most interested...'*: minutes of meeting with HAPS board, 1949, GHM.
26. *'Your stories are formulaic'*: Erle Stanley Gardner, 'A Wonderful Woman', *The Boston Globe*, 4 February 1962, p. 1.
27. *'I just can't believe'*: minutes of Harvard Associates in Police Science second annual meeting, 10 February 1949, GHM.
28. *'Because she had an orderly mind'*: Gardner, 'A Wonderful Woman'.
29. Gardner autographed the first copy: letter from Erle Stanley Gardner to FGL, 21 December 1948, GHM.
30. *'I want to have it photographically reduced...'*: letter from FGL to Thayer Hobson, 19 May 1949, GHM.

31. 'A book in which': letter from Erle Stanley Gardner to FGL, 21 December 1948, GHM.
32. 'A lively correspondence': letter from FGL to ARM, 19 January 1949, GHM.
33. 'Taking the wrong attitude...': letter from FGL to Charles W Woodson, 8 March 1949, GHM.
34. Gardner attended a second homicide seminar: '"Perry Mason" Goes to Harvard with Police', The Boston Globe, 1 May 1949, C1.
35. Meeting with Maryland Post Mortem Examiners Commission: B Taylor, 'The Case of the Outspoken Medical Examiner, or an Exclusive Journal Interview with Russell S Fisher, MD, Chief Medical Examiner of the State of Maryland', Maryland State Medical Journal 26, no. 3 (March 1977): pp. 59–69.
36. Lee recommended Fisher: letter from FGL to Huntington Williams, 5 July 1949, GHM.
37. Fisher appointed: 'Dr R S Fisher Assumes Post as Examiner', The Baltimore Sun, 2 September 1949.
38. Ultimate vision for the Maryland Office of the Chief Medical Examiner: letter from Huntington Williams to FGL, 2 September 1949, GHM.
39. 'Our belief is': MGM, Murder at Harvard.
40. 'I am of the opinion': letter from CSB to Edward Reynolds, 10 January 1949, CHM.
41. 'Mrs Lee has in the meantime joined the group': MGM, Murder at Harvard.
42. Lee asked to write article for Scientific Monthly: letter from Gladys Keener to FGL, 31 May 1949, GHM.
43. 'I would like to accept': letter from FGL to Gladys Keener, 14 July 1949, GHM.
44. 'Members of the faculty': minutes of the Harvard Associates in Police Science Second Annual Meeting, 10 February 1949, GHM.
45. 'I am not unmindful': letter from ARM to FGL, 31 January 1949, CHM.

Chapter 11: The Decline and Falls

1. 'We will be sunk': letter from FGL to Roger Lee, 28 February 1949.
2. Dr Richard Ford: Harvard Law Record, undated, CHM.
3. 'The more I see': letter from FGL to Roger Lee, 28 February 1949, GHM.

4. *'During the past ten years'*: letter from ARM to CSB, 11 May 1949, CHM.

5. *'Lurid or otherwise offensive'*: letter from Edward Reynolds to Lowe's Inc., 13 June 1949, CHM.

6. *Mystery Street* filming locations: *Mystery Street* Internet Movie Database (IMDb), accessed 28 December 2018, https://www.imdb.com/title/tt0042771.

7. MGM payment to Harvard: letter from ARM to Richard Ford, 2 September 1949, CHM; letter from ARM to Richard Ford, 12 December 1949, CHM.

8. *'Mrs Lee has asked me'*: letter from Richard Ford to George P Berry, 14 December 1949, CHM.

9. *'There is more science'*: Metro-Goldwyn-Mayer, 'Mystery Street Reviews', undated, CHM.

10. *'I must confess that it is a mystery'*: letter from FGL to Richard Ford, 31 January 1951, CHM.

11. *'I must confess that I am greatly disappointed'*: letter from FGL to Alan Gregg, 31 January 1951, RAC.

12. Harvard limiting attendance at seminars: memo from SAC, Richmond, to J Edgar Hoover, 21 December 1950, FBI.

13. *'In my opinion'*: letter from FGL to Alan Gregg, 31 January 1951, RAC; letter from Alan Gregg to FGL, 16 February 1951, RAC.

14. *'A proper deduction'*: letter from FGL to Allan B Hussander, 27 February 1951, GHM.

15. *'Captain Frances G Lee'*: Erle Stanley Gardner, *The Court of Last Resort* (New York: William Sloane Associates, 1952).

16. *'I have had to restrain'*: letter from FGL to Francis I McGarraghy and others, 5 June 1951, GHM.

17. *'In desperation, I am writing'*: letter from Margaret Roth to FGL, 9 November 1948, GHM.

18. Automotive Safety Association: letter from Frank D Miller to FGL, 27 January 1946, GHM.

19. Entrepreneur from Long Beach: letter from Arthur W Stevens to FGL, 29 January 1948, GHM.

20. *'He has read of'*: letter from John Crocker Jr to FGL, 9 February 1955, GHM.

21. *'While I am entirely sympathetic'*: letter from FGL to John Crocker Jr, 18 February 1955, GHM.

22. *'This appears to be'*: letter from FGL to Mrs Edwin B Wright, 25 October 1949, GHM.

23. *'Each member of the advisory board'*: letter from FGL to Francis I McGarraghy and others, 5 June 1951, GHM.

24. *'It seems to me'*: letter from FGL to Francis I McGarraghy and others, 5 June 1951, GHM.
25. *'We had not been visiting'*: *Lee News*, 10 September 1957, GHM.
26. Lee's visit to the FBI: telegram from J Edgar Hoover to FGL, 20 November 1951, FBI.
27. *'When informed of Mr Hoover's absence'*: Office of Director memo, 21 December 1951, FBI.
28. *'No salary from Harvard'*: letter from George P Berry to David W Bailey, 16 June 1954, CHM.
29. *'I have talked again'*: letter from David W Bailey to George P Berry, 25 June 1954, CHM.
30. *'You will agree with me'*: letter from George P Berry to Richard Ford, 6 July 1954, CHM.
31. *'So you may have'*: letter from George P Berry to David W Bailey, 17 February 1955, CHM.
32. Woodson's inquiry to the FBI: teletype from FBI Richmond to Director, FBI, and SAC, Boston, 2 February 1955, FBI.
33. *'This reception reportedly cost'*: office memorandum from SAC, Boston, to Director, FBI, 19 September 1955, FBI.
34. *'No derogatory info'*: teletype from Boston Field Office to Director, FBI, 2 February 1956.
35. *'I've been fighting'*: *Lee News*, 7 October 1957, GHM.
36. *'The cocktail hour'*: *Lee News*, 17 August 1958, GHM.
37. *'As I sit quietly'*: Lee and Lee, *Family Reunion*, p. 411.
38. *'The most serious damage'*: letter from Parker Glass to FGL, 17 February 1961, CHM.

Chapter 12: Postmortem

1. Lee's funeral: *Lee News*, 5 February 1962, GHM.
2. *'Mrs Lee was unquestionably'*: Banner, 'She Invested a Fortune'.
3. *'The only person…'*: '"Murder unrecognized" tops Harvard seminar on crime', by Mary Murray O'Brien, *The Boston Globe*, 19 November 1950, C36.
4. *'She was…my personal friend'*: Erle Stanley Gardner, 'She Would Battle for Ideas at the Drop of a Hat', *Boston Sunday Globe*, 4 February 1962.
5. Honorary degrees: 'Quartet Receives Honorary Degrees from N E College', *The Portsmouth Herald*, 26 July 1956; *Lee News*, 13 May 1958, GHM.

6. Honorary positions: William Tyre, personal communication, 2019.

7. Committee report on Department of Legal Medicine: 'The Ad Hoc Committee Report', *Corpus Delicti: The Doctor as Detective*, Center for the History of Medicine at Countway Library, accessed 5 December 2018, http://collections.countway.harvard.edu/onview/exhibits/show/corpus-delicti/ad-hoc-committee-report.

8. Department of Legal Medicine ceased operations: 'The End of Legal Medicine', *Corpus Delicti: The Doctor as Detective*, Center for the History of Medicine at Countway Library, accessed 5 December 2018, http://collections.countway.harvard.edu/onview/exhibits/show/corpus-delicti/ad-hoc-committee-report/end-of-legal-medicine.

9. Law and Medicine Center at Case Western Reserve University: Jentzen, *Death Investigation in America*, pp. 76–7.

10. 5,000 undetected homicides every year: 'How to Get Away with Murder', *True*, July 1958, pp. 48–101.

11. Murder of Marilyn Reese Sheppard: Douglas O Linder, 'Dr Sam Sheppard Trials: An Account', Famous Trials (website), accessed 24 November 2018, http://www.famous-trials.com/sam-sheppard/2-sheppard; 'Sheppard Murder Case', Encyclopedia of Cleveland History, accessed 24 November 2018, https://case.edu/ech/articles/s/sheppard-murder-case; Sam Sheppard, *Endure and Conquer: My 12-Year Fight for Vindication* (Cleveland: World Publishing Co. 1966); James Neff, *The Wrong Man: The Final Verdict on the Dr. Sam Sheppard Murder Case* (New York: Random House, 2001).

12. Death of Richard Ford: 'Dr Richard Ford, 55, a Suicide; Witness in Many Murder Trials', *The New York Times*, 4 August 1970, https://www.nytimes.com/1970/08/04/archives/dr-richard-ford-55-a-suicide-witness-in-many-murder-trials.html.

13. Donation of The Rocks: 'History of The Rocks', The Rocks (website), accessed 16 December 2018, http://therocks.org/history.php.

14. Historical highway marker: 'New NH Historical Marker Honors "Mother of Forensic Science"', New Hampshire Department of Cultural Resources press release, 22 October 2018, https://www.nh.gov/nhculture/mediaroom/2018/francesglessnerlee_marker.htm.

15. Prairie Avenue residence: 'The House', Glessner House Museum (website), accessed 6 December 2018, https://www.glessnerhouse.org/the-house/; William Tyre, personal communication, 2018.

16. *'There are two minor items'*: letter from Parker Glass to Dorothy Hartel, 9 May 1969, Maryland Office of the Chief Medical Examiner.

17. *'Troubled by the implication'*: letter from Steven A Abreu to Scott Keller and Gary Childs, Harvard Associates in Police Science, 17 October 2017.

18. Death investigation systems today: Randy Hanzlick, 'An Overview of Medical Examiner/Coroner Systems in the United States' (PowerPoint presentation prepared for National Academies: Forensic Science Needs Committee, undated), accessed 9 April 2019, https://sites.nationalacademies.org/cs/groups/pgasite/documents/webpage/pga_049924.pdf; Randy Hanzlick, 'The Conversion of Coroner Systems to Medical Examiner Systems in the United States', *American Journal of Forensic Medicine and Pathology* 28, no. 4 (December 2007), pp. 279–83.

19. Medical examiner and coroners in Illinois: 'Medical Examiner', Cook County Government website, accessed 22 November 2018, https://www.cookcountyil.gov/agency/medical-examiner; 'Coroners Roster', Illinois Coroners and Medical Examiners Association, accessed 22 November 2018, https://www.coronersillinois.org/coroners-roster; 'Illinois Coroner/Medical Examiner Laws', Centers for Disease Control and Prevention, 1 January 2014, https://www.cdc.gov/phlp/publications/coroner/illinois.html.

20. Charleston dual system: K A Collins, 'Charleston, SC: Reversion from a Medical Examiner/Coroner Dual System to a Coroner System', *Academic Forensic Pathology* 4, no. 1 (2014), pp. 60–4.

21. Not enough forensic pathologists: K A Collins, 'The Future of the Forensic Pathology Workforce', *Academic Forensic Pathology* 5, no. 4 (2015), pp. 526–33.

22. Current numbers: Denise McNally, executive director, National Association of Medical Examiners, personal communication, 2018.

23. Only sixty two per cent of cases referred: 'Medical Examiners' and Coroners' Offices, 2004', US Department of Justice, Bureau of Justice Statistics, June 2007.

24. Absence of essential tools: Hanzlick, 'Overview'.

25. Hotel room deaths from carbon monoxide poisoning: 'Health Department Issues Statement about CO Deaths in Hotel', WVTV, 9 June 2013, http://www.wbtv.com/story/22541035/health-department-issues-statement-about-co-deaths-in-hotel.

26. DNA used to exonerate: 'DNA exonerations in the United States',

Innocence Project, accessed 28 December 2018, https://www.
innocenceproject.org/dna-exonerations-in-the-united-states.

27. Problems with DNA evidence: Matthew Shaer, 'The False Promise
of DNA Testing', *Atlantic*, June 2016, https://www.theatlantic.
com/magazine/archive/2016/06/a-reasonable-doubt/480747/;
Pamela Colloff, 'Texas Panel Faults Lab Chemist in Bryan Case
for "Overstating Findings" and Inadequate DNA Analysis',
Propublica, 8 October 2018, https://www.propublica.org/article/
texas-panel-faults-lab-chemist-in-bryan-case-for-overstated-
findings-and-inadequate-dna-analysis; Greg Hampikian, 'The
Dangers of DNA Testing,' *The New York Times*, 21 September
2018, https://www.nytimes.com/2018/09/21/opinion/the-dangers-
of-dna-testing.html.

Further Reading and Resources

Museums

Glessner House Museum
1800 S Prairie Avenue
Chicago, IL 60616
Tel: 312-326-1480
www.glessnerhouse.org
info@glessnerhouse.org
https://www.glessnerhouse.org/story-of-a-house

The Rocks
4 Christmas Lane
Bethlehem, NH 03574
Tel: 603-444-6228
therocks.org
info@therocks.org

Multimedia

Of Dolls and Murder (2012, Susan Marks director)
Murder in a Nutshell (in production, Susan Marks director)
Mystery Street (1950, John Sturges director)

Professional Organizations

National Association of Medical Examiners (http://thename.org)
American Board of Medicolegal Death Investigators (https://
www.abmdi.org/)
International Association of Coroners and Medical Examiners
(https://www.theiacme.com)

National Institute of Standards and Technology Forensic Science Standards Board (https://www.nist.gov/topics/forensic-science/forensic-science-standards-board)

Scientific Working Group for Medicolegal Death Investigation (https://www.swgmdi.org/)

American Academy of Forensic Science (https://www.aafs.org)

Harvard Associates in Police Science (https://harvardpolicescience.org/)

Reports and Papers

'The Coroner and the Medical Examiner'. *National Research Council Bulletin* No. 64, July 1928

Strengthening Forensic Science in the United States: A Path Forward. National Research Council, August 2009. (www.ncjrs.gov/pdffiles1/nij/grants/228091.pdf)

Status and Needs of Forensic Science Service Providers: A Report to Congress. National Institute of Justice, 2004 (https://www.ncjrs.gov/pdffiles1/nij/213420.pdf)

Death Investigation: A Guide for the Scene Investigator. National Institute of Justice, June 2011 (https://www.ncjrs.gov/pdffiles1/nij/234457.pdf)

An Overview of Medical Examiner/Coroner Systems in the United States. Randy Hanzlick, the National Academies: Forensic Science Needs Committee (https://sites.nationalacademies.org/cs/groups/pgasite/documents/webpage/pga_049924.pdf)

Coroner/Medical Examiner Laws, by State. Centers for Disease Control and Prevention (https://www.cdc.gov/phlp/publications/topic/coroner.html)

Death Investigation Systems. Centers for Disease Control and Prevention (https://www.cdc.gov/phlp/publications/coroner/death.html)

Investigations and Autopsies. Centers for Disease Control and Prevention (https://www.cdc.gov/phlp/publications/coroner/investigations.html)

Medicolegal Death Investigation System: Workshop Summary. Institute of Medicine Committee for the Workshop on the Medicolegal Death Investigation System, 2003 (https:// www.ncbi.nlm.nih.gov/books/NBK221919/)

Medical Examiners and Coroners' Offices, 2004. Matthew J Hickman, Kristen A Hughes, Kevin J Strom. US Department of Justice Bureau of Justice Statistics (https://www.bjs.gov/ content/pub/pdf/meco04.pdf)

Collins, K A, 'The future of the forensic pathology workforce.' *Academic Forensic Pathology,* Vol. 5, No. 4, 2015, pp. 526–33

Hanzlick, R., 'The conversion of coroner systems to medical examiner systems in the United States.' *American Journal of Forensic Medicine and Pathology,* Vol. 28, No. 4, December 2007, pp. 279–83

Hanzlick R, and D Combs, 'Medical examiner and coroner systems.' *Journal of the American Medical Association,* Vol. 279, No. 11, March 18, 1998, pp. 870–74

Legal Medicine and the Nutshell Studies

Botz, Corinne May, *The Nutshell Studies of Unexplained Death.* New York: Monacelli Press, 2004

Harvard Department of Legal Medicine and the Nutshell Studies of Unexplained Death

The Nutshell Studies. 99 Percent Invisible Podcast, episode 165, 19 May 2015 (http://99percentinvisible.org/episode/ the-nutshell-studies)

Corpus Delicti: The Doctor as Detective. Online exhibit curated by Jack Eckert, Center for the History of Medicine in the Francis A Countway Library of Medicine (https://collections. countway.harvard.edu/onview/exhibits/show/corpus-delicti)

Inside the 'Nutshell Studies of Unexplained Death' – VR 360. Smithsonian American Art Museum (https://americanart. si.edu/exhibitions/nutshells/inside)

Medical Examiners and Coroners

Baden, Michael, *Unnatural Death: Confessions of a Medical Examiner*. New York: Random House, 1989

Bass, Bill, and Jon Jefferson, *Death's Acre: Inside the Legendary 'Body Farm'*. New York: G P Putnam's Sons, 2003

Bateson, John, *The Education of a Coroner: Lessons in Investigating Death*. New York: Scribner, 2017

Blum, Deborah, *The Poisoner's Handbook: Murder and the Birth of Forensic Medicine in Jazz Age New York*. New York: Penguin Press, 2010

Cataldie, Louis, *Coroner's Journal: Forensics and the Art of Stalking Death*. New York: Berkley, 2007

Cumberland, Gary, *My Life with Death: Memoirs of a Journeyman Medical Examiner*. Bloomington, IN: Xlibris, 2015

'Death Investigations', *Last Week Tonight with John Oliver*, HBO, 19 May 2019. https://youtube/hnoMsftQPY8

Di Maio, Vincent, and Ron Franscell, *Morgue: A Life in Death*. New York: St Martin's Press, 2016

McCrery, Nigel, *Silent Witnesses: A History of Forensic Science*. New York: Random House, 2013

Maples, William R, and Michael Browning, *Dead Men Do Tell Tales: The Strange and Fascinating Cases of a Forensic Anthropologist*. New York: Broadway, 1995

Melinek, Judith, and T J Mitchell, *Working Stiff: Two Years, 262 Bodies, and the Making of a Medical Examiner*. New York: Scribner, 2014

Noguchi, Thomas T, and Joseph DiMona, *Coroner*. New York: Simon and Schuster, 1983

Ribowsky, Shiya, and Tom Shachtman, *Dead Center: Behind*

the Scenes at the World's Largest Medical Examiner's Office. New York: William Morrow, 2006

Zugibe, Frederick, and David L Carroll, *Dissecting Death: Secrets of a Medical Examiner*. New York: Broadway, 2005

Other Books

Boos, William F, *The Poisoner's Trail*. Boston: Hale, Cushman & Flint, 1939

Frankfurter, Felix, *The Case of Sacco and Vanzetti: A Critical Analysis for Lawyers and Laymen*. Boston: Little, Brown, 1927

Gardner, Erle Stanley, *The Court of Last Resort*. New York: William Sloane Associates, 1952

Jentzen, Jeffrey, *Death Investigation in America*. Cambridge, MA: Harvard University Press, 2009

Larson, Erik, *Devil in the White City: Murder, Magic, and Madness at the Fair That Changed America*. New York: Crown, 2003

Puleo, Stephen, *Dark Tide: The Great Boston Molasses Flood of 1919*. Boston: Beacon Press, 2003

Spears, Timothy B, *Chicago Dreaming: Midwesterners and the City, 1871–1919*. Chicago: University of Chicago Press, 2005

Tejada, Susan, *In Search of Sacco and Vanzetti: Double Lives, Troubled Times, and the Massachusetts Murder Case that Shook the World*. Boston: Northeastern University Press, 2012

Tyre, William H, *Chicago's Historic Prairie Avenue*. Charleston, SC: Arcadia Publishing, 2008

Watson, Bruce, *Sacco and Vanzetti: The Men, the Murders, and the Judgement of Mankind*. New York: Viking Adult, 2007

Index

217, 231
Steinway piano gifted to 149
Harvard Alumni Chorus 32
Harvard Associates in Police
Science (HAPS) 183, 185, 197, 214,
232–3, 237
Harvard College 231, 232
Harvard Corporation 153, 154,
201, 220
Hauptmann, Bruno Richard 113
Hayden, Sophia 33
Hektoen, Ludvig 103
Helpern, Milton 109
Hickox Secretarial School 132
Hill, Edwin 137
Hirsch, Charles xiii
Historic Prairie Avenue District
230–1
Hochette, Eugene 74
Holmes, H H 35
Holt, Miss (librarian) 125
homicide, *see* murder
Homicide Investigation (Snyder)
195–6, 202
homicide squads 165
Hoover, J Edgar 112, 220, 222
hospital deaths 142
The House at 1800 Prairie Avenue
(Glessner) 25, 27
Howe, Julia Ward 34
Hussander, Allan B 214

I Was a Male War Bride 200–1
Illinois Institute of Technology 230
immersion 155
incineration 141, 155
independent authority 132, 158
industrial hygiene 123
insolation 141
Institute of Medicine of Maryland
200
International Association of Chiefs
of Police 219, 221
International Harvester Company
16, 36, 44, 83, 110
Interstate Industrial Exposition
(1975) 16
intoxication 127
Iroquois Theatre 45–6, 154

Johns Hopkins University 38, 199
Journal of the Massachusetts

Medico-Legal Society 106
'justice' for cash 10, 13

Karsanoma, Madame 54
Karsner, Howard T 107, 119–20,
203
Keeler, Leonard 199
Keller, W Floyd 161
kidnapping 112–13
Kingston, Thomas 70–1, 72, 73
Kirk, Paul 135
Kitchen diorama 256–7
knife crime 181

Langstaff, Percy Lee (grandson)
242
Lawrence, Dwight 37
Leary, Timothy 60, 66–7, 116, 137,
143–4, 206
LeBrun, George 10
Lee, Blewett (husband) 37–57
Lee, Frances (daughter), *see* Martin,
Frances
Lee, Frances Glessner v, viii, ix,
xiv–xv, 16, 27–9
AJMJ editorship offered to 136,
202
autopsies attended by 93, 94–8
begging letters received by 211–
12
birth of 15, 18
Boston ME plan of 146–66
brother's death affects 84
Christmas letters sent by 195
coming of age of 36
conferences held by 163–4, 170–1
death of 214, 226, 231
diary of 43
dinner hosted by 184–5
dioramas of, *see* Nutshell Studies
divorce of 51–2, 110
Gardner first meets 196–7
honours bestowed upon 160,
164, 170, 220–1, 227
Hoover meets 112–14
as house mother 56–7
ill health of 1–2, 3–4, 29–30,
147, 214, 219, 222, 225, 226
inheritance of 83
library created by 150
Magrath's death affects 128
marriage of 40, 41–57, 82

Picture Credits

Acknowledgements

The undertaking of a project like this isn't done alone. One name is on the cover, but many people were involved to make it happen. Some provided feedback or encouragement, while others helped in more substantial ways. I am thankful for all of it.

Several individuals shared documents and other material produced in the course of their own work. I am particularly grateful to documentary filmmakers Susan Marks and Virginia Ryker, and curator Katie Gagnon for their generosity.

This book could not have been written without the cooperation and assistance of William Tyre, executive director and curator of the Glessner House Museum. Tyre allowed me exclusive access to the Glessner papers, without which this book would not have been possible, and patiently answered countless questions. During my time at the museum, Gwen Carrion was graciously welcoming. I also enjoyed meeting Kathy Cunningham, who shared her enthusiasm for the Glessners. Tyre and the museum's interns have done commendable work to document the lives of the Glessner family and bring that material to the public. Joan Stinton and Cray Kennedy organized and catalogued Frances Glessner Lee's papers. The museum's blog, Story of a House, has been an invaluable resource and is fascinating reading about life during Prairie Avenue's heyday.

Dominic Hall, Jack Eckert and Jessica Murphy of the Center for the History of Medicine in the Francis A Countway Library of Medicine at Harvard were helpful and accommodating during my research. Eckert curated an online exhibit, Corpus Delicti: The Doctor as Detective, that is very informative.

I am indebted to the staff at the Renwick Gallery of the Smithsonian American Art Museum, especially conservator Ariel O'Connor, who revealed so much that was previously unknown about the Nutshell Studies. O'Connor was assisted by Gregory Bailey, Constance Stromberg and Haddon Dean. I also want to thank Nora Atkinson, Scott Rosenfeld, Dave DeAnna, Sean White and many others for their work on the exhibition of the Nutshell Studies.

I'm grateful for the assistance of New Hampshire State Archivist Brian Nelson Burford, Helen Conger of Case Western University Archives, Lee Hiltzik of the Rockefeller Archive Center, Dale Wilkins of the Temecula Valley Museum, Clare Brown of the Bethlehem Heritage Society, Nigel Manley of The Rocks, Sandra L Fox of the Navy Department Library, Denise McNally of the National Association of Medical Examiners, Jane Warren of the American Board of Pathology, Cheryl Irmiter of the Institute of Medicine of Chicago, Harvard Associates in Police Science, the Maryland Medico-Legal Foundation and Dr Kim Collins. Stacy Dorsey and Sruti Basu provided editorial assistance. Thanks also to my brother, David Goldfarb, for feedback and advice.

It has been an honour to befriend many members of the Glessner/Lee family: John Maxim Lee, Percy Lee Langstaff, Lee M Langstaff, Virginia Lee, Gail Batchelder, Paula Batchelder, Liz Carter and many others. Getting to know the wonderful extended Glessner/Lee family has been an unexpected reward.

I'm grateful for the support and encouragement of many

friends and colleagues: Elizabeth Evitts Dickinson, Kathy and Ed Rusen, Sarah Archibald, Dave Mastric, Nick Kolakowski, Tim Friend, Katie Horton, Meg Fairfax Fielding, Maria Stainer, David Rivers, Risa Reyes, Ernie Gambone, Larry Goldfarb, Rafael Alvarez and the members of the Aging Newspaperman's Club and the Ladies Auxiliary.

It's my privilege to work with a group of people who rarely receive public recognition for the important tasks they perform. They are dedicated professionals, good people interested in nothing but the truth and the best interests of the deceased. Each has, in their way, shaped and informed my understanding of forensic science: Drs Mary Ripple, Pamela Southall, Zabiullah Ali, Carol Allan, Russell Alexander, Patricia Aronica, Melissa Brassell, Stephanie Dean, Pamela Ferreira, Theodore King, Ling Li, J Laron Locke, John Stash, Jack Titus and Donna Vincenti. Dr Nikki Mourtzinos deserves special thanks for answering questions about forensic pathology.

I learned a lot on the job from Detective Sergeant Edward Wilson of the Baltimore City Police Department. Wilson is among the most proficient and skilled fingerprinters in the country. Genuine, decent, always good with a story, he personifies the everyday dedication at the OCME.

Special thank you for all the help from Eleanor Thomas, who has coordinated the Francis Glessner Lee Seminar in Homicide Investigation for many years. I am particularly grateful for the friendship and assistance of Jerry Dziecichowicz, who assigns the Nutshell Studies during the homicide seminar and keeps the secret solutions under lock and key.

I wish to thank the secretaries and clerks who picked up the slack in my absences: Amber Conway, Sandra Dornon, Tiffinney Green, Marlene Groom, Angela Jones, Sharon Robinson and Coriann Self. Especially Linda Thomas, who always has my back.

Forensic investigators past and present have been close colleagues. They are serious, well-trained and dedicated professionals who have taught me a lot: Kristine Carder, Randolph Dailey, Dawn Epperson, Bethany Miller, Melinda FitzGerald, David Foehner, Stacy Groft, Aaron Hearn, Saundra Hensley, Stephanie Kimmel, Christina Rzepecki Leonard, Gray Maggard, Courtney Manzo, Anthony McCaffity, Joseph Mullin, Brittany Munro, Keith Opher, Charlotte Rose Noranbrook, Stephanie Rollins, Bryant Smith and Kimberly Winston. People who work in the toxicology and histology labs include Abraham Tsadik, Saffia Ahmed-Sakinedzad, Andra Poston, Xiang Zhang, Cindy Chapman and Angela Dean.

The hardest-working and most underpaid people at the medical examiner's office are the autopsy technicians. Autopsy techs don't get thanked often enough for the job that they do, so let me thank them: Mario Alston, Darrolyn Butler, Ricardo Diggs, Larry Hardy, Leroy Jones, Curtis Jordan, Jessika Logan, Robert Mills, Mozelle Osborne and Raymond Zimmerman.

Also: Tom Brown, Mike Eagle, Rebecca Jufer Phipps, Dawn Zulauf, Donnell McCollough, Brian Tannenbaum, William Spencer-Strong, Dr Juan Troncoso, William Rodriguez, Dr Warren Tewes, Craig Robinson, Barbara Haughey, Samara Simmorins, Ricky Jacobson, David Koch, Stoney Burke and Dustin Saulsbury. Tim Bittner deserves special mention for his assistance bringing the Nutshell Studies back home after the Renwick Gallery exhibit, and Albert Kaniasty for being a fan.

I am grateful for the support of my boss, Dr David R Fowler. Every day at work is a seminar. I have learned much from Dr Fowler about forensic science, governance and the law, integrity in the search for truth, running a busy forensic medical centre at the top of its game, and many other things. I can't thank him enough for allowing me the flexibility to pursue this project, and taking the time to answer questions and provide information and resources. Dr Fowler is the best boss anybody could hope for.

I'm fortunate to be represented by Tamar Rydzinski, who worked with me very patiently until I got it right. She is a fantastic agent, and I am grateful to UMBC friend Bryan Denson for the introduction. I owe a debt of gratitude to Sourcebooks editor Anna Michaels, who helped shape and improve the story immensely.

Most of all, I am deeply appreciative of the support and love of my family. My wife, Bridgett, has been a patient listener and provided key insights to the material. This book represents a sacrifice for the entire family – meals and events missed, nights away from home, hours spent at the keyboard. I couldn't have done this without their understanding and patience, and their commitment to having Lee's story told. This is from all of us.

About the Author

Bruce Goldfarb is the executive assistant to the Chief Medical Examiner for the state of Maryland, US, where the 'Nutshell Studies of Unexplained Death' are housed. He is the public information officer for the Office of the Chief Medical Examiner and trained as a forensic investigator.

Bruce began his career as a paramedic before becoming an award-winning journalist reporting on medicine, science and health. Through his work with the Nutshell Studies, Bruce earned the trust of Frances Glessner Lee's family and caretakers of her estate, and was designated Lee's official biographer.